WITHIN THE GATES OF SCIENCE AND BEYOND:

Science in its cultural commitment.

WITHIN THE GATES OF SCIENCE AND BEYOND:

Science in its cultural commitments.

by

Paul A. Weiss

HAFNER PUBLISHING COMPANY
New York
1971

Published by
HAFNER PUBLISHING COMPANY, INC.
866 Third Avenue
New York, N.Y. 10022

Library of Congress Catalog Card Number: 77-138038

Printed in U.S.A. by
NOBLE OFFSET PRINTERS, INC.
NEW YORK 3, N. Y.

TABLE OF CONTENTS

Introduction

Just what is science? Science has many images but none seems to portray its substance. As I put it in one of the following Essays: "Science, to some, is Lady Bountiful, to others is the Villain of the Century. Some years ago, a book called it our 'Sacred Cow,' and certainly to many it has at least the glitter of the 'Golden Calf'— glorification at one extreme, vituperation at the other." Such statements reflect, of course, subjective *views* of science, as it appears in one-sided illumination or obscuration or through the filters and distorting lenses of the viewer. They hold no answer for the serious and unprejudiced questioner who hopes for an "objective", universally accepted, and sharply delineated description, i.e., definition, of just what science *is*.

Considering the diversity of answers to this question that have been put forth, the sceptic might go back one step and ask first whether the question lends itself at all to a categorical and definite answer. To judge from their own utterances, the scientists themselves are anything but unanimous in their opinions and attitudes. Evidently, most working scientists can do fair work, each in his field, without being overly concerned about an academic "job description" of the overall enterprise, called "science", to which they contribute and, by attribution, belong. In general, they are satisfied with a pragmatic diagnosis of science like the one Lord Bryce made of political systems: "Though we cannot define either oligarchy or democracy, we can usually know either the one or the other when we see it."

Be this as it may, unfortunately, the outsider to science, the "non-scientist", the educated layman, the public at large, the citizen who through his government shares in the support and progress of science—they rarely get to "see" science as it is: they mostly see just partial images of confusing disparity and disproportions. Bewildered, they press on with the question of what constitutes the real "body of science" behind all that hazy imagery; above all, is it a solid body or just a phantom, a spirit, a way of looking at the world?

Throughout my life in science, I have kept pondering those questions, only to learn that the illusory simplicity in which they are phrased defies any but evasive or ambiguous answers. But realistic answers can be at least approached if one breaks through the surface screen of appearances and inspects critically and with emotional detachment the real bustle of the scientific scene. To extrovert the insights thus gained from the inside as cues for orientation of both busy insiders and outside onlookers, has been the main objective in assembling in this book some of my writings that bear on the cardinal question asked above. However, instead of heading at the question straight on with the didactic dryness of the schoolmaster (as I have done in other places), my present approach is by indirection. I try to apply Lord Bryce's precept and let the reader "see" for himself, confident that he will thus get to "know" science for what it is—and what it is not—much better than if I gave some legalistic definition.

Since I include in the prospective audience also a large contingent of scientists and educators, the non-scientist reader will have a chance, if he cares, to listen in on the critical discourse of matters normally restricted more or less to the "inner circle". But it is precisely this mode of diversified and manysided exposure which gives me confidence that no one who has gone through this exhibit with open eyes and with an open mind will ever be deluded into either deifying or vilifying science.

As the reader will learn, science is decidedly not a neatly bounded compartment that could be sequestered from the rest of civilized society as such, to be either enthroned as ruler or excised as tumor; on the contrary, it had better be described as a special attribute, a property, a peculiar way of looking at the world and of acting accordingly; in short, as a pervasive and indelible *aspect of culture*.

Like most youth, I myself have not always realized the breadth and depth of this cultural bond and commitment of science. Specialized work, nose to the grindstone, is not apt to reveal it. Even the very concept of science as an exalted idea and ideal, has tended to fade with the inevitable drudgery of routine chores and the spectacle of petty and spurious polemics. No one in research on the frontiers of knowledge, shuttling back and forth incessantly between experiment and interpretation, fact and meaning, theory and practice, successes and failures, can be spared the dual experience of upliftings in rapture and downdrafts of disheartenment. There were moments when I would find it absolutely proper to grant scientific feats the accolade of "miracles"; at other times, I was dismayed by exhibitions of arrogance which callously equated science with omniscience.

Yet, gradually one learns to view science more soberly and realistically in a more neutral light. One comes to realize that the marks of credit or discredit, which one used to attach, like labels, to a figurative realm of science, should actually be transferred to its concrete constituents, the scientists—a population so diverse that, taken individually, any epithet can find a match among them. So, by and by, science assumes in one's mind an essentially pragmatic aspect: it becomes simply the domain or the house in which "scientists" ply their trade. This image of a house, with walls and doors, shared by the bulk of people in and out of science, is reflected in the reference to the "gates of science" in the title of this book.

But in a third phase of maturation, one discovers that this empirical confinement is far too narrow. One recognizes that, regardless of the limitations of the substance of science, the spirit and the intellectual discipline of scientific logic sweep far beyond those gates, their traces imprinted in the fundamentals of knowledgeable civilization—in education, law, behavior, language, economics, art.

As I look back over the more than half-century of my active life in science, I perceive clearly my gradual ascent to this phase of true appreciation of the wide scope of the scientific spirit—an appreciation which implies that science has, aside from its practical deliveries to man, a broadly *humanistic* mission. I hope that this book will emanate some of the spirit of that mission. I have arranged the chapters so as to reflect in their seriation the ascent from the particular to the general, that is, from the concern of science with its own affairs to its radiations into affairs of broad cultural concern to man. The continuity of that scale should bridge the "credibility gap", which separates bench workers, whose generalizations are distillation products of experience and documented evidence, on the one hand, from intuitive "generalists", indulging in unsupported generalities, on the other. As a credential, I append the following graph, which gives the years of publication of the string of articles. One notes that most of them lie in the narrow span of the last eight years. Considering that in the forty years preceding those eight, I published 250 articles and 4 books dealing with strictly scientific substance, one can estimate the slowness of the intellectual distillation process that has led me to the broad conclusions of this book.

Although all but one of the chapters have previously appeared in print, most of them have been re-edited for the present purpose. Above

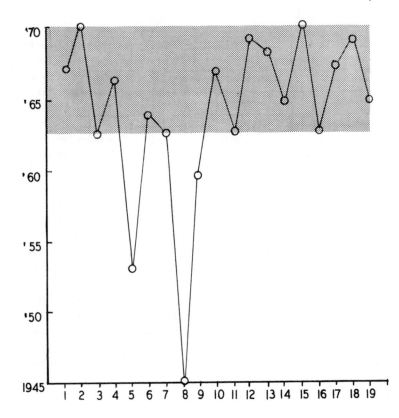

all, duplicate passages in common to two or more articles have been as far as possible deleted; this has resulted in a substantial reduction and consolidation of some of the chapters. On the other hand, ideas and propositions that recurred in different contexts and versions have of course been retained. Mrs. Helene Jordan, Editor of the Rockefeller University Press, volunteered to prune, harmonize and fit the independent pieces into a coherent chain; I am immensely grateful to her for having taken on and carried out the task with the expertise of master craftsmanship. To Mr. David Tiffany, President of the Publishing firm, I am indebted for his patience and helpful suggestions; to Mr. Jacques Strauss of the firm, for having nursed the book resourcefully from manuscript to print.

Research in Retrospect*

It would be fallacy and folly to presume that the young will adopt the ways and precepts of the past. All they can and should do, is to adapt them appropriately to the present and the future, which are theirs. In that sense, to let them share the record of one's scientific life, with all its vagaries, elations, failures and rewards, for their judicious choice of what to emulate and what to shun, becomes a mandate for their seniors. In his spirited book *From Dream to Discovery*, Hans Selye has nobly served this mission. In joining distinguished colleagues in a tribute to him on his sixtieth birthday by presenting the following "autobiographic" extroversion of my own scientific life line extending over well-nigh half a century, I find the only mitigating circumstance for doing so in the thought that it may offer further illustrative examples to validate points made in his book; and above all the key point with which Selye concludes the Introduction: "Scientists are probably the most individualistic bunch of people in the world. All of us are and should be essentially different; there would be no purpose in trying to fit us into a common mold."

Emerging from three years' service as officer in World War I, I entered the University to study engineering and biology. The motivation to do so dates back to the inspiration received from my teachers in secondary school (gymnasium), who had encouraged laboratory research and humanistic studies in equal measure. The combination of engineering and life sciences proved to have hybrid vigor, both in conceptual and technical regards. Right in my doctor's thesis (1922) on *Animal Bahavior as System Reaction*, I departed from antiquated mechanistic doctrine to introduce to the study of organisms the more flexible "system" approach, which since has come to be a standard tool in both the physical and behavioral sciences. Concurrent experimental studies on organ regeneration led me then to a logical counterpart of system theory—a pragmatic "field" concept of development, contrasting sharply with the vitalistic "field" theory of Gurwitsch. Intent

*Reprinted from REFLECTIONS ON BIOLOGIC RESEARCH, (Ed.: Gabbiani, Giulio), Warren H. Green, Inc., St. Louis, Mo., 1968

1

on exploring the actual formative factors that give a regenerating amphibian limb its shape, I tried and succeeded for the first time to graft fully developed limbs from one animal to another with complete restoration of function.

This turned out to be one of those lucky strikes which by sheer accident yield unexpected information of far greater import than what had been looked for. The pattern of regeneration of the limbs, which had been the initial issue, was soon eclipsed by the discovery of the totally unorthodox, but absolutely rigorous, regularity in the mode of their functional activity, as follows. Each muscle of an extra limb grafted near a native limb contracted always and without exception exactly together with his namesake muscle in the neighboring normal limb, regardless of whether or not the resultant movement of the graft was of any use to the animal. Regardless of how wasteful or even obstructive these duplicate movements were, they remained the same for life. Thus was discovered a principle of "resonance," or "matching specificities," of central-peripheral correspondences, which revealed how individual nervous systems can manage to come through the developmental process with the same stereotyped repertory of inherited coordinated performances despite the enormous individual variability of their embryonic histories, and wholly without the benefit of practice.

Even while pursuing this new track, I carried on the analytical studies on morphogenesis. Recognizing that organ formation was basically a cooperative product of cells and the matrix ("ground substance") in which they are embedded, I went to the tissue culture laboratory of Albert Fischer in Berlin to try to impose form on formless cultured cell masses through their matrix. By subjecting the colloidal blood plasma medium of fibroblast cultures to mechanical stress, I could indeed orient cell movements and tissue growth at will. After establishing the main effect, the identification of its mechanism was a relatively straightforward task. It revealed two components—the mechanical alignment of filamentous molecules into submicroscopic guide tracks for cell migration, and a proclivity of cells for following such tracks. The lessons learned in these experiments have later proved crucial for the understanding of the mechanics of wound healing in general and especially for the design of improved methods of peripheral nerve repair.

In 1930, after 3 years of work in various European laboratories for the acquisition of wider technical experience, I decided to accept an earlier invitation by Ross Harrison, the great experimental embryologist, to move to his Yale University laboratory. Harrison had invented the method of tissue culture specifically for the study of nerve growth. I immediately proceeded to test whether his own earlier results on enforced cell orientation would also hold for nerve fibers, as he had intimated. They did. In consequence, a general rule of "contact guidance" for protoplasmic movement could be established, soon to be supplemented by the demonstration of "selective contact affinities" between given nerve fibers and their specific pathways.

The focus of my work thus was back on nerve. I found that even completely isolated nerve centers, for instance, thoroughly deranged nerve cell pools transplanted into no-man's-land of tissue, exhibited intrinsic rhythmic automatism. This further substantiated the intrinsic autonomy of the activity of the central nervous system, which I had derived earlier from the results with transplanted limbs, and even more directly, from a series of experiments in which normal coordinated motor activity was shown to develop and persist in limbs totally lacking sensory control, either withheld from the start or secondarily removed in later life. Neverthless, one still encounters propositions that tend to concede to the central nervous system no more autonomy than to a telephone exchange or railroad station, in which incoming messages or trains (of impulses) are merely properly recombined and rerouted.

Even though it would have been most challenging to exploit the opportunities opened by this work on isolated nerve cell pools, the outbreak of World War II forced their discontinuance. The moral obligation of making one's experience available for the mitigation of human suffering became an over-riding commitment. I therefore readily placed my experience in the service of the task which I felt best prepared to serve—a search for improved methods of surgical nerve repair. My basic knowledge gathered earlier on the guidance of cell and nerve growth in culture lent itself at once to such an application. So, with the energetic collaboration of my staff, I designed and elaborated a technique of sutureless splicing of severed nerves by arterial (later, Tantalum) cuffs, which besides surgical effectiveness (and a merit citation by the U. S. Government), also yielded the following two developments of much broader significance.

The urgent need for a steady supply of arteries for splicing had led me and my associate, A. C. Taylor, to test the feasibility of using frozen-dried and stored pieces for that purpose. Having proved practicable for blood vessels, the method was then refined and extended to include frozen-dried, vacuum-storable, nerve stumps, as well as corneas, for grafting in general. Thus originated the first "tissue bank" for surgical use.

A second outgrowth of the nerve splicing technique was the discovery of "neuroplasmic flow"—an unsuspectedly intensive internal growth activity going on permanently in what had been supposed to be the "resting" nerve cell and nerve fiber. This again came about quite accidentally. Some of the arterial cuffs used were so tight as to constrict the enclosed stretch of nerve. Such locally constricted nerves were noted to develop chronic swellings at the cell-near proximal entrance to the narrows, coupled with commensurate shrinkage at the distal side. While part of the swelling could be traced (in one of the earliest biological applications of the high-powered isotopes from the Chicago Atomic Pile) to the throttling of a continuous fast centrifugal stream of interstitial fluid *between* the fibers of peripheral nerve trunks, the major force of the effect proved to be due to the existence of a perpetual, but slower, flow of the content *within* each individual nerve fiber away from its central cell of origin. The widenings up-stream from bottlenecks are simply the results of damming. From continued research on the phenomenon, combining techniques of microsurgery, explantation, radioautography, electron microscopy, cytochemistry and cinemicrography, we could ascertain that the nerve cell body is engaged in continuous reproduction of its macromolecular mass, foremost protein, which then is passed on to a conveyor-like mechanism of the nerve fiber channel for shipment to sites of internal consumption and repair, as well as for export of some products to extra-nervous tissue. My double training in biology and engineering has undoubtedly predisposed me to recognize and interpret correctly this "neuroplasmic flow" and its role in the adaptive functioning of the nervous system.

With the end of World War II, collateral work on more general cell-biological problems was resumed, establishing in greater detail the mechanisms of movement, orientation, shape, and lodging of cells individually, in artificial groupings, and in the normal organism. These studies demonstrated the high differential specificity, distinctive for cells of different tissue types, which had already been intimated by surgical experience with wound healing. It was most tellingly revealed in the "homing" in their precisely matching tissue sites of cells of a given type that had been injected into the blood stream for indiscriminate dissemination throughout the (embryonic) body. These experiments (with Andres) then led to a long series of studies (largely by Moscona in my laboratory) on the type-specific sorting out of mixed cell populations in tissue culture, and further, the cinemicrographic analysis by Taylor and myself of the manner in which cells establish contact, recognize each other and react in accordance with their respective likeness or unlikeness. This series culminated in our demonstration that random-mixed and random-reassembled suspensions of cells from differentiated organs, if placed on the vascular bed of a nurse embryo for nourishment, can reconstitute themselves into complete and typical miniature replicas of the donor organs.

With the advent of the electron microscope, I carried the studies of morphogenesis down into the submicroscopic range. Wartime acquaintance through my friend, Francis O. Schmitt, with his classical studies on collagen, led me to investigate the geometrically highly regular collagen fabric in the membrane underlying larval skin and the mode of the restoration of its characteristic pattern after wounding (with Ferris). The data pointed to the existence of a principle of "macrocrystalline lattices" in the collagen matrix, thus linking up, on the macromolecular scale, with my much earlier conclusions about the ordering role of ground substances in morphogenesis.

In general, as can be readily seen, I have tried to keep balance between analytical experimentation and theoretical interpretation. My theoretical formulations, for instance, of system behavior, of the field concept, of macrocrystallinity, of the molecular basis of cell specificity and cell differentiation, of growth control (including a rigorous mathematical treatment with Kavanau), of neuronal resonance, and so forth, have all grown out from first-hand observations and experiments and have, in turn, engendered the design of further research. Not only did I discount the imaginary categorical boundary line between experimentation and conceptualization, but I found the conventional sharp distinction between "basic" and "applied" research equally inapplicable to my way of thinking. Although most of my work would presumably be classified as "basic," I also take equal satisfaction from having earned a patent for a strictly "practical" metallurgic process: on how to confer resilience to Tantalum foil.

Besides my laboratory, teaching and literary activities in academic posts in Europe, Yale, Chicago, the Rockefeller Institute and Texas (and Visiting Professorships at 10 major Universities), I have given much of my attention and efforts to such broader problems as the role of science in education; the historical and philosophical foundations of science; the relations between science and art; the place of science in society; the husbanding of natural resources; and science in the international scene. My faculty of rendering service to those more general relations of science to human affairs (at variance with a "Two-culture" concept) has been greatly enhanced by my experience in several administrative functions, such as my service as member of the Science Advisory Committee of the President of the United States; as Chairman of the Division of Biology and Agriculture of the National Research Council; as member of the Council of the National Academy of Sciences; as special consultant to the U. S. State Department; as Chairman of U. S. delegations to the International Council of Scientific Unions and the International Union of Biological Sciences; as Chief Science Advisor to the Brussels World's Fair; and as designer and Dean of a new Graduate School of Biomedical Sciences of the University of Texas.

I am listing these activities for the simple reason that one might suspect them to be a serious encroachment on research, the basic precept for which can be summarized in the three key words: *continuity, selectivity*, and *consistency*. Let me point out, therefore, that such extraneous duties are not at all incompatible with literary and educational pursuits. What they force one to do is to make the choice among research problems competing for time and energy with a heightened sense of relevance, selectivity, and parsimony. Since my experience has convinced me that this is all to the good, I obviously cannot subscribe to the plaint of research workers that time devoted to teaching or other service functions is time misspent; for tightness of time is apt to foster concentration on essentiality, creativity and efficiency, even as it curtails redundancy and sheer profusiveness—altogether gains for both the worker and science as a whole. In my view, blanket exemption from participation in educational pursuits in academic life should be turned from a privilege into a stigma denoting some personal defect.

In further illustration of my thesis that effectiveness in one's scientific life is not confined by boundaries of disciplines of subject matter or technique, and as a plea to the imaginative and resourceful young investigators for not letting their sense of perspective succumb to atrophy from overindulgence in technical specialization, let me point to a last personal lesson. Although I have had no medical training, my research and teaching have had, in many instances, some bearing on problems of medical education and practice. As a result, I have been called upon repeatedly to serve in the role of adviser to medical schools and major hospitals (besides earning the rare award of two honorary degrees of Doctor of Medicine and of Doctor of Medicine and Surgery, as well as honorary lectureships and awards in the medical sciences). In singling out these distinctions accorded to a hybrid engineer-biologist by the medical profession, while leaving unmentioned rewards received that are more readily identifiable with my disciplinary training, I wish to stress a precept for the budding scientist: Achievement is marked not so much by what one has learned, but by how one is using that which one has learned, with eyes and mind wide-open to the immense range of *terra incognita* in the life sciences and the untapped resources and opportunities for its elucidation and penetration by observation, experiment and theory.

Whither Life Science?*

Faced with such a weighty question, one gets a sense of entering from the wings onto the stage of history, realizing that one's diagnosis may in itself bias the course of future events. One thus assumes a much heavier load of responsibility than if he were simply to predict the outcome of an experiment. After all, assessments like the one I am about to make, if carried out conscientiously and judiciously, can in the long run serve in much the same way that regular medical checkups of individuals contribute to the overall improvement of public health. Therefore, comparing my task with that of a medical examiner—in view of the still infantile stage of the life sciences, specifically that of pediatrician—I must include in my concern with future healthy growth any diagnostic signs of abnormalities, such as, for instance, symptoms of incipient gigantism or obesity.

This is a task to be tended to in the spirit of a critical clinician, not of a doting parent. Thus, I shall offer no apologies for being critical. In sober critical examination, then, what is the state of vigor of contemporary biology, measured on the dual scale of the aspirations of its own practitioners and the expectations of a public hoping for miracles by and for the supreme living being, man?

I shall not parade as soothsayer, bringing glad tidings of scientific "breakthroughs," in which some of our media of public information tend to indulge in answer to the public cry for the thrill of novelty. To those who have a flair for statistics, I propose the following instructive pastime. Go to the library and scan back copies of newspapers that have reported science items for the last twenty-five years (there was no such spate of science news before World War II as since). Note down the grand and grandiose predictions of how a given observation or insight would soon provide the cure of this disease or the solution of that mystery, or furnish new means for man to manipulate his destiny, and so forth. Then try to track the fate of those items through subsequent periods, and discover for yourself how quickly most of this erstwhile burning "news" gets cold, eclipsed, doomed to oblivion.

*Reprinted from AMERICAN SCIENTIST, Vol. 58, No. 2, Mar.-Apr. 1970, pp. 156-163 Copyright © 1970 by The Society of the Sigma Xi

Glitter and glamor are not the true marks of the steady march of science, and the hot spur-of-the-moment fascination with novelty does not last. In the first excitement, a new discovery is viewed only against the background of past ignorance, over which it stands out as a step of major magnitude. But having regained perspective, one often recognizes it as still infinitesimally small in terms of what remains to be discovered and understood. In fact, any scientific feat first presented in over-magnified dimensions is soon cut down to size and proper proportions by the skepticism and criticism of the scientific community. True, solid, and enduring scientific knowledge advances in a steady, consistent carrier wave, the trend and rate of which cannot be diagnosed from the temporary ripples of "spectaculars" any more than daily fluctuations of the stock market can be taken as indicators of long-term trends in economics.

Is there a goal?

Let us look both backward and forward from this instant in time, called "present," at which the certainty of knowledge of the past changes abruptly into the indefiniteness of a future that is uncertain; just how uncertain, varies with the designation of a *goal*. By defining a future course, a goal restrains the uncertainty inherent in blind rambling. Ostensibly, the question above takes it for granted that biology has such a goal or goals toward which research effort is being steered. But is this premise valid? Even if validated, are the goals we can discern identical with the great, august and cardinal "unanswered questions" of history, in the sense of stable, long-range beacons, or are they just auxiliary stakes set out for temporary tactical guidance at close range? In other words, does research in biology take bearings, as in navigation, from fixed stars, or does it follow the erratic lures of will-o'-the-wisps?

Is research goal-directed? What the observer of the current scene can see is only that it is vigorously on the move and moving forward along given lines. This progression is called "progress." However, the mere fact that research has direction in no way implies that it is purposefully orienting itself toward a defined far-off goal. The sheer record of progression does not reveal whether its track has been consciously, conscientiously, and considerately chosen with sights trained at some distant guiding light, or whether it has simply continued blindly in its rut, driven by the inertial momentum of past impetus. Of course, it would seem gratuitous to deal with such a question in terms of an abstract generality. After all, research is carried out by real people, who vary enormously in their individual aspirations, motivations, interests, and circumstances. So, one might answer, the pioneer still follows his star, while the dullard or drudge prefers the beaten track.

On the other hand, a comparative survey of trends during the half century of my own research experience has convinced me that the proportions and relative weights of these two extremes of the total spectrum of researchers have become so markedly reversed of late that the pertinence of the old doctrine of absolute freedom of research can no longer be accepted unreservedly. In fact, the original meaning of that "doctrine" has been perverted; for what it proclaimed was not freedom of "movement" but freedom of "choice." To merit that freedom, one must have the wish, the will, and the faculty to choose one's goal with deliberation. These virtues are not as prominent in research today as they were at the time of my apprenticeship. Examples of research production that, on the face of it, is aimless, grinding out senseless or redundant data, are mounting.

Therefore the answer to the question posed at the head of this section remains, at best, ambiguous. Some research is still decidedly goal-directed; some other research shows direction but no goal; and there is also some that even lacks direction. Moreover, what used to be clear macrogoals for orientation have gradually crumbled into innumerable disconnected microtasks; and many of the original major targets for research have become splintered, blurred, obscured, or totally lost from view. Consequently, the corresponding great focal questions whose resolution was the original concrete goal of research have not only remained unanswered but have faded to indistinctness.

True, some "great questions" are still familiar through the currency of their names; but like the names on tombstones, those are just symbolic mementos no longer denoting the essence of their defunct carriers. The problem of "organism" and "organization" is a good example; I shall turn to it below for special consideration. Other questions have simply assumed another verbal guise—perhaps more adequately phrased, though not necessarily nearer to solution: such a one is the "origin of life." Still others, such as the mind-body dualism, have been relegated to the attic of philosophy as being beyond the ken of science. Yet, on the whole, if anyone wants to find the "great problems" of biology explicitly treated in current literature, he must turn to encyclopedias or the writings of historians, "generalists," or publicists—and writers of science fiction—rather than to the literature reporting or summarizing bench research.

In passing, it should be added that the recent influx of mathematicians (other than biometricians) into theoretical biology has started to establish a promising link, albeit by shortcut, between the generalists, who see the problems, and the researchers, who have the facts, through the effort to apply rigorous mathematical discipline to the formulation of the "great problems" of biology. Unfortunately, these problems are often conceived of in terms so general, unrealistic, and grossly oversimplified that in the final account, "any resemblance to beings living or dead is purely coincidental." Even so, merely to have raised the sights to the broad unsolved questions is to be hailed as providing an antidote to the trend to myopia in bench research.

Let me return then to that trend of movement by past momentum instead of by the vision of distant goals. Some crucial questions come at once to mind. Is it inexorable? If it is, will the advancement of knowledge gain or suffer? If it is not, can its reversal be expedited, and how? The history of its origin and growth might yield some answers. To trace it, I turn from diagnosis to anamnesis.

How goals have changed

Half a century ago, when I began my explorations in biology, the field was sparsely populated, like pioneering country, and everybody who entered was thrown essentially on his own devices. Textbooks were few, comprehensive, original, and unique, almost every one of them bearing the signature of a master; but obviously there were wide gaps between the areas they covered. Yet they had one important feature in common: they tried, some more than others, to balance overindulgence in their particular specialty by pointing up the place and context of that specialty within the continuum of the living world. In this way we became aware of both the fundamental interconnectedness of all aspects of life and the appalling dearth of concrete knowledge about the interconnections.

The vistas of these wide-open spaces to be explored aroused an exhilarating pioneering drive in the curious student, who then had a relatively free rein for exercising imagination and resourcefulness to the full. He could choose his research problem for its novelty and promise and pursue it into the uncharted land of the unknown. Techniques being few and rather elementary, he could design his own adaptations to the tasks at hand. Above all, he was apprentice of a master, who exposed him to the broad perspective of the land of knowledge with its vast blanks of ignorance even as he imbued him with the discipline of minute accuracy in workmanship. Mobility of shuttling between the deep shafts of specialization and the free surface above ground in order to retain perspective and bearings thus became second nature.

Even then, of course, favored topics emerged which attracted a disproportionate share of the work force. But this did not lead to progressive clustering; it was counteracted by the suction from the wide expanse of vacua of knowledge, which, either clearly recognized or dimly sensed, attracted entrants with a spirit of adventure, unmindful of the risk of failure. What fanned that spirit was the sense of nearness to the frontiers of the unknown and the uncomprehended, offering limitless challenges and opportunities for individual accomplishment. Thus *individuals*, with little to guide them other than questions and ideas—goals visible or visualized, or sometimes just visionary—could blaze their own pioneering trails through the virgin land. The more men that manned the front, the more new paths were opened, even as some of the older ones were widened by followers. And so the power of the pioneering urge preserved a sound balance between the creation of new settlements and the enlargement of earlier ones, between new explorations and the consolidation of past acquisitions of knowledge.

Biological science was still essentially a preserve for the individual, the solitary worker, pursuing freely and unhurriedly a self-set goal selected from the broad perspective of the problems of the living world open to him. No captive of prefabricated instrumental gadgets, he worked with modest means; inadequacies were not a source of complaint but incentives for improvisation and invention. Perfection in craftsmanship and scholarship were not allowed to be encroached upon by time schedules, deadlines, and pressures for publication. In sum, research in biology was mostly left to the brains and hands of individuals in physical and social settings comparable to the workshops of the days of the guilds.

This is the science that was. Its products are still with us—but its ways have changed. Modern science has grown, by the snowballing of its own success, from an assembly of little workshops into an enterprise of the size, methods, and attitudes of a gigantic industry, with all the benefits and drawbacks such a development implies. One of the drawbacks is that a mass of single-tracked workers tends by its sheer momentum to amplify any trend once that trend has started rolling. A fashionable course thus becomes grooved ever more deeply, draining interest, attention, encouragement, and talent away from solitary prospecting ventures. As a result of these social dynamics, the research scenery is gradually becoming converted, metaphorically speaking, from a lush mountain meadow evenly irrigated by a profusion of anastomos- ing rivulets into a landscape of deep canyons with raging rivers, separated by wastelands of arid mesas. Breadth is given up in favor of depth, and universality and versatility are traded for the thrust of concentrated effort. We are so fascinated by the achievements of the latter trend that we are apt to forget the price it exacts by drying up the precious sources of discovery, innovation, and, above all, of the *understanding* of nature.

The physical branches of science seem to be mature enough to afford turning a major portion of their energies over to what in industry is called "development"—the postpioneering phase of improvement and exploitation of propitious research results. Biology, however, is still too ignorant by far to follow that course. It is not ready to be turned into a mass production enterprise; to do so would consolidate prematurely the scanty patchwork of basic principles that are truly known. In fact, promotional attempts to propel or lure biology into manufacturing drives give, by their very innocence, evidence of the immature state of our branch of science; they prove that the awareness of how remote we still are from a profound understanding of living nature has been dimmed by the glare of spectacular advances in certain limited sectors, such as "molecular genetics."

There are sectors in which brilliant progress is still being made on the old pattern by self-directed individuals, for instance, in the physiology of vision; but time has changed this approach from standard rule to rare exception. Besides, vast areas are left totally deserted and in obscurity. Who is to say what crucial clues they hold to the understanding of life which may be missed because of our compulsive submission to the spell of a few favorite topics? Will the established favorites of today keep being swelled by masses of epigones, acclaiming the familiar, and disdainful of the odd, adventurous, and risky? Will more and more workers busy themselves with fewer and fewer tasks, and will the tasks shrink to the posing of questions that fit the answers we already have? Is this trend inexorable or can it be countered? I shall now try to answer.

Old goals in new light

Growth of a body has three main aspects: (1) increase in mass; (2) mounting complexity; (3) change in proportions. Danger signs of erratic growth that bear watching, therefore, are mass increase to tumorous dimensions; loss of integration with growing intricacy; and distortion of harmonious proportions to the point of freakishness. Let me review briefly in terms of these three criteria the growth of contemporary prepuberal biology from its earlier phase of infancy.

Measured on a numerical scale—i.e. the increased piling up of items of information—growth has been steady and impressive. The increase in what we know now in certain branches of the life sciences that we did not know half a century ago, or knew only very vaguely, is truly imposing, in terms of increments over the past. Whole areas of science now heavily populated, and even overpopulated, had then neither identity nor name, let alone university departments, societies, and journals for their specialties.

Those were the days of the emergence of genetics, of ecology, of biochemistry as an offshoot of physiology. Virology did not exist, for viruses were just on the horizon. Endocrinology, pharmacology, biophysics had not yet split off from their mother sciences. Only twenty years ago the term "molecular biology," now in the daily vernacular, had not yet been coined. This differentiation of new problem-oriented or subject-oriented disciplines was further variegated by the formation of auxiliary technique-centered specialties, like electron microscopy, ultracentrifugation, tissue culture, cinemicrography, radiology, etc., each with its own problems, rules, skills, and slang. Moreover, specialties have kept right on splintering further into subspecialties and subsubspecialties, each attracting into its service increasing numbers of acolyte researchers by both the aspect of novelty and the relentless operation of Parkinson's Law.

In this manner the life sciences have grown vigorously, both in *size* and in *diversity,* exuberantly forging on without compunctions about the resulting diaspora. Some of these massive concentrated attacks on specified problems have borne rich fruit. Deservedly spotlighted, they stand out in the public mind as monolithic achievements; for instance, the deciphering of the genetic code, the synthesis of proteins and enzymes (not of "cells" or "life," as has sometimes been glibly hinted), the electrochemical explanation of nerve excitation, or the analysis of the mechanisms by which muscles contract, cells divide, and food and blood charge tissues with life-supporting energy.

But let me point out two qualifications to that success story. In the first place, none of those pinnacles was reached by blind mass assault; each trek was spearheaded by a few pioneers of exactly the kind of mind, vision, and ways of practice that I have cited above as hallmarks of the researcher of the preindustrial phase of our science. Second, most of their "breakthroughs" can be traced to residues of the catholicity of thinking of that earlier age, for they were generated largely by the interdisciplinary cross-fertilization of ideas of different parental origins to yield offspring with hybrid vigor, comparable to the superiority of hybrid corn. Molecular biology, for instance, arose from the confluence of genetics, bacteriology, biochemistry, cytology, and biophysics. This example holds a deep lesson. There is ample documentation in genetics for the innovative and invigorative value of compatible crossbreeding, in sharp contrast to the degenerative and sterilizing effects of inbreeding. The transfer of this simile to cultural evolution, of which science is an integral part, points up the risk biology incurs by overindulgence in monomaniac proliferation of ever more splinter lines, followed by smug self-isolation in those branches. As I have said, macrogoals degenerate then into microgoals and submicrogoals, ending in choiceless single dead-end tracks with no aim other than self-perpetuation.

If this were to come to pass, the growth of biology would have failed to satisfy the third criterion on my list of diagnostic signs of healthy growth: the *harmony of proportions* to be maintained by *integrative interactions* throughout the growing system would have been allowed to vanish. Biology, even in its early life, has never been truly unified. In matters of subject, interest, methodology, concepts, principles, terms, units, and standards, it has never attained the degree of unification displayed by the physical sciences. All the more is it crucial and urgent to counteract the trend to further atomization and disintegration. There is still time, but for how long?

Nothing more drastic is called for than to bring back into full view as research targets the faded age-old, unresolved "great questions," stripped of the obscurant verbiage which has enveloped them. Peel out their essential naked kernels of clearly and objectively circumscribed phenomena and properties. Let imaginative researchers draw a bead on them and find out whether the unveiled problems yield to explanations in terms of what we know (they probably will not) or whether we must expand the frame of our concepts in order to encompass and accommodate them. There are many curious and resourceful students in my acquaintance alone who are bored and dismayed by their enforced engagement on rote mopping-up operations in the quest for knowledge in sectors where the front has already become stagnant. I have no doubt that they and many like them would welcome the challenge if only the goal were presented to them concretely and realistically, and the feasibility of an approach to it plausibly demonstrated. My faith in this segment of the new generation—not necessarily large in numbers, but imbued with the vision, courage, steadfastness, and versatility of pioneer explorers—prompts my prediction that, on the whole, the downward tide of research trends from quality to quantity will be stemmed and reversed.

Our task, then, is to illuminate the old goals with the strong light of modern scientific scrutiny, and by throwing into sharp relief the solid core of our present knowledge, without embellishment, accentuate again the immensity of our remaining ignorance. The great voids and flaws in the tenuous fabric of our knowledge, now covered up by illusive verbal wrappings, which insinuate knowledge where there is none, must be exposed openly and set forth explicitly as targets for research and the conceptual integration that promises to make the map of knowledge not only more complete but more consistently coherent.

That word "must," I am afraid, will raise immediately in many minds the specter of "planned research." Let me lay that ghost to rest at once. In the first place, much of the current research effort is, unavoidably, if not planned, at least steered by two forces outside the research enterprise—the policies that control the wherewithal for research (funds, manpower, facilities, publications, etc.), and the public attitudes, somewhat fickle, which influence those policies. Yet those extraneous directive influences become effective solely to the extent to which they affect the self-determination of the independent researcher (I am not speaking here of his auxiliary forces of technicians with or without doctor's degrees). The real force that gives shape to his amorphous desire to add to knowledge is his *education*. Education can make or break him. It can give him scope for self-direction and creativity or it can mold him into a mere cog in a mass production machine. Society needs the latter kind, well trained practitioners, in increasing numbers; but we are here concerned primarily with those aiming at the advancement, rather than the application, of knowledge. If research is not properly goal-oriented, then education has failed to point out the goals and the ways to approach them. If goals have been too narrowly, too vaguely, or too forbiddingly presented, or, what is worse, concealed, the blame must again be laid at the doorstep of education. And above all, if the incipient investigator is enticed to keep on riding currents of fashion, instead of being challenged to chart his own course toward self-chosen destinations, it is his education that has been at fault. So what is needed is certainly not planned research but sounder plans for *education for research*. Many treks toward neglected research destinations might then start moving again.

To instill concreteness into this plea based on my diagnosis, let me give two examples of the basic "unanswered questions" in the life sciences which in my view have not been brought significantly nearer to solution in this half century: the problems of *organization* and of *specificity*. These stereotypes of colloquial language, which designate two of the most fundamental attributes of living systems, are highly ambiguous; yet one finds them throughout biological literature indiscriminately intermingled with the rigorously defined symbols of the so-called "exact" sciences, in a precarious misalliance between the body of science and phantoms. Phantoms make no fit targets for research. Can they not be made to materialize?

Great goals: 1. Organization

To say that *organization* is what distinguishes an organism from a sheer pile of matter sounds like a platitude. And yet in this distinction lies what poets call "the mystery of life." Popular science, more optimistic, would speak of "the secret" of life, on the presumption that a secret is more likely to be cracked than is a mystery. Descriptively, the difference between a pile of matter and an organism is, of course, quite plain: an ordinary pile of matter, scrambled, remains a pile of matter, whereas a living organism whose parts are scrambled is dead—reduced to just another pile of matter. If the comminution of any organism were reversible, restoring its life, the phenomenon of organism might emerge from mere description to scientific understanding. But it is not reversible. True, organs of multicellular organisms can be dissociated into their component cells, many of which remain viable and can be reared in isolation ("tissue culture") for countless generations of single-celled progeny. But this only proves that the living cell itself is an organism superior to a mere assembly of its constituent materials—superior by virtue of its "organization." The higher organism of which it formed a part is simply of a higher order in a hierarchical cadre of organizational levels.

The step from higher to lower levels of organization is not irreversible. In fact, we have observed cell masses, isolated from well differentiated livers or kidneys or skin of advanced chick embryos and then scrambled into haphazard heaps, reconstitute themselves into typically organized miniature livers or kidneys or skin with feathers, respectively. Yet observation is not tantamount to explanation and understanding, and scientifically the "mystery" has remained. At any rate, the experience cannot be duplicated as one descends further downward from the cell; fragments of a fractionated cell have never been shown to be capable of putting themselves together again to compose a living cell: their "organized" state has been lost irretrievably by the disruption of the system of which they had formed the elements. Logically, the epithet "life" therefore cannot be granted to subcellular units. Viruses, for instance, which sometimes have been called "alive," are not, because they cannot "live" and reproduce except inside and through the agency of a living cell. The confusion here is semantic: tin soldiers do not "reproduce"; they are reproduced, by devices and procedures contrived by a living organism—man with his brain.

Leaving aside semantic sophistry of definition, we can apply to "organization" the remark Lord Bryce made with regard to political systems: "Though we cannot define either oligarchy or democracy, we can usually know either the one or the other when we see it": we can tell the "organized" state from an "unorganized" one. But this is about where the science of life has left it. For instance, "normal tissue growth is 'organized,' cancer is not." What does this mean in concrete terms? We do not know. We read about chemical "organizers" telling tissues what to become and do; does this submit that a pile of molecules can instill an order not their own into an equally naive respondent? Now, with the recent upsurge of molecular genetics, what used to be unknown under the catchall term of "organization" has been transliterated to "information," which thereby is made to be synonymous with "lack of information."

This aberrant course departed from the classical demonstration of the ordered linear array of genes in chromosomes, which was resolved into a correspondingly unique seriation of chemical constituents arranged along enormously long filamentous molecules of a nucleic acid (DNA), comparable to the letters spelling out a message on a tape. Parts of this are then "read" by other molecules, which, in turn, translate the seriation (the "message") into a corresponding sequence of amino acids, which are the building blocks for the assemblage of proteins. So far, so good: one form of order is converted into another, one-to-one. But then what? How do we get from a bag of proteins to the organized shape and functions of a living cell, let alone to the integrated, viable masterpiece of a human organism? The standard answer one is apt to get is: "Genetic information does it." This is the point at which scientific language becomes utterly unscientific. Machines and houses are built *from* blueprints ("information" charts) but not *of* blueprints. The information must be translated into reality through the brains of human beings. Brain function being a paradigm of "organization" (="information"), we find ourselves thus caught in a tautological trap.

The truth is that the entrenched analytical and reductionist brand of scientists, who are committed to the prejudicial verdict that exclusive study of the *smallest* elements of any natural system is the royal road to knowledge about nature, have, in their concentration on ever smaller fractions of the universe, lost irretrievably the view and cognizance of the rules of order that prevail at the higher levels of cooperative *group operation* of those units. And when they are put to it to explain how, in objective terms, the phoenix can rise from the ashes, they either prove to be "organization-blind," or else bring up those terminological stopgaps which, as I said before, are blindfolds to hide ignorance.

Let me highlight the problem by just one striking example. I have pointed to the "organized" character of brain function. What does that mean? It means the operation of a *principle of order* that stabilizes and preserves the total *pattern* of the group activity of a huge mass of semiautonomous elements (in this case, brain cells), notwithstanding a tremendous range of individual variation and flux of and among the elements themselves. Our brain contains more than ten billion nerve cells, each of which averages about ten thousand connections with others; each cell, in turn, contains at a minimum ten thousand complex macromolecules, not only in constant agitation but being renewed about ten thousand times in a lifespan. Thus, looking at it from the worm's-eye view of the macromolecule, brain action must deal in a lifetime with at least 10^{22} (10,000,000,000,000,000,000,000) macromolecular constellations in various degrees of instability and impermanence. A fact that the individual molecule, of course, cannot know but which our integral brain cannot help but ponder is that throughout all that churning and changing of a population of molecules that is ten thousand billion times as large as the World's human population, we retain intact our sense of individual unity and identity, our habits and our memories.

Just what sort of principle will be revealed, or will have to be postulated, in order to account for that relative stability of a pattern as a whole despite the infinitely greater autonomous variability of its elements—*order in the gross with freedom in the small*—is as obscure for the case of brain action as it is for the coordinated activities of cell life or for the integrated wholeness of the development of an individual from an egg. It is one of the great unsolved questions of biology, temporarily bottled up under the label "organization." Other names have been coined for it (Gerard's "org," Koestler's "holon"), and I have couched it in terms of "field" theory. These were attempts to specify the problem, not to solve it. They differ from the axiomatic "soul" of the theologian or the "entelechy" and "élan vital" of the vitalist only by their intent, which is to go beyond the simple acknowledgment of the principle and to arrive at formulations and propositions of properties that can be rigorously verified by controlled tests and can thereby acquire some predictive value. It is doubtful that the current conceptual frame in biology is wide enough for this task. The influx of physicists into biology might help to widen that intellectual bottleneck and bring this fundamental problem down from the attic into the workshop. But the first thing to do is for education to make budding researchers face the problem soberly instead of looking the other way when they meet it.

Great goals: 2. Specificity

If "organization" refers to a collective property of groups of elements whose interrelations bind them dynamically into a unit of higher order, then *specificity* is one of the chief biological devices for the establishment and maintenance of such bonds. The dictionary defines "specific" as "having a special determining quality." In the living world, such qualities are used universally as means of communication, recognition, affinity relations, selectivity. The basic principle is *matched* specificities—a sort of resonance between two systems attuned to each other by corresponding properties. Man has adopted this principle from nature for many of his technical devices, from the elementary structural interdigitation between key and lock to the ingenious use of wave-length correspondence between sender and receiver in broadcasting. And when I submit that most of what is known about specific interactions in living systems is still interpreted essentially by referring back to one or the other of those man-made inventions as models, it will explain why I bring up this problem as an example of "major unanswered questions". Luckily, in contrast to "organization," at least some of the instances in which the principle is used are currently recognized as major goals of research.

The following brief sampling may give an idea of the diversity of circumstances in which living nature has made use of the principle of specificity. Starting from our personal experience: there is the selective recognition of optic wave lengths within the narrow band of only one octave by our visual system (colorvision); the tonal identification of sound waves by our ear; the identification of chemical compounds by our senses of smell and taste; the capacity of cells of the alimentary canal for selecting what to absorb and what to reject among ingested foodstuffs; the even more exclusive screening out, by each type of cell in the various organs, of its specific requirements from the passing blood and lymph stream; the faculty of cells of different tissues to recognize each other's types and to form associations like to like, which, for example, helps to restore order in the healing of complex wounds; the selectivity that enables nerves growing out from given nerve centers to make functional connections only with predestined types of peripheral tissues to be innervated; the faculty of a hormone to act exclusively or preferentially on specific target tissues, even though the agent is indiscriminately diffused throughout the whole body; the differential effect which different stimulating or depressing drugs exert on different nerve centers; and so on. Eggs accept insemination by sperm of their own species, while rejecting foreign sperm. A parasite recognizes its host and finds the proper route for invasion guided by matching chemical cues of the host. Similarly, in embryonic development many cell types execute guided migrations along ostensibly "marked" pathways before arriving at their destinations; there they become lodged, presumably bonded to their surroundings by mutual affinity.

This list, which could be greatly extended, contains a rich collection of well documented phenomena, which evidently have some fundamental principle of operation in common. But save for a very few of the listed items, we know practically nothing definite about that principle. To single out just one example, many hormones have been isolated, purified, crystallized, chemically identified, and even reproduced synthetically, but how a given one manages, on its own part, to identify and latch on to a particular matching type of cell among the myriads of cells it bathes is still nearly as obscure as ever.

However, a bright ray of hope has appeared on the horizon, coming from the field most intimately concerned with the problems of specificity because of its direct bearing on human health—the field of immunology, the self-defense of higher organisms against harmful invaders of alien and incompatible chemical constitution, whether microbes or organic compounds. A special segment of the population of white blood cells of a body that has been penetrated by the foreign chemicals (antigens) can turn out proteins (antibodies) molded to match some features of the antigen molecule; antibody and antigen thereby become related, in a vague analogy, like two adjoining pieces of a jigsaw puzzle, and as the former combines with the latter by virtue of reciprocal fitting, it captures or in some other way renders the invader innocuous. This is the process for which Paul Ehrlich was the first to suggest the metaphoric key-lock simile. But recent work in many lands has brought the understanding of the actual molecular processes involved down from that symbolic level to realistic hypotheses linking up with the advances in molecular genetics. If strengthened and widened by further research, this might become the advance post from which the universal principle of matching specificities could be brought nearer to our understanding.

Epilogue

The practical examples of the preceding sections intimate why the outlook in biology seems not all gloomy. I believe, though, that progress could be faster, steadier, and on a broader front if the research forces could distribute themselves more evenly and widely over the vast field remaining to be explored. There is need to rekindle target- or goal-consciousness and the will to make deliberate choices of goals with a deep sense of relevance, as counterpoise to the downdrift of mass movement along lines of least effort with nothing but piles of trivial and redundant data in its wake. Much as I admire the progress in the life sciences in this century if measured as a relative increment over the past, it must appear diminutive to anyone who is aware of the enormous distance yet to be traveled—and traveled the hard way—to reach a true, comprehensive, and consistent understanding of the phenomena of life.

This assessment of the current state of the science of life will seem to some to be too sweeping, to others too restrained. Phrased in the plural form—life sciences—it would indeed have to be qualified, as some branches are far ahead of others in their development. At any rate, with due allowance for the margin between optimistic and pessimistic interpretation, my assessment clearly disavows the contention that we are in the midst of a *"knowledge* explosion". The semblance of one has come from using the wrong yardstick. No doubt, there has been a data explosion, liberally equatable with an *"information"* explosion, though not all of the collected data are truly informative. Furthermore, since a data-oriented research enterprise is prodded by its sponsors, supporters, administrators, and auditors, who provide and control its wherewithal, to publish serial installments of work progress as tangible evidence of productivity, if not necessarily creativity, we are also faced with a *publication* explosion. But *"knowledge"* explosion? Not by criteria of measurement on a scale of relevance. Major steps in our approximation to the missing answers to the great unsolved questions in biology seem not to have come significantly oftener in the second half of the past hundred years than in the first; some were more massive, perhaps, but the pediatrician is wary of the distinction between growth and obesity.

(For a more detailed critical discussion of the factual and conceptual state of life science, the reader is referred to a book by the author, LIFE, ORDER, AND UNDERSTANDING: A THEME IN THREE VARIATIONS. Supplement to The Graduate Journal, The University of Texas, Austin, Texas, 1970.)

Science Looks at Itself*

Science looks at itself. This title evokes the picture of a lady looking in a mirror. Do you believe that she would ever take an honestly detached view of herself, objective and critical? And if she did, would she pass on to you the mirror's unflattering revelations? But science, purporting to be free from the human frailty of self-delusion and claiming for itself the right to criticize, must also be prepared to accept criticism—to become self-critical. We scientists proudly proclaim the present as the "Age of Science." But, mind you, people also speak of the "Age of the Child," without implying that there may not be brats as well as angels. Science, to some, is Lady Bountiful, to others is the Villain of the Century. Some years ago, a book called it our "Sacred Cow," and certainly to many it has at least the glitter of the "Golden Calf." Glorification at one extreme, vituperation at the other—are these perhaps grotesque reflections from distorting mirrors, as in a fun house? How does it look in an undistorted view?

Although I shall try to sketch this view objectively and critically, you must keep in mind that, steeped as he is in the discipline of the scientific method, even the scientist, who after all is human, can never quite escape unconscious biases. Consequently, the title *A Scientist Looks at Science* might have been more appropriate, for what I shall give you is essentially a personal view. But, luckily, I find that it is shared by many other experienced men of science.

First of all, you will recognize that science is on the move, expanding evermore in scope, diversity, and impact on man's future. Almost every day brings new developments, new insights, and new vistas. Recruitment draws in ever larger groups. The public, looking to science as a substitute for magic, adds to this gathering momentum through faith and hope, as well as through funds, so that within a century a sparse array of solitary workshops has evolved into a gigantic mass-operation of industrial dimensions.

*Reprinted in part from THE GRADUATE JOURNAL, Volume V, No. 1, pp. 43-59, 1962; and in part from "The Message of Science". Occasional Paper No. 1, The Rockefeller Institute Press, 1959.

This eruption of science into a major social enterprise is a climactic step in the evolution of our civilization. As such, it bears the signs of any evolutionary crisis. Science, like any organic system, must rely for its proper development and function on a reasonable degree of harmony among the many different parts that constitute its operating body. Or speaking metaphorically, its gears—concepts, methods, terms, units, managerial devices—must keep meshing properly if the composite machine of which they form the parts is to remain fit to operate, even as its pattern undergoes the evolutionary remodelling. However, when the usually conservative and steady evolutionary drive goes on a spree, with each part trying violent, novel excursions, unmatched and unadjusted to those of other parts, the inconsistencies among the innovations are bound to set up strains and stresses within the evolving system. Given time for adaptation, such inner conflicts can be reconciled, and the new integral structure will survive and prosper in its new form. Yet, evidently, the faster the change, the less time there is for adaptation and the greater the risk that the new structure may lose cohesion and collapse.

This is precisely the risk with which we are faced today in science. Old standard patterns prove no longer adequate for the immensely expanded and differentiated conditions of the present, let alone for the wider prospects of the future. By a patchwork of unrelated corrective efforts, we try to meet each contingency or stress signal separately as it arises, often to find that the very measures that relieve one symptom create a whole group of unexpected new ones. We have barely begun to grope for that integrative wisdom which would ensure to the emerging new estate of modern science that inner consistency without which it cannot remain strong, viable, effective, and equal to its task. Whether or not you are aware of them in your workday routine, the stresses and strains of our expanding universe have already produced some rather serious danger signs. And if one tries to trace the origin of these stresses, one finds it in the incompatibilities between the different nostrums administered to alleviate the growing pains in the various areas tributary to science, such as research, education, publication, financing, administration, manpower development, and public account-ability. In each one of these areas, new problems spring up continually, followed by a frantic search for separate symptomatic remedies. Yet, in essence, they are all part of a single common syndrome in need of conjoint focal therapy.

Some conscious efforts in this direction are under way. The major agencies and institutions and foundations concerned with the support and pursuit of scientific research and education are becoming increasingly cognizant of the fact that to fit science into its *new mold* is not a job that can be done piecemeal. Harmonizing the separate components in evolutionary development requires that they be seen and understood in their interdependence, which calls for vision, broad perspective, and judicious appraisal. But, obviously, no such appraisal can have substance unless it is based on a clear view of just precisely what the substance and objectives of science are. And here a further difficulty enters, namely, that the baseline itself is changing. That is to say, as science tries to adjust to its growing scope, the environment in which it operates and which, in some measure, bears on its objectives does not remain stationary, either. *Science*, after all, does not live in a vacuum. It is generated by real people, in a real setting of cultural, intellectual, economic, and social conditions, and these realities are likewise in a process of precipitous evolution. So science, in addition to all its internal adjustments, will also have to keep in tune with the developments of the social scene, of which it is an integral part.

Taking both needs together, it becomes perfectly evident that a comprehensive, penetrating and open-minded review, rethinking and re-evaluation of all the fundamental aspects of this expanding enterprise called science is imperative if we are to forestall the possibility of failure and disintegration inherent in the blind trial-and-error, hit-or-miss game of evolution through laissez-faire. The problems are perplexing and every scientist has a stake in their sane solution.

It is a fact that practically all groups responsible for sponsorship and support of science have reached a fair diagnosis. As for the therapy, however, they have not gotten much further, fundamentally, than they have with cancer. Nor do I think that any formula or medication for science contrived by even the wisest minds can be effective unless it is absorbed and responded to by those working at the grass-roots. Planning is one thing, but enlightened compliance is something else again; (enforcement, let us hope, to remain just a nightmare). Enlightenment presupposes open eyes and minds, clear prospects, unobstructed vision, and undeterred drive toward the envisaged goal. These precious faculties are hard to come by, yet they are most vital if science is to prosper as it should.

In the great unrelenting campaign of knowledge versus ignorance, all students of science must, for their own intelligent self-direction learn to comprehend the objectives, the strategy, and the tactics of the campaign. With the object shown, explained, appreciated, and accepted, they can orient themselves voluntarily toward it in their own conscience. Only then will the budding scientist be able to join this common enterprise responsibly as a free agent, instead of being impressed into enforced compliance with what some masterminding group might have decreed for him within their blueprint for scientific or social progress.

This latter possibility is by no means fiction. In saying this, I am not thinking necessarily of the endemic political pressure for the establishment of a separate Department of Science in the government, but I have in mind the indoctrination and eventually, no doubt, command performances of scientists in the service of prescribed utilitarian ends, as has occasionally been propagated. Repugnant though this antidote to social irresponsibility may seem to you, as it does to me, do not be blind to the validity of its underlying premise, which is that progress implies directive movement rather than random motions; hence a society bent on progress might have to abrogate the freedom for random movement which some mistakenly regard as a cherished prerogative.

Surely, a joint adaptive effort to meet the obligations of the new age of science needs direction. Need for direction is self-evident. The crucial argument concerns its source: direction from above or self-direction of the individual? Of course, the issue is not really so sharply drawn, for any system of science under whatever social and political doctrine contains free agents as well as underlings. The question is rather one of sound proportions between both and the degrees of freedom and self-determination left to either. Since science, I believe, cannot possibly flourish in the long run except with the fullest freedom for the competent individual to exert his mind, I would extend, rather than restrict, the scope of individuals in science and consequently, since direction there need be, strengthen the case for self-direction. A heightened sense of responsibility for judicious self-direction seems to me the only effective antidote to the alternative that someone in or out of government, benevolent or otherwise, would commandeer science and scientists.

Yet, self-direction, as in navigation, requires beacons and bearings to point the destinations and chart the course. At this point, if science had a face and could look in the mirror, it should see itself blush, for I believe that, on the whole, it has neglected of late to make these aids to navigation sufficiently explicit to those entering the field.

I believe that it has failed in three regards, bearing respectively on its conduct, its spirit, and its mission. I therefore shall devote my further discussion to these points, hoping to add, if only in small measure, to the sense of direction—self-direction—of those who enter science. The scientist has three solemn tasks: to augment scientific knowledge, to cultivate the scientific spirit, and to practice living by its code.

The growth of knowledge is as intricate and complex as is the growth of organisms. Research, as the gathering of data, is only the beginning. Data in themselves do not make sense. To become effective, they must be sorted, ordered, diffused, correlated, rearranged, digested, and rated in their bearings on concepts and theories which they may confirm, contradict, or modify. In this process of digestion, the worthwhile data, the foodstuffs, may lose their identity, and the gatherers may lose their credit lines.

You realize, of course that science is no longer an affair of solitary dreamers, explorers, and inventors, but has become an intricate, almost industrialized, mass endeavor. While the basic instrument of the scientific process is still the human individual with his brain, there is no longer such an individual as the complete and perfect and all-around "scientist," and it takes the combined aptitudes of many to serve in the collective endeavor that is science. It takes the observer, the gatherer of facts, the experimenter, the statistician, the theorist, the classifier, the technical expert, the interpreter, the critic, the teacher, the writer. It needs the help of all hands at all stations, from the research man who conceives a new idea to the assistants who prepare solutions or tend cultures or animals; from the mechanic who builds a new instrument to the artist or photographer who prepares indelible records of micro-scopic specimens or physiological tracings; and last, not least, from the man who willingly gives of his time and effort in order to help obtain and distribute some of the most basic tools of science—fellowships, research grants, materials, and jobs—to the one who willingly accepts them to good advantage. They all work for a common cause and should feel above the unjustified and undignified popularity contests that center on such monomaniac questions as: Who is "more important," the "basic" or the "applied" scientist? The explorer or the instructor? The technical expert or the philosopher? They are all needed—each in his proper station. They should be rated not by what they are doing but by how they are doing it.

Competence, resourcefulness, scholarship, craftsmanship, imagination, self-criticism, discipline, honesty, responsibility, and logical clarity are the only valid criteria of merit; not whether one devotes himself to exploring the vegetation of the jungle or the permeability of a cell membrane. Good work in any line will bring success. Given some luck, discoveries will come abundantly, as Pasteur said, to the "prepared mind." Opportunities are the richer the wider the field and the more there is yet to be discovered; chances the better the more freely an individual of good sense can strike out for himself, free from the tyranny of fashion and the lure of popularity.

The realization of this interdependence is a prime prerequisite to achieving greater effectiveness in the scientific process. Yet, it must go hand in hand with continued emphasis on the role of the individual mind in this process. Let us delegate what can be delegated to machines, but reserve for the human mind what it is uniquely suited to form—concepts, thoughts, and ideas. Not every mind is fit for this kind of endeavor; hence, to impress those less qualified into its service means lowering the efficiency of scientific progress. Yet, not to give full scope and opportunity to those who do have the necessary endowment is even worse, and certainly accounts for the spectacular waste of our most precious resource—human ability.

We indulge in this waste in several ways—*educationally*, by premature specialization, which narrows the chances of a budding investigator to fit his occupation to his aptitudes, and by overtraining and indoctrination, which limit his vision and power for intelligent self-orientation; *administratively*, by overloading the born research man with routine teaching or committee duties, or by forcing the effective teacher with no special bent for investigative work to do so-called research of mediocre quality; and *economically*, by disproportionate support of what happen to be the "hot" and popular trends of the day. Too little encouragement is given to the person willing to risk prospecting in new areas, new ideas, new methods, provided he has the proper imagination and discipline; too little to the crossing of conventional barriers of departmentalization and to adventuring in uncharted territory.

Now, it may seem that I am advocating here conflicting attitudes: first, group collaboration and then again assertion of free individual self-determination. However, these are not contradictory, if properly understood; in fact, in the reconciliation of group necessities and individual freedom lies the secret to scientific, just as to social, progress.

Of course, no single individual has all the necessary techniques and abilities at his command to do a full-sized job in science. Therefore, individuals have to supplement one another. This leads to team work. Perhaps "team" is a bad term, because it implies the presence of a driver. This is not always necessary. If you just give people of diverse talents and trainings a common focus, then unity of purpose and unified group success may readily emerge. Unfortunately, direction pointers of that kind are often missing. We shy away from them because of a certain unjustified stigma attached to the word "planning," misunderstood to be synonymous with "regimenting," that is, enforcement of a given plan. When you go on a trip to strange country, you do not pretend that anybody is regimenting you by giving you a road map; he is only telling you where the roads are, or where he thinks they are; but whether you use them and where you go is up to you as an individual. You still are in the driver's seat. The individual, however, can hardly be expected to choose intelligently his fitting station in this complex system unless he can choose from a clear over-all perspective. Instead, he now gets rather disparate, fragmental views, slanted from different isolated sectors. Along with this loss of unified perspective, there has grown a certain callous acquiescence in glaring discrepancies and cross-purposes, both as to subject matter and procedures. To cite just one example, there are almost as many disparate and mutually incompatible concepts of brain function as there are specialist approaches to its study. And yet, it is, of course, all the same brain. Why is the present generation so unmindful of gross inconsistencies among the verdicts of the different branches of investigation? Why? Because they have been narrowly indoctrinated by specialist sectarian traditions. There was a time when a student would be exposed to a wide variety of views, but now he is usually under the thumb of one local institution, one professor, one particular group, one doctrine, and he continues to groove himself ever more deeply in that particular rut.

This narrowing of both vision and range of concern is a natural by-product of the progressive fragmentation of science and of trends in our administrative and support policies in science. Fragmentation, in turn, is a by-product of that high degree of necessary specialization which is the key to mastery of any subject. But fragmentation without unified perspective leads to those imbalances and stresses to which I referred before. It leads to what one might call the draining force of favorite and fashionable lines. The principle is old. A pioneer trail, frequented heavily, develops into a boulevard. Such arteries have a way of draining traffic from competing smaller roads, eventually obliterating them. In science, too, the paths laid out by pioneers, improved and widened by their followers, tend to become popular and crowded highways attracting those who look for easy travel. People stream into them because of some prophecy or illusion that at the end lies the solution to this or that fundamental problem. Yet many such supposed royal roads have turned out to be roads to nowhere. In our present state of groping uncertainty, unable to predict just where the breakthroughs will come, we cannot possibly afford to gamble on singling out just a few roads for massive advances, if this involves, as it does, the risk of draining vital resources from all other, and perhaps from potentially more profitable, sectors in between.

This might be likened to the dynamics of irrigation. The heavier and swifter the major streams, the larger will be their drainage area, so that instead of finding ourselves with a uniformly irrigated and cultivated land of knowledge, we will end up with an erosion landscape, with a few major fertile canyons separated by vast arid mesas. I am afraid our social hydrodynamics is working in just that direction. As manpower, funds, and facilities keep growing, they are increasingly funneled into established lines to the point of inflation, instead of being more equitably apportioned over the entire research front for ever-new probings into the unknown. A gold rush justifies itself by its returns. But when its claims rest on no firmer base than rumor, misinformation, or promoter's optimism, it does incalculable harm, not by its own futility, but by diverting prospectors from broader explorations.

Thus fragmentation threatens not only to destroy perspective but also to distort research and teaching into bizarre patterns. As science advances, we see more and more new problems opening up, more of the old conclusions in need of reappraisal, but we have neither the manpower nor the resources needed to man this widening front, for they are being siphoned into the easy channels of mass application. Where the need for exploration is greatest, explorers are scarcest. Adding to this the fact that as the number of scientists increases, the gain tends to accrue more to the ranks of the less imaginative than to the ranks of the highly gifted, our predicament is clear: it is not that we shall learn "more and more about less and less," but mostly the opposite—that we shall remain so sorely ignorant about ever more and more.

How is it possible that in our state of ignorance we commit ourselves with such abandon to the pursuit of relatively few and far-between courses, at the risk of the collapse of the whole front? True, fragmentation has set the trend, and loss of perspective has blinded us to its risks. But the basic motivation to follow the easy course lies, I believe, elsewhere—in the psychology and sociology of contemporary science.

You realize, of course, that the well-channeled roads of mass traffic are also the ways of least effort and resistance, offering the security that lies in numbers and the comfort that comes with conformity. To travel them now does not call for the vision and daring and devotion of the pioneer who built them. Procedures are neatly mapped out, equipment ready made, and tangible results are the more certainly assured, the more narrowly circumscribed the task. While the contribution of the individual may be infinitesimal, the cumulative product of the crowd adds up to an impressive record in which each participant may claim credit. The risk is small and the reward assured. And this, of course, appeals to those who crave security. Coincidentally, our prevailing system of research support by project grants plays into their hands and confirms them in their attitude.

The project system, which allocates funds for a specific purpose, is admirably suited for developmental work; that is, for tasks that can be clearly circumscribed by one who knows essentially what he wants to find and can spell out in detail how he will go about finding it. It likewise is suited to the testing of an existing theory, to the broadening of an existing set of data, to the improvement of an existing technique or to the elaboration of existing doctrine. At any rate, it places a premium on the continuation of existing trends rather than on the exploration of news ones, and the very source of scientific discovery, the inductive process, the prospecting of the wholly unknown, is given little chance.

Now, fortunately most of the agencies endowing research, whether public or private, have come to realize this situation and do not always hold a grantee to the delivery of specific goods he has contracted for, as long as he keeps on delivering some useful goods. But even when they subscribe to the philosophy of some free, unprescribed, and unpredictable research, they feel ill at ease for fear that the powers whose funds they administer might disapprove. This eying of possible public reaction makes research money, except for periods of national emergency, flow more readily into conservative projects of predictable outcome than into more imaginative ventures of greater risk, yet infinitely more promising of future profit yield. Thus the average investigator, who shuns unorthodox ventures, and his average public sponsor are actually well in accord: they both want to play safe.

The roots of this development do not lie wholly in sociological and economic conditions. Part of them lie simply in our education, and this realization points to a remedy. A generation that is raised, for better or worse, with security rather than with aspirations and with comfort rather than exertion as the designs for living is, after all, not well equipped to take the gamble of a pioneering life in science, or even to underwrite the risks of others willing to take it.

Fortunately, however, there is a brighter side to this. I do not believe that the course I have just described is inexorable and could not be reversed by a sound educational philosophy. Pioneering, after all, is not a mass procedure. It does not take many men to make a discovery, and we have a goodly quota of apt candidates in our student population. I see them daily: curious, determined, bright, and eager to advance the frontiers of science. Trustingly they turn to us for guidance, and what do we do? This may be a harsh pronouncement, but we misguide them. We misguide them by giving them a biased and overoptimistic picture of our present state of knowledge. While we dwell on our accomplishments, of which we may be rightfully proud, we are less candid about the vast expanse of the unknown yet to be conquered. We give them hard and fast answers where uncertainty ought to be stressed, we pass debatable opionions for facts, we pretend knowledge where there is none by hiding plain unknowns behind suggestive allusions. In short, we impart to them a sense of smug satisfaction that the essential information is all in and that nothing remains to be done but to round it out and fill in some missing links. How can we then expect them to see what we so carefully conceal? Instead of training them to face up to the unknown, we help them turn their backs to it. And why do we do this? Again, to give them a sense of security, I suppose, and false security, at that. This we can change.

Adventure, effort, perspective, a sense of relevance, and personal responsibility must be put back where they belong in science, in the front ranks of essentiality. Minds are meant to walk, not to be carried. Those of us who are teachers, investigators, and administrators must prod our students to assert their individual potentials. The scientific process is based on the insecurity of adventure, and if we want to revitalize our whole research structure we have to do something about bringing people up in this spirit and with the mental and moral stamina to "take it." Risk-taking must be restored to respectability. However, lest it lead to sheer waste motion in random straying, it must be coupled with (1) a clearer exposition of the nature of the scientific process, its objectives, rules, and methods, and an honest and true perspective of the problems in each field, particularly the unsolved ones; (2) a heightened sense of responsibility on the part of the investigator so that he will be more conscientious and selective in the self-direction of his efforts; and (3) help to each proven man in finding a type of work for which he is genuinely suited, and giving him the means to concentrate on it.

Whichever way we phrase these problems and proposed solutions, they all return us to a common nucleus—the human individual. No organizational design becomes effective or defective save through the men and women who execute it. It may be sad that this needs emphasizing, but it does; particularly in view of some current illusions about the potentialities of so-called team-work. No one familiar with the scientific process can share the hope that, by hitching large numbers of scientists to a common treadmill, their aggregate effort will, by some sort of collective super-intelligence, turn out discoveries of staggering novelty. Discovery always takes shape in single brains. The building up of teams of workers of different training and viewpoints is a wonderful device to supplement, but not supplant, what only the individual mind and intellect can do—think. In science, there is no substitute for human intelligence, so let us not act as if there were. If many of the secrets of nature still lie unknown behind closed doors, let us not spend most of our efforts on ramming in those doors by blind mass pressure, but rather let more individuals get busy looking for the keys or figuring out the combination of the locks.

To accomplish this, let us single out early those budding investigators who have native curiosity, imagination, and drive and put them in their proper place in the front lines of exploration before they are sucked into the ranks of mass routine. They can be rescued from mediocrity, if we would only encourage them to assert leadership, productive scholarship, and pioneering spirit; show them the virtue of taking calculated risks; help them sense the thrill of personal achievement; make them discover pleasure in effort and exertion, as in sports; and imbue them with the constant urge to probe for new directions, new objects, new techniques, and, above all, new concepts and new insights gained by views taken from unusual angles. Cunning and daring must find favor again over sheer plodding, and critical self-direction must take the place of drifting with the current. Let us restore respect for systematic and unhurried work, and arouse suspicion of the flashy, but ill-supported, claim that trades passing notoriety for lasting truth, and raise that sense of responsibility and pitiless self-criticism without which even the best man is prone to go to seed.

These thoughts are addressed to all those in education, administration, direction and support of research, with opportunities to detect and develop potential leaders. To sum it up, if all of us, in full awareness of what a growing science needs in order to thrive, will direct our individual efforts to this common need, even at the expense of comfort; and if we can carry on our tasks in a beneficent climate of healthy economics, public understanding and intellectual freedom, the prospects of science in our age are indeed bright. Knowledge will grow and, like a growing tree, throw off as fruit a rich crop of tangible deliveries for the prosperity and welfare of mankind.

But is that material yield all that science has to offer? To be sure, we must not sneer at gains in hardware and in pills. If, through the works of science, more men will attain a higher-than-marginal standard of living—with starvation, pestilence, and pain ever-more-narrowly retrenched—it will have been quite a feat. But there is something more that science can offer. Enchanted by the fruits shown on the market, we let ourselves be too readily distracted from looking at the process by which the tree that bore those fruits has grown. This growth process itself conveys a message—my second point—and it is this: If science has been so patently successful, could man not emulate that success formula in some of his other, thus far less successful, undertakings?

The formula is no secret. It is called "scientific spirit." Its power stems from the strict mental discipline and critical detachment that it imparts to those who live and practice by its code. And if living by this code can help men lead more satisfying lives, so as more fully to enjoy and share promised release from want and drudgery; if, just as an example, scientific advances will not only bring man more leisure time, but scientific spirit will spark him to enjoy it in creative self-improvement, instead of as a passive onlooker at prefabricated mass performances; if science will not just extend man's life span, but render the content of that life span more purposeful; if science can convince man that many of the evils and errors and convulsions of the present age stem from his ignorance and neglect of the very code of science; then science will truly have given him another noble gift—a basis for responsible and judicious self-direction as a design for living.

For we take it to be axiomatic that within the frame set him by God, Nature, or whatever other symbol you use to refer to that principle which sets his limits, Man is free to choose his course for better or for worse. And in this choice, a dose of scientific spirit can help him to avoid predictably disastrous turns and missteps. Man may make foolish uses of scientific *products*, but the scientific *spirit* can teach him reason. At any rate, science is not to blame for man's misdirecting scientific knowledge to evil ends.

Now, just what is it that marks this spirit as superior to the mere application of logic, the Golden Rule, or just plain common sense? The answer is: the categorical demand for *validation* and *verification* of each premise, each contention, and each conclusion by the most rigorous and critical tests of evidence. Every rule and law has to be tested and enforced, and nowhere else is the penalty for error or infringement so prompt and telling. Misjudging public pressures may do no more than sweep a politician out of office; but miscalculating wind or water pressures in the design of towers or dams will surely doom those structures to collapse. Thus, by reward and punishment, *scientific method*, the embodiment of scientific spirit, teaches man to discipline his thinking and his actions based on thought.

This discipline of the scientific method, broadly applied, can go far toward clearing the underbrush of superstition and prejudice that hamper civilization in its march. By its incisiveness, the scientific spirit will leave its mark wherever men strive to overcome obscurity and obscurantism.

But it has limitations. According to the code of science, no positive assertions are final. All propositions are approximations, and indeed are provisional, pending conclusive proof that all alternative propositions are untenable. Viewed in this light, science is seen to advance more by denying what is wrong than by asserting what is right—by reducing, and eventually eradicating errors, rather than by heading straight toward some preconceived final truth.

Look at it this way: Mankind is facing the vast realm of the unknown, which must be conquered. From any point along the frontier of knowledge, the imagination and curiosity of individual men start treks that radiate in all directions into this virgin jungle. Through trial and error, one gradually comes to single out the right path, as the successful survivor from the multitude of tested and discarded blind alleys. Now, what endows a trek into the wilderness with such survival value? What makes it right? Simply the fact that it has not remained a blind and isolated venture, but has met, instead of missing, other new or familiar lines that had struck out from other points, merging with them in mutual reinforcement. Success lies in the confluence of thoughts from many diverse directions.

This is of first importance. A blind path driven into the unknown stays blind, its fate unknown, until it meets with other paths, the intersection giving both a valid check of their respective bearings. The unknown is not conquered until it has become so thoroughly pervaded by this network of trails that trains of thought can travel from any place or any subject in the universe to any other place or subject without encountering stops or gaps or frontiers with a sign "Do Not Trespass." This is what gives to science its coherence and consistency, with a stable, interconvertible intellectual currency of terms and units, modes of operation, and standards of proof or disproof. But remember that the way in which science gains this structural unity and strength is by gradually removing the inconsistencies and incongruities within the system: by the systematic reduction of margins for error.

In taking this course, science has adopted the time-tested method of organic evolution, but on an infinitely faster scale. According to current concepts, organic forms evolve as follows: Within each species a major stock of heritable characteristics is passed down conservatively from generation to generation. Every so often, changes—so-called mutations—spring up in the basic repertory. When these are recombined in the offspring from slightly divergent parents they may lead to novel characters. These emergent properties, never before subject to the test of survival value, more often than not turn out to be failures, blind alleys. The few new products, however, which are improvements, assert themselves by their competitive success and mark an enduring forward step in the advancement of the species, provided they benefit the total interbreeding population.

Mutations, thus, are like the blind probings of advancing knowledge; in both, success comes not from designing the fit, but from routing out the unfit. Yet, thought processes—the probings of the mind—while following the model of genetics, are infinitely faster. The unit of genetic probing is the time it takes for a generation to test its endowment and either win or lose the test; for man, about a quarter century, one generation. Knowledge's mutations—the novel ideas emerging from spontaneous inspirations or from hybrid crossing in a single mind of two unrelated parent lines of thought—take much less time to prove their soundness; so little time in fact, that in a single generation we have witnessed the most startling advances of modern physics, chemistry, medicine, and agriculture.

This, then, gives man his unprecedented chance for rapid progress, but progress, let me repeat, arises, as in evolution, from the incessant weeding out of error. Thus, truth in scientific terms is not approached as one would seek a goal—by heading straight toward a distant beacon, visible or visualized. The individual scientist may proceed that way, but as for science as a whole, what it regards as truth is but that strip of possibilities left over after all demonstrable untruths have been trimmed away. And this will remain a fairly broad band of uncertainty, including the indeterminate, the unknown, the indeterminable, and the unknowable.

It is a sobering experience for the scientist thus to acknowledge the finite boundaries of his reach. It takes humility and courage to live with partial answers, and it disturbs complacency. Yet, if this critical scientific spirit can cure more men of their cocksureness that they already know the answers to questions yet unsolved, then science will have given man a new resolve to search and strive again, not just to conform; to face his problems, not to accept pat solutions; to exercise his ingenuity, instead of dully abdicating to authority. The scientific spirit will thus rekindle flames which one of science's products—mechanization—threatens to smother.

But then again, by the same token, science must judge its own scope with no less critical detachment. This precept is not popular. With the exuberance of youth, science has often maintained not only that it is a cure-all for mankind's ills, but that it can prescribe ultimate goals to guide man's conduct. A mature science cannot condone such juvenile extremism. It must take into account the other claimants to a share in human destiny. And if it is to thrive and serve humanity, it must range itself among them as a partner, not set itself on top as the ruler.

The creative arts; philosophy; the kernel of religions (not of creeds); the lessons of the course of history; all of these are companions of science in shaping mankind's fate. Never mind that they at times have also shown monopolistic arrogance; this does not exculpate the scientist from blame if he does likewise. His own code holds him to curtailing error, and positive conclusions must remain confined to what is testable and can either be verified or negated. True, this code entitles science to pry into those other areas as auditor of their accounts, and sure enough, it finds a host of errors in their books. But the accounting done, there still remains wide open that broad band of beliefs in which the scientist can have no say being beyond his testing range. There rest the mysteries of the basic order and direction of the universe and of the ethical, aesthetic, and moral principles by which men live.

Of course, there have been scientific (and also pseudoscientific) doctrines purporting to explain such things as beauty, decency or sympathy. They may be right, but by science's own dictum they cannot prove it, because they cannot prove that those of opposite doctrine are wrong. So science would do well to concede and retreat to its proper province. Where science tries to be objective, barring the arbitrariness of the observing subject, the arts, by contrast, express man's urge to break out from the strait jacket of reality and find an outlet for his subjectivity. While science prefers to deal with classes of phenomena that are predictable, all history, by contrast, relates the singular, unique, and unpredictable. Science may be able to tell us what very probably will not happen, but it cannot tell us precisely what will happen next. Religions, in their plurality, reflect ethnic, social, and psychological differentiations among men that history and science might treat rationally. But by science's own verdict, religion as such, attesting to man's awareness of the limits of his rational cognition, retains its unassailable position alongside science, because it cannot be invalidated.

Science, to be consistent, must take this position of critical and modest self-appraisal and sober recognition of its own limits. No sophistry or verbal trickery, of wishful thinking or political design, can hide this need for those who see the broad perspective of our times. If science claims no greater share of man's allegiance than it can ask for on scientific grounds, if it will behave as educator rather than as conqueror, then the resentments, the suspicions, and the injunctions of those who have feared the aggressive expansionism of a youthful science will subside, and the barriers of prejudice can be let down on all sides. Civilization needs us all. Let us be friends. That is what I call "closing ranks."

What we must look and work for is a broad humanism where science is accepted understandingly by all men in all walks of life, not for its fruits alone, but for the ideal of rational thought which it can carry to its highest culmination. Yet at the same time, the men of science themselves must ever be on guard against the danger of specialist isolation in tunnels of mechanical robotism and rote performance, to the neglect of other human values. Science must neither let itself become de-humanized nor power-drunk. It has a mighty, not an almighty, mission.

I have spoken *of* science, but not *for* science. Some men of science share my views, others do not. Which have the greater number on their side, I do not know, nor does it matter, for the soundness of such arguments is not decided, like elections, by majority vote. New mutations or new ideas, when they arise, are always at first in the minority: but fitness makes such budding germs of progress spread. And from my station of individual judgment and free thought expression I make a final plea. I am alarmed by signs that an abuse of science may lead to humans being treated as merely "cases" for a gigantic statistical processing mill in which they are to be levelled to standards of the average, the common and the mediocre. Therefore, I make a plea to science to reacclaim diversity as a source of progress (for uniformity means death), including the diversity of human minds in their responsible expressions. And then I make another plea to the nonscientific humanists not to regard themselves as prime custodians of civilization, shunning science as if it were inhuman. Let none of us lodge in the Master's Mansion, but let us all move down into the servants' quarters, so that we may work together for human progress in harmonious cooperation. The tasks are large, our forces limited. No group can do the job alone. So, let us all close ranks, the men of science with those in other walks of life, for humanism and against the dehumanization of our culture.

Now, how much chance is there for such a meeting of minds and harmony of effort to become reality? In 1959, Sir Charles Snow delivered the Rede Lecture at Cambridge, THE TWO CULTURES AND THE SCIENTIFIC REVOLUTION, which aroused wide interest and comment. In it C. P. Snow exposes, deplores, and well nigh despairs of the widening gulf between what he calls the scientific and the traditional cultures, meaning the opposition of ideologies and attitudes of men of science and men of the arts.

In a thoughtful editorial, the British journal NATURE has tried to integrate Snow's thesis with my *Message of Science*, cited in the foregoing pages. NATURE comments as follows:

> If the scientific spirit can teach man reason, the message of science must, however, first be accepted by man, and it is Sir Charles Snow's contention that one of the two cultures he predicates as existing does not and will not accept that message. . . .
>
> The conception of the Message of Science and the place of the scientist in our civilization which Dr. Weiss expounds in this

address . . . . could well elicit the response he seeks from the non-scientists if it can reach them. But while Dr. Weiss recognizes as clearly as Sir Charles Snow the gap between the two cultures and the imperative need for cooperation between scientist and non-scientist, he does not indicate how the gap is to be bridged. It is true that, if his counsel is followed, scientists could do a good deal to remove the prejudices and suspicions which have enlarged the gap—or at least to remove the substance of those prejudices and suspicions; but something more is required to restore unity to the intellectual life of Western society, or even to provide a meeting place of the two cultures. The lack of comprehension of science and technology on the part of the non-scientist . . . must be removed also, and this, as he sees clearly, is a problem of education.

Indeed, the major key to the solution is education. Merely to speak of a solution introduces an optimistic note; for it implies that the purported cultural rent is not beyond repair. But must we even accept it for a fact that there is already a real rent running through the fabric of our culture, dividing a scientific from a nonscientific half? If so, of course, the two should be rejoined, the rent be mended. In terms of education, I suppose this means that each half should be given more instruction about the other, properly weighted to redress what C. P. Snow correctly diagnoses as the existing imbalance in disfavor of science. But then, this treats the matter as if there were two adversaries that had to be reconciled, rather than two partners whose bonds are to be strengthened. Yet, if the latter point of view is the correct one, then education's task would be to blur rather than sharpen the distinction between the two spotlighted extremes. Rather than as a strict antithesis, it should present them as the two ends of a continuous graded spectrum; it should stress increasingly the cultural content and role of science, but remain no less mindful of the nonscientific mainsprings of our culture.

Above all, it should uproot the absurd clichés and caricatures of both which have grown in the public mind and must not be allowed to be perpetuated among the young. If education can prevent those misconceptions from forming which equate science with technological gadgetry; history with anecdotal recitals of events; literature with an arbitrary judge, rather than creator, of values; and knowledge with a hodgepodge of miscellaneous data; then, I believe, the dreaded schism between science and nonscience need never come about.

And here is, I submit, where the main challenge lies for liberal arts colleges and their counterparts in universities and adult education programs. The unity, universality, and cohesiveness of culture, including science as an integral part, must be demonstrated and documented convincingly, not just professed in platitudinous generalities. This calls for the most critical selection of suitable and telling examples from the history of ideas, concepts, and discoveries to illustrate the mutual interaction between scientific maturation, on the one hand, and human progress and social evolution on the other. Such a disciplined unified overview should constitute a potent antidote to further fragmentation and dismemberment of what we call our culture. Even though only a minor fraction of the population will go through this experience, and only part of them will truly benefit from it, they are the ones whose judgment and voice will carry influence.

What I am pleading for, therefore, is that we strengthen in our educational system those programs in the middle layer which will resist the growing pressure for ever narrower specialization and fragmented professional training, and which will concentrate instead on raising an enlightened citizenry with real comprehension of what the universe, including man, is all about. However, let us be clear on one point. This is no easy task. To accomplish it will take more than running shallow, "data-" or "principle-oriented" survey courses. It will require the development of critical and balanced thinking in the student by exposing him methodically to sample exercises in areas in which scientific and extrascientific dictums have been at variance. He must learn to identify sham arguments based on inconsistent premises, incomplete evaluations, or dogmatic assertions. Education must fully return to the original literal meaning of the word, which is "to bring out" the student's faculties, not just "to stuff in" a lot of data.

But no such program could succeed unless the student himself were again ready and eager to be guided to such a station of broad and judicious overview of our civilization and of his role and duty in its preservation, instead of narrowly confining himself to the mere acquisition of tricks of the trade. Among the students of today are the leaders of tomorrow. Theirs is the task to keep our culture unified. But we, the teachers, ought to show them how; that is, provided we ourselves still know how.

And on this point, I have a practical suggestion. Let every college and university furnish each member of its teaching faculty with annual subscriptions to two periodicals from an approved list, with the only proviso that members of nonscientific departments choose them from a scientific field and vice versa or, better still, from publications of such broad cultural scope as to encompass both scientific and nonscientific content. Having such unfamiliar reading and thinking matter within reach at his desk or bedside table ought to go far in saving many a teacher from becoming ever more deeply grooved in that specialist isolation which even now keeps most of them from mustering the time, interest, and energy needed to secure the same literature from the library. The extra expense for the school budget would be incommensurably small in proportion to the potential effect of keeping teachers fit to bring up students to hold together the Two Cultures, if there be such.

Science in the University*

The great tides of change which have swept over the academic world, as over all our world, have moved familiar landmarks, submerged inhabited ground, and thrown up new islands to be explored. New fields of inquiry have emerged, old fields of inquiry face new problems, vast public support is thrown behind certain lines of endeavor, and not others. It is not surprising that this continuing process of change has produced in us a habitual attitude of re-examination and reappraisal of our goals, our assumptions, our values, and the distribution of our efforts. And, since the academic world is nothing if not articulate, this re-examination involves a great clamor of voices. Forward-looking men, who have foreseen the emerging patterns and find significance in them, welcome the changes; but at their side are the faddists and the opportunists and the unstable folk who would welcome and exploit *any* change. Sober and judicious men, who see the losses that come with tumultuous change, regret the breaks in continuity and the washing out of old landmarks; but at their side are the inert and the timid and the self-interested who would resist and condemn any changes.

Carnegie Corporation of New York, Annual Report, 1952, p.13

Because we are struggling to meet this multiplicity of rapidly changing aims through continual alterations in our educational system, it is perhaps not surprising that our educational world is in a continual ferment. But this ferment, though it is far-reaching, does not necessarily mean chaos. A modern and rapidly changing society inevitably must have a diverse and a rapidly changing educational system. Our society will be shocked from time to time by unexpected and startling events throughout the world. Such events may stimulate us to re-examine our educational procedures. But we cannot amend our educational system overnight, or suddenly remove our educational deficiencies. Our

Reprinted in abbreviated form from THE CONTEMPORARY UNIVERSITY: U.S.A. (Ed.: R. Morison). Houghton Mifflin Co., Boston, pp. 152-185, 1966. —Also in Daedalus, Vol. 93, no. 4, pp. 1184-1218, 1964.

system must be kept on an even keel, our educational goals must
be kept clear; we need to work steadily and not impulsively,
constantly to improve our system and to accept change as
inevitable and desirable.
*Education for the Age of Science. Statement by the President's
Science Advisory Committee: The White House, May 1959*

Preamble

Science has burst upon the stage of modern life with more aplomb
than foresight, and the universities must face and come to terms with
the precipitous changes that this so-called "scientific explosion"
impresses on our culture if they wish to retain their claim to leadership
in cultural evolution rather than to accept the passive role of drifters in
the wake of wholly extraneous trends. To examine the growing impact
of science on the universities is a timely and urgent undertaking; it
should, indeed, be made a continuous process.[1] There are two sides to
the problem. The university must find ways to keep accommodating
the legitimate expansive claims of science, but at the same time it must
protect itself against disproportionate expansion of the scientific
sectors beyond the stress limit at which the very ideal of a university as
a cohesive body would collapse.

From the manner in which the case of "science and the university"
is often stated within and without the academic precincts, one almost
gets the impression of adversaries in court or challengers from hostile
camps. It is deplorable that so much of the debate, on which weighty
decisions and actions hinge, should be carried on in a spirit of doctrinal
antagonism, with myopic concentration on extreme aspects of what in
truth is, or ought to be, despite diverse facets and graded scales, an
integral continuum—man's quest for knowledge.

By contrast, my main object in this essay will be to expound the
proposition that the issue of "science in the university," together with
all its subissues must be removed from the arena of conflicting
intellectual contentions. We ought not act like umpires in a game of win
or lose. The more one poses the issues in terms of mutually exclusive
alternatives and looks for universal master keys to their solution, the
further away one actually gets from any prospect of realistic resolution.
Attempts at categorical solutions—the symptoms of administrative
expediency—are doomed to failure.

For instance, the question of whether the universities should expand or contract their scientific engagements cannot be resolved in simple quantitative terms. A quota system is hardly applicable to any branch of learning. The issue is complex, and the only fruitful manner of approaching it is by untangling its intricacy, bringing the full diversity of its many detailed components into view, and shaping from them, after re-evaluation, programs sufficiently elastic to meet the unprecedented opportunities for growth, as well as the resultant stresses, that lie ahead.

First, let me clarify terminology. Just what are we talking about when we speak of "science" and when we speak of "the university"? After all, we are to deal with real institutions, not just with ideals or allegories.

What Is "Science"?

A search of laboratories or libraries for a representative and comprehensive miniature sample of "science," true, pure, and simple, would come to naught. The term is an abstraction. It simply signifies a collective operation of mankind in which countless different efforts and aptitudes are brought to bear conjointly on those aspects of knowledge that deal with nature. The basic motivation of science is man's curiosity, his wish to learn and know, accentuated by his practical experience that benefits are to be reaped from knowledge.

The quest for knowledge of itself is good, regardless of the uses men make of their knowledge, wise or foolish. Although only that part of knowledge which lends itself to verification or negation by the evidence of observation, experiment, and measurement is the legitimate province of natural science,[2] the land within those borders is so immense and variegated that no separate fraction of it can be taken to portray science truthfully. One-sided portrayals of science either as the exalted search for absolute truth or as a mundane preoccupation with practical results and products are symptoms of narrowly restricted vision, perceiving only limited absorption bands from the broad total spectrum covered by science. In consequence, the man of practical affairs more often than not tends to identify science with technology, whereas the academic purist conversely prefers to exclude from his definition of science all its practical applications in agriculture, engineering, medicine, statistics, and so forth.

However uninformed and short-sighted such distinctions may seem, there is no glossing over their widespread use and uncritical acceptance. The staggering internal diversity of science is not generally appreciated. Since this is surely not the occasion to list the multitude of diverse activities included in science, let me quote a passage from an earlier attempt I made to illustrate the point for my own field of biology (Science, vol. *118*: 33-34. 1953):

> Biologists, in the sense of miniature incarnations of universal biological knowledge, no longer exist. Biological science has become a group enterprise with many servants in varied stations. . . . Anyone contributing to this collective task constructively, competently, and conscientiously, thus becomes a biologist. Consequently, it takes all kinds of biologists to make the biological world, none of them able to carry on without the others. And biology needs their full diversity. . . . .
>
> It needs the student of evolutionary history as much as it does the experimental physiologist; the precise recorder of morphological data as much as the analytical biophysicist and biochemist; the investigator of molecular interactions as much as the student of supramolecular organization, of the order of events in space and time.

If it seems impossible to find a unified formula for even a section of science like biology, how much further from reality is the notion that science as a whole is uniform and can be treated as a single simple entity. The university could help to combat this notion by ceasing to lump all "science" into a membrane-bound homogenate. This, of course, might lead to an administrative monstrosity, but it would at least engender a more balanced overview of what "science" in the university really means. It would stress the enormous differences in kind, composition, and maturity of the different constituents of that "scientific" compartment, as widely disparate in their requirements of aptitudes and facilities as theoretical physics and descriptive botany. At the same time, it would blur the demarcation line between science and the humanities by recognizing their blending in philosophy, history, and even art.

I leave for later the question of how far the university is committed and how far it can afford to go in catering to this vast array of tributaries and ramifications of science without becoming what Robert Hutchins referred to as an "academic service station." For the moment, I would rather raise the sights upward to a feature of science which deserves special emphasis in the present context. It lies in the spiritual values imparted to those who share in its pursuit. That spirit of science, more than any specific training, is a most powerful ingredient of education, if education is defined with Corner as "preparation for effective living."

As I have stated more explicitly in the preceding article, the power of that scientific spirit "stems from the strict mental discipline and critical detachment that it imparts to those who live and practice by its code: this critical scientific spirit can give man a new resolve to search and strive again, not just conform; to face his problems, not accept pat solutions; to exercise his ingenuity, instead of dully abdicating to authority. The scientific spirit will thus rekindle flames, which one of science's products—mechanization—threatens to smother."

Why, then, are the broad cultural aspects of science not more generally recognized in the academic community? That failure constitutes a black mark not for science but for the faulty manner in which it is customarily taught.

There is no glossing over the fact that "liberal education" versus "scientific training" is turning from a slogan into a battlecry. Were both sides only to learn more about each other, the misconceptions and perverted meanings might readily subside. Of course there is a marked asymmetry to be corrected; for whereas scientists by and large respect the cultural mission of the humanities, the humanistic values and social virtues of science, in contrast to its utilitarian aspects, are rarely appreciated in the other camp. The lack of symmetry in mutual relations between scientists and non-scientists, which forms the core of C. P. Snow's "Two Culture" argument, is an indisputable fact. As a result, the profound relevance of science to education is still widely underrated. But since this is based, it seems, on sheer lack of acquaintance rather than on misjudgment, there is hope for remedial action.

It will have been plain from this discussion that I rate science, properly presented, as a major rather than an auxiliary component of "Liberal Education." Here is further supporting testimony:

No one discipline or combination of disciplines provides the unique avenue to the liberation of the mind. The natural sciences—in the first flush of enthusiasm—once thought that they had the golden key to enlightenment, but sensible scientists no longer make this assertion. On the other hand, thoughtful people will find just as ridiculous the currently fashionable characterization of the physical and biological sciences as almost the antithesis of a liberal education—fit only to produce soulless technicians, illiterate in philosophy, innocent of moral values, and strangers to the creative life of the mind and spirit. The physical and biological sciences provide as great play for the creative spirit as do the literary fields. There are as many technicians-without-values in the fine arts as in the sciences. The intellectual climate in which we live has been fashioned in no small part by the physical and biological sciences, and no educated man can ignore their contributions, nor indeed frame a philosophy without them.[6]

So much for the role of science in general education. The reciprocal contributions of a literal education to the making of a good *scientist** have been stressed so often and so convincingly that it would seem superfluous to labor them once again. Two aspects, however, call for comment. The first is that it seems unnecessary to single out the scientist as specially benefiting from a broad liberal education, the chief aim of which is, after all, to turn out educated, responsible, and judicious citizens. The second aspect, which has two facets, presents greater problems. It raises the old question of the optimum ratio between the irreducible common denominator of a general education

---

*I am using the term here in its more exalted sense, as defined, for instance, in the statement by the President's Science Advisory Committee on "Scientific Progress, the Universities, and the Federal Government" (The White House, November 15, 1960), on pp. 4-5. "By the word 'scientist' we mean someone who is fit to take part in basic research, to learn without a teacher, to discover and attack significant problems not yet solved, to show the nature of this process to others—someone, in short, who is equipped to spend a lifetime in the advancement of science, to the best of his ability."

("for effective living") for all professionals, including the prospective
workers in any branch of science, and the essential requirements for
professional preparation ("for greatest effectiveness in one's chosen
occupation"). But it also raises the new question, emerging with the
growth in volume of science, whether that optimum is alike for
everyone going into science. Is it the same for those who are destined
by unusual aptitude, vision, aspirations, dedication, and courage to
approximate the ideal of all-around "scientists," capable of promoting
knowledge by steps of telling significance, as it is for the ever-growing
proportion of those who neither desire nor would be qualified for such
an august station, but who are content to execute competently tasks of
limited scope, as partners in that glorious campaign for human
betterment that goes by the collective term of "science"?

The process of differentiation of tasks in our society has reached
the stage at which corresponding differentiations in the schools
preparing for those tasks become unavoidable—in the case of science,
moreover, requiring further adaptation to the heterogeneity within the
field itself. The voices advocating earlier specialization among science
students are growing louder; but so are the counterclaims for keeping
higher education unified through at least the early years of graduate
school. It surely would be disastrous if one were to allow the branching
points to be determined by power equilibria between vocational
empiricists on the one side and academic purists on the other.

There are auspicious beginnings of a penetrating general discussion
of this issue, but the deliberations seem to suffer from an unwarranted
timidity. It looks as if there were no choice except to emasculate either
liberal education or professional propaedeutics, whereas what is called
for is not a decision in favor of one against the other, but rather a
combination of both in balanced proportions. The same applies to
decisions about teacher training, technician training, administrative
training, and other fields, as well. The problems cannot be solved by
extremists, either by ultraconservatives rockbound in status-quo positions or by ultraprogressives submitting to the momentum of political
and economic pressures. Unquestionably, the growing differentiation of
the scientific process has created the need and explicit demands for a
corresponding educational differentiation that would split the various
specialized branches of the academic tree even further down into and

off their common stem. However, if this process were allowed to go too far, the whole trunk would lose coherence and fall apart. And since this limit will appear different to the men living in the trunk and to those living in the branches, "science" cannot claim to enter the negotiations with a single unified voice.

The pressures for an earlier separation of the branches of professional training from the trunk line of general education are, of course, a reflection of the progressive fragmentation of science into ever more specialized branches—a familiar subject for both complaints and justifications. The trend is here and must be faced. Its impact on the university is clear. The challenge, I believe, can be met only by better differentiation of What for Whom? Differentiation, rather than standardization, must become the key objective of the modern university. It seems to me quite feasible to resolve the conflict between the increasing clamor for *early technical specialization,* to fill the growing manpower needs of industry and government, and the equally vigorous assertion of the primacy of a *broad general education* as the sole means of salvaging that rare and precious resource of the future, the creative scientist. All that would be required would be a modulated application of both principles in different proportions of emphasis designed to fit the different types of candidates—those bent on simple training in the "tricks of the trade" at one end of the scale and those eager for a broad background of knowledge at the other.

It is worth noting that a common misconception blames the employers—industry and the professions—for the overemphasis on specialized training in universities, while my experience has been that by and large they would prefer to have academic institutions furnish them with open-minded, roundly educated people, albeit with general technical competence, rather than with indoctrinated specialist robots who would have to be retrained "on the job" anyhow. The main pressure for early specialization seems, on the contrary, to come from the prospective employees, the crowd of individuals who are heading for a limited occupational field in which to earn a living and who want to get there as directly and quickly as possible. Since this applies to large numbers of prospective physicians, chemists, veterinarians, teachers, engineers, and others, one can rightfully question whether it is justifiable to shortchange on their account the more highly motivated and qualified minority of budding genuine and creative scientists by forcing them to share the same pablum with the average, who do not care for a richer diet.

Having said this, let me add at once however, that much as I advocate discriminative treatment for different groups according to their respective aspirations and aptitudes, I still think it would be ruinous to surrender to the growing demands for almost pure professional or vocational training at the expense of breadth and flexibility, comparable to the raising of sterile workers in an ant colony. Thus, having made the case for separating, though on a graded scale, "scientists" from specialized practitioners, I gladly associate myself with Gerard Piel in his remarks on the education of the engineer:

> Having distinguished science from engineering by implication here, I should like to set that distinction aside. Such distinction always raises troubling metaphysical, not to mention social, questions of hierarchy and pecking order. Let it be said simply that understanding and control are inseparable. Engineering, as the closest coupling of science to society, is too widely celebrated for its utility and not enough for its creativity. What is more, engineering derives as much historical significance from the challenges it lays to understanding as from the applications it makes of understanding. . . . To careers in science, therefore, society must summon independent spirits. This is no work for the artisan equipped with slide rule and handbook, for the intellectual mercenary with his talents at auction. The survival and welfare of an expanding world population hang on the vigorous expansion of the public domain of science and on the efficiency and equity with which it is exploited. Men of science must be independent men, with the vision to comprehend the context of their work and the courage to assert their independence in it.[7]

After accepting such a high-principled design for socially responsive science education, how can one translate it into practice with due regard to the growing diversity of needs, interests, talents, and economic limitations which the university must face? Can the university inherited from yesterday measure up to today's desiderata, which will be tomorrow's necessities? This, then, at last raises the question: Who is this "University" to which we are referring in the singular?

Who Is "the University"?

It will be noted that I have posed the question in the personified form of "Who." The explanation is that "the University" is indeed a personified abstraction. In a realistic view there is no University— singular; all we have is universities—plural. Whether there ought to be a more unified concept, and whether it should then be translated into practice, are matters which have been debated for more than a century. For the purpose of our discussion it seems quite evident that, like "science," "University" remains a generality with little definite meaning. Not even the most general definitions will hit the mark. When John Henry Newman, the later Cardinal, described it in 1852 as "a place of teaching universal knowledge," but promptly added that "this implies . . . the diffusion and extension of knowledge rather than the advancement,"[8] he certainly did not anticipate that the latter qualification would be thoroughly disavowed by the academic developments of the decades to follow with their ever greater stress on research. The point is clear: Since the category of "university," like the category of "species," embraces a wide variety of specimens and is subject to continuous evolutionary change, any concept implying uniformity or constancy would be illusory.

Adopting this evolutionary simile, we are at once faced with the question of whether evolution is goal-directed. On the whole, organic evolution is now considered to operate blindly, or rather by hindsight. If so, the new efficiency device it has created—the human brain, with its capacity for reasoning—is radically changing evolutionary methodology in that it can replace hindsight by foresight. In other words, if universities generated and tossed about by capricious currents of cultural and political history, have come to be the hodgepodge of institutions disparate in purpose, character, performances, and size which they appear to be, is it compatible with human intelligence to let their future courses continue equally capriciously and unrelatedly? Or should one try to redesign the system to adapt the product of the past for a more unified and concerted service to society in the future? The reason that I phrase these questions as antitheses is that I believe them to be unanswerable in this form. And yet public pronouncements that sound like answers to them are legion. Let me paraphrase some samples of argument both for radical remodeling and for continued laissez faire; both *for* and *against* a fundamental reorientation.

Pro: The university should rise above being merely an assemblage of individuals employed for statutory service on teaching curricula or research contracts or for the privileged pursuit of their scholarly predilections. Its members should develop a strong sense of cohesion and group responsibility as a "community of scholars" with common purposes, stemming from common ideals and responsive to common needs of society.

Contra: Universities should content themselves with offering facilities for able individuals to develop, display, and proffer their intellectual wares, a sort of market, like the Greek *agora.* They need have no common collective goal or pattern so long as they do competent and honest jobs.

Pro: The university should not be a shelter for individuals indulging principally in tasks of no immediate and readily demonstrable utility to a society ever-more clamoring for practical services and concrete deliveries; one of its major aims should be to relieve the manpower shortages in the professions, particularly those which enable the population to share the benefits of scientific progress. Accordingly, it should train more medical practitioners and engineers—especially the latter—even if, in doing so, it has to curtail more esoteric lines of traditional university interest.

Contra: Our world is already precariously close to being torn asunder by stresses engendered by unprecedented innovations too numerous, precipitous, modish, transitory, and mutually unrelated for the safe maintenance of equilibrium as our society keeps evolving. Therefore, and precisely in the self-interest of society, it is imperative that at least one steady focus—the university—insure continuity of progress by asserting and strengthening its traditional role as guardian of the cohesion of knowledge, the balanced perspective, and the long-range outlook, not letting its unhurried, steady, scholarly pace be upset by fancies, fashions, or group pressures of the day.

Pro: The university should abandon its self-arrogated station as a sort of global arbiter purportedly entrusted with guardianship of the common values inherent in all human cultures. It should rather concentrate on promoting tangibly the self-interests of the particular national or group culture to which it owes allegiance, self-interests which, in a competitive scientific society, would place science and technology foremost.

Contra: The university should be dedicated broadly to the universality of truth rather than letting its scope be confined and even corrupted by narrower considerations. It must retain its traditional freedom for supranational, supradoctrinal, suprapolitical thought, expression, and action. Science, by method and subject matter predisposed for such universality, must act as pacemaker for the emergence from sectarianism of all the other cultural endeavors of mankind.

This list of opposites, which could be amplified and documented by many convocation addresses, illustrates the inconsistency among the popular concepts of the essence of a university, and hence the absurdity of trying to reduce the relations between science and "the University" to a single uniform rule. Instead, the profitable course for universities and for the scientific establishment is to accept the great multiformity of both and to try to effect *the most congruous match between their respective patterns.*

Both science and university are now in this phase of groping for new patterns more suited to the conditions of the present and their extrapolation into the future. In this search, such one-sided dogmas as are listed in the preceding pages, can serve at best, like Scylla and Charybdis, as perils to steer clear of: the safe course lies between them, the keyword being *balance.*

More specifically, we are led to the following conclusions, based on the recognition that what is called "the University" is in reality a most variegated system of institutions differing individually as to objectives, methods, service, size, and rank; and what is called "science" is likewise a highly composite enterprise. So is society. Evolutionary trends, organic as well as cultural, have always been in the direction from loose aggregation of independent units toward combination into integrated higher-order systems. The change from independence to cooperative *interdependence* endows the merged constituents with heightened viability and endurance, for their very diversity gives the compound system the versatility needed to maintain its vital integrity amidst the incessant unpredictable fluctuations of the world around it. In return for submitting to some restraints on their degrees of freedom, the parts derive from their association not only the benefit of mutual support, but above all the opportunity to develop to their full potential those particular individual faculties which are most specifically their own.

Naturally the greater is the degree of diversification and the resultant specialization of parts, the greater also becomes their dependence on the system as a whole, and consequently, the task of integrative regulation; the greater, in further consequence, becomes the danger that the regulatory faculties of the system will be taxed beyond the limit and break down. To maintain steadiness of progress, evolution has therefore had to keep teetering between opposite pulls—balancing trends towards ever greater differentiation, which if excessive would portend eventual disintegration, against trends in the direction of ever greater uniformity, which would, as in inbreeding, lead to sterility and loss of flexibility for adapting to changing circumstances.

Evolutionary reasoning can condone neither anarchic individualism nor an autarchic scheme of mass conformity. Applied to the universities, this means evolutionary repudiation of both extreme indulgence in individual predilections and absolute submission to any uniform mission,—that is, other than the call to serve. Universities must not renounce diversity and individual identities, but they must learn to contribute harmoniously to a *group* performance less haphazard in its total aspect than heretofore. In short, they must ascend from the state of a loose *mosaic* to that of a cohesive *system* of diverse, mutually complementary and sensitively interacting parts, or partners.

I submit that nothing short of such a collective, integrated system of plural universities with diverse functions can fulfill the ideal overall function of "the University." Any attempt to make any one existing university over into a miniature version of this total scheme is bound to end as an exemplary showcase of mediocrity and triviality, for, in trying to be comprehensive, a single university would have to spread itself so thin that it would lack depth and quality. The differentiation of both knowledge and its users has gone too far for any single institution to be able to attain the necessary critical mass for dealing with the total spectrum comprehensively, profoundly, and competently. Yet, united in groups, universities can measure up to the requirements. They therefore should band together into integrated compounds, as in the evolution of the higher organisms' single-celled precursors, joined to form many-celled communities, taking advantage of the efficient principle of "division of labor." Instead of being "a community of scholars," I visualize the university of the future as being a *community of scholarly institutions.*

At present it is neither. In fact, as I have said earlier, the university—singular—does not even exist except as an allegorical abstraction. This does not mean that individual universities may not have definite general goals, as well as the will to pursue them. But one need only strip their histories of rhetorical adornments to realize how limited their power to stay on self-set courses has been. Great leaders with vision or special-interest groups with more limited objectives may design blueprints for the future, but as the latter come to materialization, their development is so deflected and distorted by outside influences beyond the control of the originators that the original design is largely obliterated. University histories are full of examples of how environmental factors unrelated and even inimical to good educational philosophies and practices have often defeated self-determination: political pressures and lures; manpower needs; alumni whims; deficiencies of pre-university education; fiscal stringencies as well as the temptation to accept compensatory economic bribes; excessive intrusion of unacademic managerial technicians; and, at times, even a fifth column of contrariness within the faculty.

Faced with such vagaries, some institutions have had the moral and financial strength to hold as firmly as possible to their self-set course, while others, lacking either clear goals or determination or resources, have kept from drowning only by riding the waves of opportunism. But here they are, these products of history, each one performing some major or minor service, useful despite their utter disparity, from the most highly principled, almost monastic, centers for the search and propagation of truth at the one end to mercenary trade schools and diploma mills at the other. Confronted with the gamut of institutions, the question is not whether diversity should be renounced in favor of any one academic ideal, or not even at what point along the scale the epithet of "university" becomes inapplicable, but rather what degree of institutional diversity is essential in order to meet the enormous diversity of needs of our differentiated society and to match the wide spectrum of motivations, interests, and aptitudes of individuals to be served.

The latter point is not always taken into account realistically. It is fortunate that our society, being in need of mounting numbers of practitioners in medicine, in law, in schools, and in parishes, can count on a large quota of citizens who want, quite simply, to be just competent physicians, lawyers, teachers, priests, without aspiring to the more exalted stations of scientists, jurists, scholars, or theologians. So truly the graded scale of colleges and universities reflects the graded needs, wants, and aspirations of people. Therefore, next to the replacement of individual self-sufficiency by integrated realignment in collaborative groups, the universities of the future face the added task of identifying more precisely the needs of the culture, the society, and the people they must serve and of subdividing and apportioning out among themselves their offerings accordingly. Personal preferences and predispositions for work bench over library, for theorizing over gadgeteering, for naturalist observation over dynamic analysis, for dealing with people over dealing with concepts, for professional and economic success over sheer satisfaction in self-improvement, must all be honored instead of being frustrated in a common mold purporting to serve them all—and matching none.

Unquestionably, a critical re-examination of the degree of correspondence between the current patchwork of university offerings and the pattern of needs would reveal major incongruities. Should corrective action toward higher congruance then be undertaken on the small scale of the individual campus? Hardly the right solution, for let us suppose there arose a powerful move to train, for instance, more doctors, engineers, or business administrators. Would not any given university, responding to the call by enlarging the respective schools, then have to choose between the equally undesirable alternatives of trying to maintain its former proportionate structure by inflating the less marketable branches, or else abandoning the latter to a relative eclipse? Surely the solution would lie in recourse to the principle of the *collective system,* instead of an illusory *universal* role, a realistic *partial* one, thus preventing its energies from being distracted, diluted, and dissipated by ancillary commitments, historically or prestige-dictated, which no longer accord with its context; while at the same time the proportions of the whole can be preserved by other members who select partial tasks of compensatory or complementary character.

The proposition I am here expounding is the evolutionary compromise between conservation and progress. Since no single university can encompass any longer the full scope of the ideal "universal university," it should resist the urge "to be all things to all men" and "to go it alone." Instead, each one should concentrate its major energies on those selected sectors of the total field of knowledge which it is supremely qualified to investigate and teach. To some extent this practice has already come into effect as a matter, if not of principle, at least of economy. Every institution has certain areas of strength which it tends to cultivate more than others. Yet the significant distinction between this outcome of accident and necessity on the one hand and, on the other hand, the orderly scheme to be envisaged for the future, is that the differentiation among universities in the past has been so piecemeal and incoherent that the various pieces do not fit together to form the harmonious whole that a university system, as here advocated, should represent.

For the formation of a truly effective and viable system, a certain minimum number—a critical mass—of institutions would have to come together, review their respective functions and capabilities, and, with the least possible incursion on individuality and sovereignty, work out an integrated plan so that collectively they would so supplement each other as to cover the total continuum of knowledge in all its essential scholarly and professional ramifications. Three major considerations would have to guide such integrative efforts: the filling of significant gaps, the correction of serious disproportions, and the lessening of redundancy, particularly where strength could be gained by merging separate units that had remained weak because of isolation or inadequate support. For a concerted program of this sort to succeed would, of course, presuppose, in addition to the re-allocation of educational tasks and subject matters, the harmonization of standards of performance, the free movement of students, and the facultative exchange or sharing of staff members within the association.

Without elaborating the point, it seems that efficient super-universities, "communities of scholarly institutions" of this description, could appropriately be set up by regional compacts. Each association would comprise a suitable assortment of privately endowed universities, high-grade liberal arts colleges, and professional schools. Administrative obstacles to the inclusion of state and municipal institutions and of land grant colleges might also be overcome eventually. There are signs of a growing recognition of the need for such a combining of forces and concerted programing in higher education, as, for instance, in a measure of program coordination among the universities of the Southern Conference; in similar arrangements among regional groups of colleges;

and in the establishment of such organizations as the Southwest Graduate Research Center, the Midwest Interuniversity Library Center, and the Brookhaven Laboratories of Associated Universities, Inc. It would seem timely to amplify and expedite similar trends wherever they appear, with the deliberate aim of furthering the emergence of the "Integrated University Compact" of the future through the linking of existing autonomous institutions of higher learning into self-regulatory networks.

In such a framework it will be easier than it is at present to satisfy the growing variety of educational needs by a corresponding variety of programs without having a rigid one-to-one connection between any given program and any given institution. By definition, the integrated group would contain collectively such a complete set of major offerings that any essential program, however broad or narrow, could be composed from them simply by combining an appropriate selection of items from that comprehensive list into program packages.

As one can readily appreciate, this scheme would be both economical and efficient; it would curtail the boundless proliferation of institutions; it would conserve and concentrate the finite resources of academic talent, funds, and facilities; it would encourage the pursuit of novel "interdisciplinary" combinations of potential "hybrid vigor"; and it would have the necessary plasticity to adapt to changing circumstances. On the other hand, it would, of course, necessitate a far greater liberalization of student transfer among institutions—a feature reminiscent of the great universities of bygone centuries—as well as greater equalization of standards at reasonably high levels. It would place greater burdens of responsibility on both administrations and students, the latter having to give up a good deal of the sense of security engendered by current lock-step tactics of indoctrination and "togetherness," in favor of a wider range of the insecure, but personality-building, freedom of choice.

Such an ideal university system of the future is both conceivable and practicable. It would achieve the restoration of the very principle of *continuity, unity, and universality of knowledge* the loss or abandonment of which our universities bemoan. The basic common trunk of the tree of knowledge, presented in the early years of study, would be allowed to branch gradually by successive dichotomies of choice from the more general to the more specific, albeit with numerous anastomoses, in the methodical and consistent manner attainable solely in an integrated system; only the terminal branches would become relatively more consolidated as separate "schools," and even then not wholly single-tracked. Transition from "liberal" to "professional" education, from "undergraduate" to "graduate" preparation, from "basic" to "applied" areas, would be fluid, the terminology merely a matter of administrative convenience.

This prognostication of the emergence of harmoniously integrated university systems is based on evolutionary logic. Universities are integral parts of society. Both are in counterplay. Society is in a phase of rapid evolution. If universities were to stand still, they would be left behind to wither. Society, though suffering, would survive; universities might not. So universities must meet the changes of the social scene by corresponding adaptive alterations of their own patterns.

However, in calling on higher education to adapt itself to the evolving social environment, one must not lose sight of the reciprocity of the relation. The social environment must, in its turn, be receptive for adaptive claims fed back to it from the university system. Their greater service to the community would also entitle the universities to assert their leadership in intellectual matters, with full partnership in all cultural affairs, exercised most effectively through the leaders and influential members of society which they educate.

To maintain the highest possible standards of *education for responsible leadership* remains one of the prime obligations of the universities, those of the future even more than those of the past. Of course, to strengthen and broaden *mass education* is equally vital, in that it shifts the basis of public acceptance of leadership from compliance with persuasive dicta to the understanding of convincing arguments. This is indeed only repeating what has been stressed so often—but cannot be stressed too often—that while educational goals and standards must be raised on all fronts, the most important task is to give that scarce supply of superior talent, paired with responsibility, a challenge and opportunity to develop native faculties to their maximum; this means placing quality above quantity, with a premium on excellence. Public support for this precept is one of the adaptive contributions society must make if the evolution of both universities and society is to be kept in a dynamically self-adjusting correspondence.

Science in the University

The range of inner flexibility in the integrated university system I have outlined would reduce the question of "the" place of science in a university to absurdity, for it could allow for as many different places, roles, and relations as the growing and ever more highly differentiated field of "science" can command. We read in the White House report "Education for the Age of Science":

> Science, engineering and technology have obviously been responsible for a host of conspicuous changes at all levels of our modern civilization. There is much reason to expect that such changes will continue, and will indeed accelerate. There is no way to turn back the clock or to turn off scientific advance. There will be no international moratorium on science or technology. The people of the United States, on the most practical grounds, must accept and support these propositions.

Lest this arouse the specter of scientific dominance, let me quote further from the same report:

> One of the great strengths of this nation is the diversity of its citizens. No man or council of men dictates what our people individually should do, or how they should be educated. Each of us is remarkably free to pursue that which interests or profits him personally. Out of this great diversity of individual expression comes great strength and wide capability. The diversity should be husbanded. But it cannot long be fruitful if it breaks the nation into isolated groups. Going his own way, a man must understand why other men go theirs, and must respect their right of choice.
>
> A primary objective of an improved educational system should be to bridge the gaps between important segments of the American people. There are many such gaps, even among highly educated people; between scientists and artists; between intellectuals and non-intellectuals; between scientists, humanists, and social scientists; between scholars, research workers, and teachers; between pure scientists, applied scientists, and engineers; and there are others. Such gaps inhibit the close collaboration

between groups which is essential to improving the intellectual atmosphere and developing a better and stronger society.[9]

and from a later report from the same source:

Even in the interests of science itself it is essential to give full value and support to the other great branches of man's artistic, literary, and scholarly activity. The advancement of science must not be accomplished by the impoverishment of anything else, and the life of the mind in our society has needs which are not limited by the particular concerns [i.e., scientific] which belong to this Committee and this report.[10]

In summary, the possible distortion of harmonious proportions in the pattern of education as a result of the phenomenal expansion of science is not only clearly recognized; science itself cautions against it. To maintain balance, or to compensate for disequilibrium, could be accomplished much more easily in a diversified collective system than within the rigid framework of a single institution. This applies to the correction of imbalances not only of subject matter but also of functions. And because the issue of disproportionate attention to science in the functions of research, teaching, and public services is such a lively one, I would like to give it special attention in the light of what I have said before.

Essentially, the major functions of a university, as I see them, are the following four:

(1) The preservation, critical interpretation, and synthesis of existing knowledge.

(2) The furtherance of the acquisition of new knowledge, and the development of the intellectual and technical tools required in this process.

(3) The training in the application of existing knowledge to the practical needs of man.

(4) The transmission and dissemination of knowledge and of its implications and applications.

Even though universities are assisted in these tasks by libraries, museums, governmental and industrial establishments, professional societies, and the like, "the university" still stands as the integrated center where all four of these functions become confluent and interact freely for the common benefit of all of them, and hence for the best utilization of knowledge for the common good. The super-university of the future would be in a uniquely favorable position to give balanced attention to all aspects.

In each of these four categories the problem of maintaining sound proportions between the expanding scientific domain and the other academic commitments recurs. Can it be met by mutual accommodation without radical dislocations? Let us look at a few concrete examples for each of the four fundamental functions.

(1) *The preservation and synthesis of existing knowledge.* Greater concern with the history, structure, and cultural values of science has created not only an opportunity but a genuine demand for a far more active interplay between the sciences and the humanities in education. The historic and philosophic spirit in science still suffers from atrophy. Usually the fruits of science are taught without explaining the nature and roots of the tree that has borne them; preoccupation with the most recent advances is allowed to obscure the fact that they have grown steadily from a historic past. Yet it becomes increasingly important to impart a feeling for the continuity, consistency, and cohesiveness of science to the future leaders of a generation that is overly impressed by the spotlighted glitter of ephemeral novelty. There is, moreover, a goldmine of conceptual and factual material buried in the past literature of science which is practically ignored and unprocessed, bypassed in the manic rush for "doing research." Unless "doing without thinking" is to be conceded supremacy over thoughtful work or even over "thinking without doing," history and philosophy must assume a major task in science education. But they must tackle it not by the expedient of supplementary courses in "History of Science" or "Philosophy of Science," least of all of the purely chronological and anecdotal variety, but by instilling the prospective teachers and workers in science with a true appreciation of the historical and conceptual foundations of scientific thought so that they may learn to see and teach current developments as threads in an intellectual fabric extending from the past into the future.

But then, would not those same historians in the humanities profit reciprocally from closer contact with their scientific colleagues? I am not thinking of the utility of scientific techniques, such as the dating of historic documents by radio carbon, the use of pigment chemistry to check the authenticity of famous paintings, or the recourse to the statistics of cryptography in deciphering ancient tablets. These are taken for granted. But has full advantage been taken of advances in social and comparative psychology to trace the underlying motivations of major historic movements beyond the standard references to political and economic trigger actions; or of the role of modern operational physics, with its relativity and indeterminacy principles, as a possible contributor to the instability of values in our time? These are matters not just of casual interest but of broad concern for the understanding of our culture. And as he gains acquaintance with scientific principles, the humanist will also learn to appreciate better the nature of their origin from what the uninitiated often regard as trivial and redundant labor—namely, the enormous series of painstaking observations, elaborate measurements, intricate experiments and calculations—activities as germane to the purpose of "the university" as are field trips for the excavation of ancient cities or learned commentaries on literature or music. The case for harmony is further strengthened by the cross-linking between science and art through mathematics and esthetics; and there are many other illustrations of the continuity, rather than demarcation, that exists between the sciences and the humanities. Such fruitful interaction is not promoted by expressions of mutual disdain, particularly in view of the fact that the purported cleavage of culture into scientific and humanistic halves, in my opinion, is a plain artifact, merely a relic of medieval divisions of knowledge.

(2) *The acquisition of new knowledge.* The criterion of relevance as guide in the self-selection of one's academic tasks applies also to one of the knottiest problems faced by the universities, namely, the disproportionate expansion of scientific research within their walls. This issue has far too many facets for me to give here the critical evaluation which it would deserve. Instead of reiterating arguments now rather widely discussed, I shall confine myself to accentuating a few aspects that I do not find properly spotlighted in current debates.

The first pertains to the assessment of the degree and rate of expansion of the scientific domain. There is talk of a "knowledge explosion." Undeniably, the spurt of growth of science in this last century has been, as some would call it, "breathtaking." However, if it is referred to as "staggering the imagination," one wonders whether this does not mean the imagination of the unimaginative. Besides, the lack of historical knowledge and perspective deplored above has given current events an appearance of spontaneous eruption. With proper perspective, one would have recognized that this sudden explosion has really been the orderly result of a continuous evolutionary process, steadily accelerated and amplified.[12] In comparing today's picture of the universe, of matter, of life processes, and even of mind with that of fifty years ago the progress made appears truly dramatic, but what is not usually pointed out is that in this progress we have discovered and identified more gaps of knowledge and more new problems to be solved than we had ever known existed; more even perhaps than the positive solutions we have found. Indeed our ignorance, that is our conscious realization of what we do not know, is growing so rapidly that the resulting vacuum attracts increasing numbers of curious minds. It is this which establishes the legitimate expansive claim of science.

Yet there is another side to the coin. The vacuum is also sucking in masses of "fellow travelers" who ride the currents of prevailing fashions, neither truly conscious of the problems to be solved nor qualified to contribute to their solution except in the auxiliary services I have listed earlier. In other words, the ratio of productive over creative scientists has increased enormously by the numerical inflation of the former group. As a result, what we are facing is not a knowledge explosion but a veritable inundation of informational data finding vent in a corresponding "publication explosion."[13] Instead of a problem-orientated selectivity and goal-directed uphill striving, much present research follows the downhill course of least resistance, carried forward largely by inertial forces. I have no direct substantiation for this conclusion for any of the scientific disciplines other than the life sciences; but I have been given to understand by colleagues in other fields that the situation is about the same all round.

Given this fact, the universities have an even heavier responsibility now than they have ever had before to husband the dwindling proportion of scholarly and singularly creative individuals. They are the ones on whom society must rely for the steady and balanced continuance of scientific progress in accordance with the rigorous research discipline of the past. They are the ones whom the universities must single out, protect, promote, and furnish with optimum conditions. Not only do their efforts have an infinitely higher prospective yield than do the routine operations of the average scientific workers; above all, their example resets for others the mark of morality, discretion, critical judgment, self-discipline, and dedication to that higher plane from which it has been slipping as a result of the massive influx of rote performance.

For the same reason, it is vital for the universities to resist pressures for undertaking more sharply delineated so-called "project" and "contract" research than may be useful as a training device. The project system, which allocates funds for a specific purpose, is admirably suited for developmental work, that is, for tasks that can be clearly circumscribed because we know essentially what we want to find and can spell out in detail how to get there. It likewise is suited to the testing of an existing theory, to the broadening of an existing set of data, to the improvement of an existing technique, or to the elaboration of existing doctrine. At any rate, it places a premium on the continuation of existing trends rather than on the exploration of new ones; and the very source of scientific discovery, the inductive process—the prospecting of the wholly unknown—is given little chance.[14]

In recognition of this fact, granting agencies have come to establish a triple scale of research support as "project grants," "program grants," and "institutional grants" in ascending order of latitude and descending order of specific predelineation. In general, this scale of degrees of freedom has worked well, but the pressures to narrow the range of indeterminacy and risk-taking in publicly subsidized research continue nevertheless. Their source lies in the bankruptcy of trust and in the widespread lack of comprehension of the nature and workings of the scientific process, for which the accounting system of industry and commerce is utterly unfit. Unless universities, as the last bastions of "free enterprise" in science, take a resolute stand in this matter, the efficiency coefficient of scientific yield will decline further.

One safety provision against excessive administrative intrusion into research policies lies in the fact that experienced scientists participate in policy formation and program evaluation. Although this involves a diversion of creative scientists from creative work, the use of expert consultants for evaluating scientific merit has by and large proved successful. Even if, at times, the rate of turnover of membership on such judicial boards and committees has exceeded the rate of maturation of sufficient people with the necessary judgment, perspective, and experience to fill the needs, the yield has still remained infinitely better than would have been possible if any of these programs had been administered by scientifically uninformed and inexperienced professional administrators. I am not saying that there is no room for improvement in current screening procedures. What I am saying is that some modicum of mature scientific counsel is a better safeguard against the waste of public funds than are incursions into the research process of legal and accounting procedures which operate with criteria of "performance" and "productivity," which are tailored for contract work and marketing, but are quite inapplicable, and indeed demonstrably detrimental, to scientific proficiency. Faced with the demand for tighter controls over the utilization of government funds for scientific research raised recently by the Congress, a demand which naturally has aroused anxiety and protest, the scientists themselves must share part of the blame for this retrenchment, insofar as they have failed to counteract the gradual relaxation of standards of selectivity and efficiency. But the remedy must come from efforts by the universities themselves to resurrect those standards of research morality, and not from external policing.

This leads back to my earlier emphasis on the sense of relevance, which is so easily lost in the narrow, deep, and dark shafts of rote performance in a given specialty. Because of this, and in order that the universities may reassert their moral right to plead for freedom of research, untrammeled and uncontrolled, it is imperative that they shun any sort of investigative engagement that does not qualify on two counts: that it hold promise to contribute both to the advancement of knowledge and to the building of a person possessing knowledge and the ability to use it. The motto for scientific research in the university should become again to turn out scientific *personalities,* not scientific *products.*

Only those who have been through the process can truly understand how far superior is an education that has let the student experience the thrills as well as the disappointments of exploration, the elation of success in resourceful effort, and the disciplining power of tests of evidence which his participation in active research engenders, as compared to book learning and passive submission to second-hand indoctrination. I thus conclude that *every kind* of institution in the diversified spectrum I have outlined—yes, even teacher training schools —would stand to gain from having some degree of scientific research conducted on its campus, motivated not chiefly by the need for training specialists but by the disciplining virtue of research in developing critical thinking.

(3) *Teaching and training.* In modern times, the general principle of the indissolubility of teaching from research is gradually becoming the rule. Sporadic opposition to it by educational tacticians is as one-sided as is the contrary move by technically preoccupied scientists to let handiwork in laboratory or field crowd out the cultivation and exercise of intellectual endeavor. Once again the question is one of balance—not a "Whether-or-not," but "How much for Whom and When?" In full awareness that the student's time, resources, energies and absorptive faculties are limited, I still submit that a more sizable share than in the past can be spent on research without encroachment on the effectiveness of teaching, provided the following four premises can be fulfilled.

(a) Elementary research experience should be encouraged on the high school level. A trend in this direction has lately made some notable gains. Its denunciation by opponents as nothing but a recruiting drive for technical professions only serves to show how little the detractors know, and partake of, the true spirit of science, and hence how important for a balanced outlook in life it is for future generations to be spared similar blind spots. On the other hand, it would be ludicrous to defend some of the current high school manipulations and exercises in science as introductions to research, let alone to the spirit of science. If science is misrepresented to the young as an array of glamorous "spectaculars," the seed is sown for later anticlimactic disillusionment, perhaps even dishonesty. But trimmed of frills, some laboratory and field practice to sharpen observation, controlled analysis, and critical evaluation of the phenomena of nature cannot be started too early in life. As for the colleges and universities, such earlier initiation to research would certainly relieve some of the competitive demands of research for time that otherwise would have to be taken from teaching.

(b) Contrariwise, the teaching load in higher education can certainly stand radical curtailment. This is not the place for a philippic against the cramming of curricula with offerings from both the ultraconservative and ultraprogressive fringes of the academic scale—petrified wood at one end and excessive fertilizer, crop-destroying, at the other. But let teaching practice squeeze the water out of its own substance and revert to concentration of and on essentials, and let research likewise set an example of relevance-mindedness, and time will cease to be the limiting factor for tending the legitimate needs of both.

Implied in this proviso is that book-*learning* be made to recover from its progressive degeneration into book-*teaching*. Teaching is teacher-student-polarized; learning is bipolar interaction. A good deal of the sheer imparting of information can be relegated to automation through audio-visual aids and television with their powers of condensing instructional material into its most expert and efficient form and then disseminating the concise product. Much of the teacher's time can thus be freed for those other aspects of education in which there can be no substitution for personal effectiveness—inspiration, discussion, criticism, and interpretation. Instructors can then rise again to the role of educators, and students, from passive recipients to active acquisitors of knowledge.

(c) No rigid formula should be set for the proportion of research in teaching programs. In general, the proportion should increase gradually from high school through college to graduate or professional school, but otherwise wide latitude must be left on each level for the variety of individual and institutional objectives. In this sense, an integrated group of institutions, allowing among them for both maximum and minimum requirements, could meet the diversity of future needs better than any single institution pegged to a standard average.

The same argument, however, applies just as cogently to the variety of individuals within an institution, division, or department. What ratio of teaching to research is proper? There can be no universal answer. It seems essential not only for every prospective teacher to have participated in some research activity, but, conversely, for every professional and research man in science to have had some experience in teaching; for having to explain matters to students does more than clarify one's own thinking. It trains the faculty of articulating one's own thoughts and observations. As editor of several scientific journals, having had to face the serious deterioration which good research results suffer from inept description—and I suppose that hospitals and industries could add corroborating evidence from the transcriptions by interns or engineers of patients' histories or product tests, respectively

—I am disheartened by the neglect of the art of communication in the rearing of scientists. As in the case of the history of science, I see the antidote not in remedial courses in "Science Writing," except as a stopgap measure, but in increased opportunities for the student and young instructor to express himself in public, exposed to benevolent criticism.

Having thus recommended a modicum of both research and teaching experience as beneficial for every scientist, regardless of his eventual destination, let me reiterate at once the great variety of human aptitudes and talents to be dealt with. There are first-rate investigators who are poor teachers, and there are first-rate teachers with little flair for or proficiency in research. The former gains by doing some teaching, and the latter grows by making some investigative effort of his own; but neither can be forced into a common mold by a procrustean operation. Yet this is precisely the practice of many college and university administrations, which seem to rely mechanically—the college on a man's industriousness in teaching, the university on the volume of his research publications—as tests of achievement and criteria for promotion. The former thereby stymie some really promising investigators, while the latter divert highly effective teachers from their true calling into "grinding out research." This pressure for mediocre research output, growing in proportion to the abundance of research grants, is doubly pernicious, because not only does it add to the glut of inconsequential data; what is worse, it places resourcefulness and excellence in teaching, by implication, into a rank of inferiority. Fortunately, there have been sporadic signs lately that this inequality is beginning to be redressed. One realizes that science, like music, needs not only good composers but good conductors and performers as well.

(d) No less insidious than the gauging of the creativity of an academic man by the number of published papers to his credit, at least in science, is the attempt to rate academic service and effectiveness, whether in teaching or in research, in terms of man-hours—the punch-clock mentality. What is the time scale of an idea, of a discovery, of an invention? Can accountants be persuaded that moments of deep thinking, even off-campus, or a flash of genius, even during "off-hours," can undo or save years of expensive labor? Or are we possibly heading for a time when quantification of teaching and research performance will go even beyond the simple counting of the number of hours spent on the job and multiply it by caloric output as a measure of intensity of work?

I realize the magnitude of the problem facing many an administration in coping with vast numbers of students and faculty by other than impersonal methods. Nevertheless, save for service functions, automatic quantitative ratings will never provide a valid measure of academic performance in science. The answer may lie in giving human experience and judgment wider play. Appointments are made on a basis of faith and trust. Why, then, is not that spirit allowed to persevere throughout the appointive years? I have commented on a sad decline of risk-taking in research support;[16] perhaps risk-taking in individuals is likewise diminishing. At any rate, there seems to be no better yardstick for judging optimum relations between research and teaching in science education than mature, sober, balanced judgment, taking into account the objectives of the institution, the special functions of its subdivisions, the diverse needs of its students, the variegated complexion of its faculty, its finite means and facilities, as well as the necessary reconciliation of economy and efficiency with the principles of freedom for individual self-development and self-expression. On the point of economy, it is well to remember that, in general, it will be easier to get $n\%$ greater efficiency out of available funds, services, floorspace, and equipment than to obtain an additional $n\%$ more money, $n\%$ more manpower, $n\%$ more space, and $n\%$ more instruments.

(4) *Adult Education.* The preceding comment touches on the growing subsidy by government to the conduct of science and the concomitant increase in the awareness and concern of the public for how its funds are spent, which may portend a mounting pressure for a greater measure of control. To quote from a White House release cited earlier:

> Perhaps the most important single task of the universities is to see to it that their own standards of freedom and excellence are maintained in a period of growing connection with government. While we do not share the notion that government money is necessarily subversive of university freedoms, it is obvious that large-scale Federal spending, like any other form of patronage, has its hazards.[17]

In the long run, this hazardous trend can be effectively countered only by bringing up an enlightened citizenry with comprehension of the nature and ways of science. Hopefully, as I explained earlier, the new generation now in school will already be better grounded in science than are their elders. However, in the interim, until they mature and have decisive voices, there is a partial vacuum in the adult population's contact with science, that in the interest of both ought to be filled. There is a patent need to introduce more science into adult education programs. Some will reply that this is already being done on an increasing scale. I disagree. With very few outstanding exceptions, what is offered in courses of "General Studies" or "Adult Education" is usually either some practically or even vocationally oriented display of "tricks of the trade" or a rather dull, second-hand rendition of the elements of a specialized branch of science. Rarely is there the broad portrayal of science with its lights and shadows—its life, spirit, exhilarating adventures and satisfactions as well as its code, restraints, discipline, and frustrations; its grounding in disinterested curiosity as well as its unlimited bounty for man's self-interests; its enormous untapped potential as well as its inner limitations. This story is seldom told to the public from the rostrums of universities.

In line with the idea of integral programs within groups of institutions, perhaps it would again be preferable to have a favorably located member of the group assume a major responsibility in this field with due assistance from the other affiliated institutions, which thereby would be relieved of some of their "extension courses." The main thing, at the present juncture, is to give wider circles of the public an appreciation not only of the fruits of science, but of the nature of the tree that bears them and of its deep rooting in our culture.

Conclusions

I have tried, in this essay, to moderate between conflicting versions of the impact of science on the university. Extreme positions commonly betray confinement in remote corners from which only a limited aspect of a field can be seen. Although one may regret that many of the discussions about "science" and "the university" nowadays bear signs of such partiality, based partly on unfamiliarity and partly on prejudice, it is far more significant to note the constructive efforts that are being made at synthesizing the separate views into a broad, well-balanced overview and presenting the total picture dispassionately in undistorted perspective. I have quoted examples from such efforts. More could be added. From their study I am encouraged to believe that the basic propositions set forth in this essay are shared by others, even though not universally. These basic tenets, in summary form, are the following:

I. Science is a major integral part of our culture, not just a service function. Its spirit is of as much concern to man as are its products.

II. The growth of science has naturally a critical impact on the future of the universities as centers of knowledge and of learning. Caution, lest growth turn into overgrowth, is indicated.

III. Harmonious growth is predicated on the reconciliation of conflicting and competing trends by mutual accommodation. Science and nonscience are not opponents but partners in a common enterprise.

IV. As such, both must adjust to the emerging evolutionary change in their educational tasks by re-examining their respective roles conjointly with a deep sense of value and relevance, so as to concentrate on essentials, husband talent, and bar the infiltration of extraneous diluents. This applies to both teaching and research.

V. Both society and knowledge are in a process of progressive differentiation and particularization, which must be recognized and even assisted, but which must be kept from degenerating into tight compartmentalization and disintegration as a result of the abandonment of vital interrelations among the specialized components. The universities, as custodians of knowledge, have a solemn duty to preserve "unity amidst diversity." They must offset splintering by efforts at re-integration within their whole structure and its substructures.

VI. Differentiation has proceeded to the point at which neither the diversity of objectives and fields of higher learning nor that of people's aspirations, needs, and aptitudes can any longer be served with competence within any single institution. True, schools of higher learning have also differentiated and specialized, albeit somewhat haphazardly. However, their total pattern is not sufficiently congruous with the patterns of need of either society or knowledge. Therefore, to remove present and to avert future incongruity, the universities will have to counterbalance specialization by combination into integrated groups—the only realistic method of protecting the creative potential inherent in diversity against the dulling effects of uniformity, standardization, and mediocrity. In a diversified system, science and nonscience can find their proper distribution and proportions without pitting exaggerated claims of "social superiority" against an outmoded status quo doctrine of "cultural superiority."

VII. In order to achieve integration in such enormously complex systems as science and the educational continuum, it will be imperative to rise above the analytical method of singling out from an intricate problem simple component pieces for isolated solution, and to adopt the sprouting young methodology of "system thinking" appropriate to networks of intimately interdependent functions. Like other major activities of society that have already benefited from such integrative treatment, such as economics, traffic, national defense, natural resources, and others, education is such a network system and deserves like treatment. Science education cannot be viewed and dealt with rationally save in this context.

REFERENCES

1. See, for instance, three reports from the President's Science Advisory Committee: "Strengthening American Science" (The White House, December 27, 1958); "Education for the Age of Science" (The White House, May 24, 1959); "Scientific Progress, the Universities, and the Federal Government" (The White House, November 15, 1960); obtainable from the U. S. Government Printing Office, Washington, D. C. 25; and "Symposium on Science in Education," *Proceedings of the National Academy of Sciences* (U. S. A.), vol. 43, no. 7 (1957); and many others.

2. Paul Weiss, "The Message of Science," *Bulletin of Atomic Sciences,* vol. 15, no. 7 (1959), 274-277.

3. Paul Weiss, "The Challenge of Biology," *Science,* 118 (1953), 33-34.

4. G. W. Corner, in symposium on "Science in Education," *Proceedings of the National Academy of Sciences,* vol. 43, no. 7 (1957).

5. Weiss, "The Message of Science."

6. Carnegie Corporation of New York, *Annual Report* (1952).

7. *Engineering Forum,* Ford Motor Company (June 21, 1961).

8. Cited from Quincy Wright's address "What Is a University," *Bulletin of the American Association of University Professors,* vol. 30, no. 167 (1944).

9. pp. 4 and 15.

10. "Scientific Progress, the Universities, and the Federal Government," p. 3.

11. Paul Weiss, "Experience and Experiment in Biological Research." Symposium on "The Experimental Method in Biology from the Time of Antonio Vallisneri to Present," ed. U. D'Ancona, Padova, *Science*, vol. 136, no. 3515 (1962), pp. 468-471. (Chapter 7 of this book).

12. Derek J. Desolla Price, *Little Science, Big Science* (New York: Columbia University Press, 1963).

13. As regards the distinction made here between "knowledge" and "information," see "Knowledge: A Growth Process," *Science*, vol. 131, no. 3415 (1960), pp. 1716-1719. (Chapter 9 of this book).

14. Paul Weiss, "Medicine and Society; the Biological Foundations," *Journal of Mt. Sinai Hospital*, 19 (1953), 716-733. (next chapter).

15. Weiss, "Experience and Experiment in Biological Research."

16. Weiss, "Medicine and Society; the Biological Foundations."

17. "Scientific Progress, the Universities, and the Federal Government."

Medicine and Society: The Biological Foundations*

That medicine must rest on a firm foundation of biology is a truism. Biology is the science of life. Man is alive in a world full of other life relevant to his existence. In his basic constitution, functions, and reactions, the human organism is a biological system, developing, growing, maintaining itself, responding, behaving and adjusting according to the laws governing all life. Thus, to dwell on the dependence of medical progress upon biological knowledge would seem as redundant as to labor the fact that engineering is rooted in physics, chemistry, and mathematics. In fact, throughout history, medical motivation and observation have added to biological knowledge as materially as has biological understanding to the advancement of medicine.

However, let me make clear at the outset that I realize that this does not imply that medicine is just "a branch of the biological sciences," as it is sometimes called in pardonable short-hand language. Medicine is rather a hybrid of two parental lines, only one of which lies in the sciences of objective measurement and logical deduction, while the other stems from the subtle but subjective powers of evaluation and judgment of the human mind, to be tapped whenever the doctor faces the individual patient, the single case in its uniqueness. Science does not deal with unique events. It only encompasses them. It deals with the general rules, usually statistical, in common to large numbers of cases—the average behavior. Physics does not deal with a particular electron or a given atom; meteorology not with a specific cloud in its uniqueness. No two cells will ever behave exactly alike, no two disease courses duplicate each other down to the last detail. Lest this semblance of indeterminacy disquiet you with the suggestion of indeterminism in the universe, let me point out that it need mean no more than our own inability to predict precisely and infallibly the

*Reprinted from JOURNAL OF THE MOUNT SINAI HOSPITAL Vol. XIX, No. 6: 716-733, 1953

Address delivered at the Centennial Symposium of Mount Sinai Hospital in New York City, November 29-30, 1952.

individual event. The physicist, knowing full well the laws of wave motion, which all waves must obey, is yet unable to predict the precise shape of any particular wave on the ocean, molded by a unique constellation of currents, winds, wakes, tides, reflections off the bottom and backwash from the shores. Predictive science takes an interest in individual cases only for what they may hold in supporting old, or directing new, generalizations and theories. It then discards them as nonrecurring items. Scientific prediction can be positive about . what cannot happen and what might happen, but it can only approximate reality in anticipating just precisely what will happen in the individual event. This is where the physician cannot afford to be a scientist. His interest must sharpen as it focuses on the single, unique and nonrecurring specimen, the human patient whom he wants to help.

Thus there are two strains running through medicine, one of impersonal scientific method, which furnishes the rules and tools for guiding judgment, and one of personal decision applying guided judgment to the unique case at hand. The trend over this past century has been for the scientific strain to grow in vigor and volume. This should be no cause for alarm, since the two strains are not competitive, but supplementary. And truly in the expanding universe of human welfare, there must be plenty of room for both happily to expand in unison.

As science with its method and knowledge and tests and checks provides personal judgment with ever-safer guides and narrower margins for error, it expands legitimately into what the ancient ministers of the healing art might have claimed to be their proprietary rights. Commensurately, however, it frees time and energy for the cultivation of human values and the powers of human application. Let us not overlook that the human body contains some of the subtlest precision devices of discrimination and evaluation. Our eye can detect a few quanta of light, our nose a few aromatic molecules. True, we can design technical apparatus of equal sensitivity to register elementary stimuli, but for the perception and evaluation of the most varied patterns and combinations in which they appear in nature, there is no substitute to that discerning power of the human mind which we call judgment. The time and effort that science saves us on the one hand could then be profitably spent on training and sharpening by practice those peculiarly human faculties.

There is a danger, though, that we may fail to develop them to their full power or let them atrophy from sheer disuse. Then, of course, as you give withered muscles the support of braces, so the sciences will have to come to the rescue of withered minds with the poor substitute of automatic rules, preventing at least the worst malfeasance and the fatal error.

Perhaps we are heading that way. When there are not enough teachers of native talent to go around to fill the needs of an expanding educational system, particularly when the really good ones cannot be attracted to a station of economic and often social inferiority, society, depending now more on the lesser lights, has to protect itself against incompetence by giving them some hard-and-fast mechanical rules of conduct. Likewise, if an expanding program of medical care should fail to fill its quota from those with native talent and calling for the profession, science will have to provide ever firmer guide ropes to make sure that even those with blurred vision will not fall off the safe trail, dragging their charges with them. Science will never dehumanize medicine. But conceivably it might one day be called to the rescue of a dehumanized medicine.

I made these introductory remarks to convince you that I am not one who would grant a monopoly to the scientific approach to medicine. Having made this clear, let me then proceed to deal with those aspects of medicine which lie definitely within the right of domain of science. If medicine is to rest on a firm base of biology, let us examine that base to see whether it is being adequately broadened, strengthened, and secured to support the continued growth of medicine.

Biology is in a state of flux. The most dramatic change that is occurring in our days, the key to the understanding of all the rest, is what might be called our industrial revolution, that is, the rapid conversion of our science from small-scale workshops of individual craftsmen and apprentices to the mass proportions of an industry, with all that goes with it: more workers, more administration; higher production quotas and more specialties; more rote and less call for initiative; standardization mixed with the rule of fashions—yes, even vested interests and jurisdictional disputes. Research, education, publication, budgetary policies—they all reflect this tide as they grope to adjust to the new pattern.

In the conviction that the change is here to stay, undoubtedly for better rather than for worse; that it calls for major adjustments; and that such adjustments can be made rationally and methodically only if we see clearly where we are heading; I shall try to outline some of its symptoms. The principal ones are: an organizational regrouping within biology; progressive fragmentation of biology into innumerable specialties, with corresponding loss of unity and communion; countered by deliberate efforts at reintegration and cross fertilization by combination of formerly separated lines, particularly new tributaries from the physical sciences, and the advent of team work; spectacular progress in certain favorite channels of massive application, at the expense of relative starvation of other urgent tasks, hence distortion of proportions of the field as a whole; a dearth of pioneering spirit because of reduced motivation and opportunity for adventure, along with heightened concern for personal and intellectual security; perhaps also some decline of standards of scholarship and workmanship, trading quantity for quality; and above all, a growing realization of the impact of science on human welfare, and the growth of a mature sense of responsibility of the scientist toward society, and, in traces, of society toward the support of science.

As for the grouping and classification of the biological sciences, it may be useful to remember the artificiality of the labels under which they run. As Abraham Flexner said in this connection, "Medicine is an indefinite portion of the vast field of biology.... For purposes of effective attack, the area to be explored, itself only tentatively marked off, has been provisionally divided, but the several portions really have no distinct individuality. On the contrary, they merge into one another and are liable to regrouping whenever they are surveyed from a new point of view." While our teaching and research system still employs the classical pigeonholes of zoölogy, botany, bacteriology, anatomy, biochemistry, physiology, pathology, and so forth, the study of life actually forms a continuous spectrum from which different interest groups have merely cut out different absorption bands depending on their own absorptive faculties. Such subdivisions are not only an administrative expediency but can be highly effective when they have task-force character, that is, are charged each one with occupying a well-defined sector of a field. But just in the latter sense, those traditional designations have lost much of their original meaning. A colleague recently defined a zoölogist quite pertinently as a man who does his work in a zoölogy department; were he to do the same work in an anatomy department, he would be classed as an anatomist, and in a physiology department , as a physiologist. A glance at modern cell biology, endocrinology, or neurology bears out this operational definition. The old lines of demarcation have become erased, and the fields they used to circumscribe have become, as Flexner put it, "liable to regrouping." This regrouping is definitely under way.

Many of our traditional classifications were based either on forms of life, as in bacteriology, botany, and zoölogy, or on methods of approach, as anatomy (for dissection) and biometrics (for measurement). With the growing realization of the general validity of certain basic principles common to all forms of life, a more natural organization of biology according to inherent principles is gradually superseding the old pattern. Thus, investigators and teachers have begun to draw promiscuously on bacteria, plants, animals, and man for knowledge and illustration of the principles of cell structure, metabolism, growth, heredity, excitation and coordination, adaptation, ecology, and evolution. Many of the greatest advances of biology have come in places where different specialties have combined forces in conjoint study. The spectacular development of genetics in this country has profited immensely from the correlation of facts from such diverse fields as cytology, animal and plant breeding, biochemistry, immunology, statistics and taxonomy. As a result, the old alignment gives way to a new, more natural, and more consistent order. The important thing in the present context is that in this new order, the biology of man is due to be included as an integral part. Genetics courses will encompass human heredity, development be taught with reference to wound healing and tumors, and animal behavior with an eye to social psychology. But even as old disciplines escape the straight jacket of obsolete trade marks and become confluent, the new currents again break up into new local whirlpools, and fragmentation into ever more compartments goes on at an ominous pace; which brings me to my second point—the splintering process.

Fragmentation goes with specialization, and specialization is a mark of scientific progress. Mastery requires concentration, which means narrowing. The gibe about the man who gets to know more and more about less and less is not quite just. Science needs that man. The only question is: Can it entrust its progress wholly to his hands? Our answer to this question today may shape or warp the future course of biology and medicine.

Subdivision of tasks under a common plan and with a common goal in view is good accepted practice. Splintering into isolated and independent columns is something that only a science of sufficiently advanced maturity, which has a common goal and common rules, can well afford, a science whose basic framework of concepts, principles, terms, and units has become consolidated and unified. Physics has evidently reached this stage, and chemistry is near it, but biology most definitely is not. Biology is only just emerging as an exact science. It is still groping for its basic principles and concepts. The blank spots on its map of fundamentals are legion. Its vocabulary is still fraught with the subjective terms of primitive and nonanalytical observation, its problems are formulated in ambiguous symbols. There is no common master blueprint from which the various specialists could each take home a different assignment for independent piece work with reasonable certainty that their final products, when assembled, would fit together into a rounded and harmonious whole.

The point I wish to make is that biology can continue to make healthy progress only if its task forces start with a comprehensive view of the problems in the field, keep this total perspective in view and do not lose it when they retreat into their various working quarters. This requires not only effort but determination. The difficulty grows as the horizon widens and information grows in bulk. Helpful devices are interdisciplinary conferences, review articles, and informal exchange of views. Biological education likewise is beginning to present an integrated picture of the province of biology, rather than a smattering of miscellaneous data. However, all these countermeasures are still so thinly spread that unless greatly amplified, they could hardly offset the growing momentum of disintegrative overspecialization.

Let us take, for example, the nervous system. It represents problems of molecular organization, histological structure, geometry of connections, biochemistry of metabolism, chemical and electrical correlates of conduction and transmission, pharmacological response to drugs; problems of coordination, specificity, integrative, regulatory, and interpretative functions and their derangement, as well as the whole problem of the developmental mechanisms through which all of this has come about. So the histologist, physiologist, biochemist, embryologist, psychologist, psychiatrist, and so forth, each picks out a partial aspect, analyzes it with the best of techniques available, according to the most rigorous scientific standards known to him, only to discover, if and when he meets the others to compare conclusions, that these do not quite jibe. They come up with as many different versions of the brain as there are technical approaches, overlapping in good measure, to be sure, but largely also inconsistent and conflicting; and yet, the brain is still one and the same. I could cite several recent symposia in ample illustration of this contention. Yet the study of the nervous system is perhaps one of the most heartening examples of active resistance to specialist isolationism. Here, clinician and anatomist, psychologist and physiologist, cytologist and biochemist, and other cross-combinations, join forces to clarify their common objects and perhaps straighten out their inconsistencies. And so in other areas, such as genetics. But there are fewer and fewer people who are still sufficiently conversant from firsthand experience with the basic facts and problems of the whole of biology to arrange their own research and teaching in the light of such over-all perspective. Most others now inherit a narrow specialized sector of the field and learn about the rest only in formalized and watered-down second-hand tales—or fables.

This whole development is, of course, a corollary of the growth of our science. In the old days, which means not much more than a quarter of a century ago, a biologist still had training and experience in all the major manifestations of living systems, and it was still within the grasp of a single man to give a fairly comprehensive and well-balanced lecture course in biology in its totality. A single journal such as the Journal of Experimental Zoology would carry articles on development, genetics, protozoology, nutrition, insect physiology, endocrinology, ecology, animal behavior and what not. In those days, it was easy to keep one's bearings and balance in the total scheme even as one applied oneself to rather specialized investigations. But nowadays, we tend to bring our students up to stay in rather closely demarcated channels. Scientific journals and societies frown on diversity and purify their contents to embrace smaller and smaller parcels of subject matter or technique. And making virtue of a necessary evil, they are begetting a narrow-minded sectarianism, which biology in its state of immaturity and loose coherence can ill afford.

Commuting between different branches of biology, one often finds that they have highly unrealistic, if not fantastic, notions of each other's subject matters. It is not so disturbing that they disagree as that they do not sense it or, worse still, do not care. I am not speaking of conflicts that cannot be resolved but of the conflicts, as well as opportunities, that go unnoticed because of self-inflicted myopia.

Of course, there have always been seclusive tendencies in our, as in any, science. But never before could the resulting incongruities assume the perilous mass proportions made possible in our day by the inflated volume of scientific production. The danger that the various segments of biology will succumb to the centrifugal pull and fly apart on separate tangents is a very real one.

This danger of particularization in biology is partly offset by the reverse tendency of divided branches to combine in the attack on certain focal problems. Desirable as is this cooperative trend, it sometimes also aggravates the problem. This happens in those cases in which supposedly converging lines have different notions of just what the substance of their common object is. For instance, there is a growing and welcome influx into biology of students from the physical sciences who have had no first-hand acquaintance with real biological phenomena. In their innocence, they then often contrive models of organic systems so utterly fictitious that they bear no resemblance to living beings at all. Models must bear some pertinent relation to the real thing. To choose them fittingly, one must know the real thing. Otherwise, one ends up with something perhaps quite interesting in itself, but wholly irrelevant to the elucidation of life. Even so, the principle of conjoint and concerted effort has been one of the potent antidotes to our growing schisms. Even so, fragmentation without commensurate restoration of total perspective proceeds at an increasing pace. If allowed to go too far, it would lull the young generation into a sense of complacency about the true state of perfection of biological knowledge.

It is important, therefore, to point out that notwithstanding all our wonderful progress in biological research and theory, most of our core problems still lie in deep obscurity. We do not know the physical basis of intracellular organization, the principles that sort biochemical processes and diverse molecular realms in space without the aid of rigid mechanical frameworks. We do not know much about what causes orderly substance transport within cells, nor do we know the motive mechanism of cell locomotion. We do not know how cells recognize each other, their foods, their enemies, and how they can react selectively to their environment. We still have no more than shrewd guesses about the process in which constituent chemical units fall into places all at once to replicate a model compound, and only in the presence of the latter; nor do we know what activates and checks and reawakens the powers for growth in development, disease, and aging. Even less do we appreciate, let alone understand, the supracellular principles of field character which order the cellular community both in development and in the coordination of our nervous functions, and whose disturbances may yield freaks in the former case, mental disorders in the latter. This is just a small but fair sample of our state of ignorance. In such an unsettled state, it is unsafe to give up the cohesiveness of unified perspective, which tight seclusion in separate specialized compartments tends to crumble.

Another hazard in giving young minds a grossly overmagnified picture of contemporary accomplishments, is that it dwarfs appreciation of the vast stock of older data on which they rest. Again, if biology were in a state of maturity comparable to that of the physical sciences, that stock of knowledge would by now have become fully ordered and incorporated in a consistent code of rigorous and universally accepted principles and laws. However, as I said before, biology is not yet in this lucky stage. True, a few areas, such as genetics or evolution, have managed to compress a large number of empirical facts into some valid generalizations. But most areas have not yet succeeded in finding unified conceptual formulae. Much less do we have a system of rules and principles that would tie the various areas into a conceptual superunit. Then how can we justify the careless unconcern by which we let the record of the past recede into oblivion before it has been properly extracted and condensed into some master concepts?

Therefore: Let us restore the scholarly approach which takes a balanced view, derives the present from the past and goes on to project it into the future, with no undue enlargement of the present. We must humbly acknowledge the vastness of our ignorance, point to the exciting vistas of discoveries yet to be made and to the countless opportunities. By stressing the challenge of the unsolved biological problems and indicating ways to their solution, we can attract and inspire the superior minds who now see little scope for their ingenuity in a field part nature lore, part technical routine, with not much premium on daring enterprises. This is a real task for our educational policy, and granting concurrence of research, administrative and economic policies, it can succeed.

The splintering of biological sciences will, of course, continue unabated. But we now have the opportunity to reweave the separating threads in new and fruitful combinations.

As a practical example of such regrouping, let me cite the reclassification of the biological sciences which I devised in 1951 for administrative use within the National Research Council, but which, since it reflects our modern trends, has since been applied more widely. It sorts biology into six major areas based on inherent principles of life as follows:

1) *Molecular biology*: concerned with the elementary compounds, their interactions, transformations and the attendant energy balance.

2) *Cellular biology*: the behavior of the organized cell, especially the coordination of molecular events underlying orderly structure and function.

3) *Genetic biology*: covering the laws and mechanisms of heredity, that is, the continuity of generations as well as their progressive transformation in evolution.

4) *Developmental biology*: including growth, development, repair and reproduction of the individual.

5) *Regulatory biology*: dealing with the coordinating and integrating mechanisms, such as the nervous system, endocrines and homeostasis.

6) *Group and environmental biology*: dealing with the relations of the individuals to one another and to their environment, including ecology, psychology, and sociology.

You will note that there is no longer any reference in this scheme to particular forms of life, but that every biological phenomenon can be defined in terms of one or more of these six categories. The value of such a system lies in the shift of emphasis from technical specialties to focal problems. Habitual communion, for instance, among all the different specialties studying the nervous system, or among all the different groups interested in growth, whether it be the growth of bacteria, plants, animals, or human tumors, should result in more unified concepts than if the several lines were kept in segregation. In short, such schemes facilitate re-integration.

Striving for integration does not mean turning the individual investigator into a superficial jack-of-all-trades. It merely means to develop in him the urge to mind more than his own business so that he will compare and check and reexamine all he does in the light of what goes on elsewhere. For this purpose, critical surveys, as well as conferences and symposia, bringing together briefly specialists from different areas, are of great help. Of even greater value would be a more extensive exchange of workers among different laboratories for longer periods. We then may overcome the factional isolation of teachers and investigators, and the narrow indoctrination of the students which stems from it.

Speaking of increasing specialization and division of labor, if we are to adjust to them with a minimum of duplications or omissions, we ought to have some clearer understanding on who is to assume what tasks. For instance, with their growing emphasis on the human individual, research and teaching in medicine are bound to concentrate on areas directly related to human health and ills. Reflected into pre-medical education, this will lead to greater preoccupation even in the more basic fields with man or mammals most closely resembling man's organization. Considering this trend, it becomes incumbent on the biological sciences as such to take increased responsibility for the more general aspects of bacteriology, cytology, histology, anatomy, physiology, biochemistry, and so forth. Indeed, much that is still traditionally considered the preserve of the medical school, could profitably be ceded to biology.

The biological sciences, in their turn, could do much more to give the budding medical student a firmer grounding for his later understanding of the machinery of the human body, its faculties and limitations. A standard course in embryology that is no more than an illustrated travelogue conducting the student through the changing scenery of the embryo by pointing to landmarks of ridges, craters and pipe lines, without telling him the how and why of the changes, is hardly the right introduction to the proper understanding of pathological phenomena of clinical concern, such as malformations, wound healing, regeneration, dystrophy, aging and neoplastic growth, all of which are but variants of what the normal embryo displays. Is it not high time to tell him more of our modern knowledge of the dynamics and mechanisms of embryonic processes and the causes of their deviations? Would he not get a better grasp of the vague concept of "constitution" by being shown more of the realistic background of genetics and ontogeny on which this constitution rests? Would he not become more adept at nerve repair if we explained just how nerves grow, are guided and connect? Would it not be good preparation for psychiatry to give him some biological acquaintance with animal behavior, instinct and memory, so that he may better appreciate what is specifically human and what is not? Undoubtedly, by intelligent and cooperative planning, one could do a lot to make the pre-medical experience in biology more pertinent, adding not only to the perspective of the clinician but also to the orientation of the investigator who has come through this training.

Whichever way we phrase it, we come back to the human individual. This is the second plane on which we have to work. No organizational design becomes effective or defective save through the men and women who execute it. It may be sad that this needs emphasizing, but it does; particularly in view of some current illusions about the potentialities of so-called team work. "No one familiar with the scientific process can share the hope that by hitching large numbers of scientists to a common treadmill, their aggregate effort will, by some sort of collective superintelligence, turn out discoveries of staggering novelty. Discovery always takes shape in single brains. The building up of teams of workers of different training and viewpoints is a wonderful device to supplement, but not supplant, what only the individual mind and intellect can do—think. There is no substitute for human intelligence in science, so let us not act as if there were. If most of the riddles of life processes still lie obscure behind closed doors, let us not spend most of our efforts on ramming in those doors by blind mass pressure, but rather let more people get busy with looking for the keys or figuring out the combination of the locks." (Chapter 3, p. 35)

To accomplish this, Let us teach young investigators the tolerance that goes with understanding; explain the workings of the scientific process which lives on all of these: methods, data, facts, conclusions, theories, hypotheses, and concepts, all of them equally vital; restore a balanced attitude between the extremes of the pure fact finders and gadgeteers at one end, and the pure theorists and speculators at the other, and debunk the arrogance of their monopolistic claims; restore respect for systematic and unhurried work and arouse suspicion of the flashy, but ill-supported, claim that trades passing notoriety for lasting truth; and raise that sense of responsibility and pitiless self-criticism without which even the best man is prone to go to seed.

Then, if we select the right young leaders and bring them up the right way and show them the immenseness of yet-unconquered problems full of the unknowns of biology, and if we have the courage to call these unknowns by their names, if we don't cover up our ignorance by pretentious words, if we phrase the problems as objectively and as precisely as a realistic approach to them would demand, if we present existing knowledge soberly and honestly without implying more than what we know or can legitimately extrapolate; in short, if we expose biology as challenging to the best of minds, then, I believe our progress is assured, and it will be balanced and steady. When I say we, I mean all those in education, administration, direction and support of research, with opportunities to detect and develop potential leaders.

This leaves out, of course, a large, and presumably the larger, fraction of the scientific population who have just average ability, not much originality, yet come to science with a will to serve. I am not talking of the laboratory technicians but of those who aspire to a professional career in science. As competent specialists in limited areas, they are in increasing demand in industry, government positions, and as teachers in institutions of higher learning. They are eminently useful, indeed indispensable, in what in military language would be called the mopping up and occupation duty and the logistic support of all the front lines. Like the leaders, they end their formal training with a Ph.D. degree. Yet, this cannot conceal the fact that a true division of labor between the two groups is gradually emerging. The sooner we give official recognition to this fact and create a respectable status for the growing corps of needed technical specialists, the better for them and for the rest of our science. There is no reason why high-class technical experts in, let us say, electronmicroscopy, biostatistics, electronic recording, x-ray analysis, histochemistry, anthropometric measurements, assay of nutrients, and so on, who have neither a flair nor a gift for original investigative work, should feel forced into it to make the grade of respectability, just because academic tradition has pronounced research as a virtue in itself. Such expert service personnel with doctoral degrees should be certified as valuable and full-fledged members of the scientific community with no explicit or implied pressure for research production. That class already exists in hospitals and some other institutions, but it has not yet spread into the academic places where it is badly needed.

In general, the biological sciences are understaffed, both academically and technically. Increased recruitment is needed, from the high-school level up. Such recruitment is, of course, up against a serious handicap—the inequity of the economic status of the academic profession. I do not want to go into statistics which would only boil down to the familiar comparison between the salaries of college professors and scrub women. The trend becomes the more alarming, the heavier the bid for scientific talent from industry, medical practice, and governmental agencies, all of which can afford to pay higher financial rewards. True, the academic profession has always accepted financial loss in trade for a scholarly atmosphere. But this rationale is rapidly disappearing. Academic load grows heavier while industry and practice often provide attractive opportunities for scholarly activities. As the economic gap widens, we may yet see a larger quota of high-grade research workers veer off from academic life, depleting the sources of scientific progress, at a time when they ought to be augmented. In realistic view, therefore, unless academic institutions can be secured against this drain, all the envisaged measures for assuring biological progress will come to naught.

Unless corrected, the trend could lead to a disastrous disruption of the structure of our science. This is a matter of national concern, hence, there are those who would look to government for relief. I would rather see help come through the growing realization of self-interest of those who benefit from the products of academic institutions. After all, much of the fundamental work on which industrial progress and medical practice rest comes from the universities and private research institutes, as a free gift to public welfare. Considering the added service of training, by which academic institutions mold human raw material into half-finished products at no cost to the consumers of such manpower, it becomes plain that more of the proceeds of these achievements will have to be plowed back into the academic process of teaching and investigation if the productive flow is to be maintained. Tax legislation allowing industry and the professions a larger tax-free share for contributions for educational and investigative purposes might act as stimulant.

As for the investigative process, however, the largest beneficiary is the public itself. Therefore, we must intensify the campaign to spread more widely a true understanding of what the scientific process is, the good it does and what it needs. The public must be made to see that the acquisition of knowledge proceeds in a single coherent and continuous stream, which constantly delivers the stuffs that feed and shape our civilization. It yields them as naturally as a tree bears fruit if properly nurtured, irrigated, and protected. But neither will a cut-off branch bear fruit, nor can you grow fruit directly on the soil by short cuts. We must not tire of explaining this truth and illustrating it over and over again in order that the public may, in due course, learn how to invest its contributions to science most soundly and to best interest. We evidently do not promote such understanding by our publicity techniques, which turn the spotlight merely on the recent fruits, many of them indeed unripe and sterile, while keeping the rest of the organic tree, which has produced them, unilluminated. If what they want is fruits, they must start with the seeds, the proper soil and climate, and tend the orchard.

This brings me to my conclusion. The biological sciences are one of the most profitable investments of society. To raise the efficiency of their yield to even higher quotas, we need further fundamental knowledge; hence, we must strengthen the academic institutions that can get it. The public has a major stake in this, but is not quite prepared to understand and underwrite the riskier phases of the process. Meanwhile, progress basic to human welfare must not be held up waiting. Thus, pending public enlightenment, the next best thing to do is to have the trustees of public funds who know the story of scientific progress, or at least ought to know it, improvise proper measures.

The public, through taxes and annual collections, contributes a large share to foundations and organizations supporting biomedical research. Many of these foundations must be commended for the wisdom with which they allocate a part of the proceeds to the support of the basic biological sciences and their investigative program. But the very fact that they are explicitly commended reveals a feeling that they are acting somehow "above the call of duty"; and that they have to justify to the uninitiated the propriety of such investment. Thus, they will obviously tend to stay at least as close to their specific practical objectives as they can reasonably do without betraying their basic faith in the need for the support of fundamental science. Unwittingly, they add to the mentioned tendency of premature grooving and freezing of our science into a few major channels at the expense of broad and unrestrained exploring; thus adding to the distortion, rather than to sound proportions, of our research pattern.

In order to correct this and to make public investment in biomedicine more profitable, I would propose that all foundations, organizations, and individuals who contribute financially to the advancement of medicine assign a fixed fraction of their budgets, perhaps no more than 10 per cent, to a common pool for the promotion of the biological sciences as such, with no earmarks, no qualifications, and no restrictions other than those of accepted accounting procedure. This pooled fund ought to constitute the risk capital of the biological sciences, to be used for exploration, pro-specting, and the support of the imaginative, critically controlled, but often unpredictable ventures into the unknown. It should be used as a mobile reserve for the support and encouragement of men with ideas, rather than of routine projects, and the rekindling of the dying flame of the curiosity and vision of the pioneer, which is the irreplaceable source of fundamental scientific progress and without which the scientific process is doomed to run down toward a thermodynamic death.

These have been a few symptomatic, although somewhat sketchy, comments on what, in my opinion, is in the cards for the academic patchquilt of biomedical education in its groping to transform itself into a more rational pattern adapted to the needs of our evolving social scene, as we can foresee it. The rapid increase in population, the even greater increase in both claims and need for biomedical education, and the pressure for including ever-wider strata of the population in the benefits of the advances of medicine and the social services—all these developments have reached a momentum which can no longer be met by pragmatic nostrums. No longer will it do to correct errors of the past, one by one. Developments are getting too precipitous and times are too short for symptomatic remedies. The time has come to take a bold look forward in order that, for once, we may get ahead of the game. With future objectives clearly focused, the tactics by which to get there can be worked out, sometimes by foresight, at other times by trial-and-error. On no account, however, does blind continuance of the tactics of the past measure up to the challenge of the future tasks.

A Model Program for a Graduate School

Introduction

The preceding chapters have been essentially reflections on the state of health and growth of science—more narrowly, the life sciences—in the setting of our contemporary universities and society. Assessing the effectiveness of the service actually rendered by universities in comparison with that which they could optimally render to both an expanding science and an increasingly differentiating society, certain deficiencies, calling for adaptive change, were recognized and identified, at least grossly. The broad scope of the general principles and objectives involved, portrayed in correspondingly broad brush strokes, did not permit the spelling out of the desiderata in sufficient detail to serve as guide to concrete action. For instance, one reads in the preceding chapter:

> "Let us teach young investigators the tolerance that goes with understanding; explain the workings of the scientific process which lives on all of these: methods, data, facts, conclusions, theories, hypotheses and concepts, all of them equally vital; restore a balanced attitude between the extremes of the pure fact finders and gadgeteers at one end, and the pure theorists and speculators at the other, and debunk the arrogance of their monopolistic claims; restore respect for systematic and unhurried work, and arouse suspicion of the flashy, but ill-supported, claim that trades passing notoriety for lasting truth; and raise that sense of responsibility and pitiless self-criticism without which even the best man is prone to go to seed."

One might rightly ask how this is to be accomplished.

Therefore, to become more specific, I am inserting here as an appendix a program for a modern graduate school, designed decidedly with an eye to the future, drawing on the lessons of the assessment of the current academic scene. A major move toward such a forward-looking program was made in 1953 by The Rockefeller Institute for

Medical Research in New York, when its then-incoming President, Detlev Bronk, planned and effected the conversion of what had been a pure research institution into a novel version of a graduate university (afterwards renamed The Rockefeller University). When I was called in 1964 by the University of Texas to establish a similar program for a new Graduate School of Biomedical Sciences in Houston, I had, besides my own ideas and prior experience, acquired in the planning and conduct of the Master's program of the Division of Biological Sciences of the University of Chicago, the benefit of a decade's connection with the Rockefeller program. The gist of these experiences is given in the following sample outline for a graduate program, which, although tailored originally for a biomedical school, is applicable in its essential precepts to graduate education in science in general and, with proper adjustments, to extra-scientific precincts of learning as well.

It will be noted that the program is distinctly student-oriented. Its focus is on giving the student both the incentive and the opportunity for optimum self-development of his individual faculties. But, inasmuch as it makes him relate his own development to his prospective role in the advancement of knowledge and civilization, the program is Janus-faced, looking after the interests of both the student and society. It is a program for mutual commitment of teacher and student to harmonious cooperative effort. Perhaps examples like the Rockefeller experiment and its sequel in the program outlined here can serve as proof that the purportedly lethargic attitude of unconcern about the future, ascribed to universities by a student generation awakening from a no-less-reprehensible state of somnolence, has not been quite so universal as has been imputed.

OBJECTIVES

Graduate Education

The aim of education is knowledge: more specifically, (1) the acquisition of knowledge; (2) its application; (3) its dissemination; (4) its critical evaluation; and (5) its augmentation. The hierarchy of educational systems deals with these five objectives in a progressive order, with (1) at the most general lowest level and (5) at the summit.

Graduate education converges on the upper end of this scale, beginning in the middle of (2). It leads from rote to judicious application, from the blind acceptance of rules to their critical reexamination and adaptive improvement, and from sheer productivity (of data) to creativity (of novel concepts and methods). It thus calls increasingly upon those powers which are the unique province of the critical and creative human mind.

Unquestionably, modern society needs ever-more professionals thoroughly trained to apply and spread the available products of knowledge for the benefit of the people. But it also needs more of that scarce supply of truly creative minds through which knowledge is expanded so that deeper insight into nature may yield products more rationally, efficiently, and amply. It needs, much as in music, not just performers and conductors, but, above all, composers—in science, individuals endowed with imagination, skill, resourcefulness, drive and perseverance. These traits, though latent in various degrees in many individuals, fail to develop to their full potential unless they are detected, cultivated, and exercised. And, since their pattern varies from individual to individual, each gifted student is a separate special case requiring careful individual attention. His study programs must be tailored to his special needs to bring his superior faculties to full fruition. To subject him to no more than routine mass training would doom those faculties to atrophy.

Research

"Education" literally means "to lead forth," not "to pipe in." Since this places learning by experience from active practice above learning from rote memory, the principal teacher in graduate education is research. Research itself, however, has many facets and degrees of relevance: from sheer data compilation to invention and discovery; from wider application of the known to deeper penetration into the unknown. This scale reflects degrees of both visibility and vision—of what there is open to view and what one actually sees. While vision is a personal trait, visibility is an external feature. The gifted student, endowed with a wide perimeter of vision, must not be made to chart a course through a program that artificially restricts the visibility of the vast areas of what is, and what is not yet, known. Yet, many academic programs insist on building just such artificial blinders into their structure, purportedly for the sake of fostering concentration and mastery in given specialties. Instead of being provided with a map of the land of knowledge, with both its travelled lanes and its vast blanks, students are thus funneled into rigid channels which they can broaden and groove further, but from which they seldom escape to make discoveries through novel explorations. This is a proved way to train practitioners, not to prepare explorers; to produce followers, not to encourage leadership; to satisfy the clamor for quantity, at the expense of excellence. It is a poor way to raise creative minds and to advance the sciences broadly, harmoniously, and quickly.

The need for the perpetuation and deepening of existing trends of specialization is not to be disputed. However, unless the resulting fragmentation of the life sciences is offset in equal measure by efforts to preserve an integrated perspective of how the fragments fit into the total picture of the living system, chances for new and telling advances in the life sciences are significantly reduced. Continued work along established older lines, done competently, but not necessarily from a broad perspective, unquestionably leads to jobs which need to be filled; fresh work along new lines, or recombined old ones, however, carries the promise of major discovery and important progress. In general, graduate education should provide students with a choice of either course.

But there should also be *some* graduate schools that place a special premium on those students who possess the curiosity, talent, and courage of pioneers and who prefer the potentially more rewarding course of intellectual or technical adventure to the comfort of routine activity. Being blessed with a superior native endowment implies a moral obligation to develop it fully for service to mankind as well as for personal gratification. Some graduate schools must make it their special goal to help the individuals thus endowed and motivated fulfill that mission. New discoveries can be expected to come from the imaginative recombination of formerly separate lines of investigation, from striking out in new directions, and from the reorientation of older ones. To prepare himself for such opportunities, the student pioneer-in-training must not derive his direction solely from the inertial momentum of the past, but must be led to reorient himself with regard to, and in full view of, the vastness of the unsolved problems that lie ahead. Yet, at the same time, he must also be instructed in the expert use of the tools and procedures on which he must rely in whatever problem he aims to tackle.

Thus, the following emerge as the main objectives of a graduate school for pioneers:

(a) Well-rounded, broad exposure of the student to the cohesive entities of problem areas that are at present fragmented in numerous separate, and often unconnected, channels of technical specialization.

(b) Training in depth in one or several skills of potential bearing on a given restricted problem area.

(c) Selection of students who hold promise to profit maximally from the combination of (a) and (b)—the "T-square" education scheme.

(a) is a matter of over-all design of programs; (b) a matter of individual instruction; (c) of individualized admission and screening standards of high caliber.

PROGRAM

Outline

For the special example of graduate education in the life sciences, the implementation of the outlined objectives should be guided by the following key precepts.

(1) All teaching programs should be organized with major emphasis on continuity, consistency, and inner coherence so that the student may learn to relate any particular thread of specialized work or view to the integrated fabric of the life sciences.

(2) More specifically, all students should be offered a "core" program of lectures, demonstrations, and exercises, giving them a critical synopsis of the present state of knowledge in the life sciences; of its historical, technical, and conceptual development; of its achievements as well as of its gaps, inconsistencies, and incongruities; and of the promising avenues to its future progress. The selection of topics should be made with an eye to their relevance and balanced proportions, without undue bias toward fashions of the day.

(3) The student should be made familiar with essential methods and techniques current in biomedical research; deficiencies in his

preparation should be corrected by course attendance in neighboring institutions or by tutorials.

(4) The student should acquire competence in a few technical or methodological specialties and must learn to master at least one.

(5) Doctoral research should be tailored to the individual interests and aptitudes of each student, preferably by encouraging him to combine a variety of approaches in the exploration of a given problem in novel ways. This will foster his chance of breaking in a new line of thought and investigation peculiarly his own for further development in his subsequent career.

(6) The student should be given opportunity to develop appreciation for the nonscientific aspects of our culture, such as the arts, and, conversely, for the role of science in our civilization and for its obligations in serving society.

(7) In general, deliberate efforts must be made to counteract the growing fragmentation of the life sciences by rearing a new generation of pioneers endowed with a broad perspective for critical self-orientation, but at the same time trained in the disciplined application of their talents to a chosen, preferably self-chosen, path in a given discipline.

Execution

In compliance with this program, Ph.D. degrees should be given in "Biomedical Sciences" without explicit reference to subdivisions. "Departmental," or other sharply compartmented designations should be omitted in the interest of flexibility and versatility. To counter the risk that the abolition of categorical distinctions might lead to an undesirably amorphous scheme, the program should be structured not along traditional disciplinary lines, but around *key problems* presented by the living organism. The student must be made to sense that all phenomena of life are interrelated and interacting and that he must keep his eye on this integrated continuum even as he concentrates his work on no more than an infinitesimally small sector. Organizational emphasis will thus be shifted from disciplinary margins, which tend to hem the student in, to focal issues, from which his mind and work can radiate out. Such focal issues would be chosen from the major problem areas of molecular, genetic, cellular, developmental, regulatory (organ-ismic), behavioral, environmental, and evolutionary biology. This pattern is broad and flexible enough to accommodate unpredictable future developments in the life sciences, including additions and regroupings, as new needs and opportunities arise.

The core program should present to all students well-rounded accounts of both the state of knowledge and the open problems in those priority areas. A major part, at least of the first year of graduate study, is to be allocated to this portion of the program. During this period, time and emphasis should gradually be shifted from lectures and seminars to practical exercises and research propaedeutics. The pre-sentations should be rather strictly programed as regards logical sequence and proportions, and be amply supplemented by modern visual aids, laboratory demonstrations, library assignments, exhibits, and discussion sessions. Experiences gained in this core program will give the student a broad outlook and firm basis from which to formulate his doctoral research, as well as the necessary critical perspective under which to pursue his research and evaluate that of others.

Concurrently, the student should be given specific introductions to the various technical and mental disciplines of general applicability to modern biological research, including, for instance, methods of biosta-tistics, enzymology, microbiology, ultra-structural analysis, electro-physiology, cell culture, surface chemistry, radiation genetics, chroma-tography, microsurgery, etc. Having obtained some general acquaintance with many of these disciplines, the student will then select one or several of them for further methodical specialization under the expert guidance of an appropriate staff member.

Each of the technical skills thus acquired is pertinent to several of the program areas listed above. By applying them in various combina-tions to the investigation of common problems (e.g., brain function, wound healing, parasitism, etc.), the student's thinking and working will gain that essential second dimension which cross-connects the single-tracked channels of the established disciplines into topically unified programs. Each student should be expected to think and operate on a dual scale; he should learn to be no less concerned about consistency of subject matter than about clean methodology and technique. While he will thus be solidly trained in a given specialty, he will also be enabled to orient and rate his specialist endeavors with regard to their broader bearing on the clarification of life processes, normal and abnormal.

In order to succeed, this program requires a faculty of highest professional competence, breadth of knowledge, cooperative team spirit, and enthusiastic dedication to educational ideals. The growth of knowledge has made it practically impossible to assemble a resident faculty which, in addition to those traits, would have command of all the subject matter essential for a balanced presentation of the life sciences. Therefore, the resident faculty must be supplemented by a large contingent of visiting lecturers, specifically selected to fill in the gaps, on regular repetitive appointments.

From the core program, the students should then branch out into their individual doctoral programs. In this, prime attention should be given to superseding the lock-step training of the ordinary under-graduate curriculum by offering full opportunity for individual self-development. Originality and independence in the exploration of a problem area will have to score much higher than would sheer plodding along well-trodden paths. In the selection of doctoral projects, the heavily trafficked routes of greatest popularity, already pursued superabundantly in many institutions, should rank second to the more neglected problem areas of high significance and promise. This calls for considerable personal attention to each student by the faculty. Conversely, the student will have to make the most of the available aids in self-development, such as libraries, practice laboratories, and outside lectures.

To grow to leadership and, in turn, to raise leaders, a person must be more than informed; he must be broadly cultured. Therefore, it is incumbent on a high-class graduate school to give the student opportunities for furthering his cultural interests by participating in lectures, exhibits, field trips, and literary exercises of broad cultural scope; in this way, he will experience intimately the fertile interaction between science and the humanities. Moreover, wherever practicable, the presentation of scientific subject matter should be interspersed with references to the philosophical and historical foundations of scientific methodology, as well as to the relation of biomedical sciences to human attitudes and welfare. In addition, seminars and discussion sessions should aim at developing not only the student's sense of factual accuracy and conceptual perspective, but also his facility at articulating and communicating his thoughts clearly and concisely.

Summary

The students of today are the developers of tomorrow. The best among them, therefore, must consider it their calling to build for the future—and not just to perpetuate the past. A forward-looking system of higher education must offer them full opportunity to do so, and in an age of expanding education, society can ill afford not to offer them that opportunity.

The task of a graduate school is to provide the highly motivated, curious, imaginative, disciplined, and skillful student with guidance and an environment in which to bring his creative urge to full fruition. This is the meaning of "education for excellence." It calls for what I have called above a T-square scheme of education—an education both in breadth and in depth: in *breadth*, by widening his horizon so that he may encompass the wide perspective of the unfragmented total range of phenomena and problems in science, instead of being made to train his sights myopically on a few narrow sectors of temporary prominence; in *depth*, by teaching him thorough competence in special technical disciplines and their application to the solution of important problems.

The former object can be served by a *core program*, strictly designed for integration and over-all balance of proportions, to be offered in a coordinated plan by resident and visiting faculty members; the latter object, by intensive individual guidance of each student in his research, taking into account his aptitudes and predilections.

All of these activities should stress student participation in research, critical research evaluation, and educational exercises. Attention should also be given to the enlargement of the student's *cultural* horizon by facilitating contacts with the humanities.

Traditional curricular constraints should be held to a minimum. Research should be fostered in areas where ignorance is great, not only in those of most conspicuous recent progress. Mature investigators might be expected to choose their own research, whether wide or narrow, orthodox or inventive, according to their own judgement and sense of responsibility. Their gifted students, however, should be allowed to diversify, rather than just replicate and amplify, the course of their research preceptors.

Consistent adherence to the outlined policy is bound to bring about a new generation of Ph.D.s steeped in the spirit of striving for excellence through effort and destined to advance the life sciences on a broad front—for their own satisfaction and gain in doing it and for the growth of human knowledge and understanding that comes from it. Evidently, such a program is suitable for only a limited segment of the graduate student population. It would seem in the interest of our society to afford them this exceptional challenge to prove and enhance superior native talent instead of condemning them to the level of performance of the average, which rightly rules the programs of education for the broad masses of practitioners and enlightened citizens with less exceptional endowments.

Experience and Experiment*

"Experiment versus Experience". If I had had to give this talk in French, I could not even have phrased the title as I did. For "expérience" in French means both experience and experiment. Yet there is a fundamental difference between the two. Experience means familiarity with happenings in the world. It is our cumulative record or store of judgments and suppositions, which we have formed by conscious or subconscious evaluation, from countless observations, impressions, and comparisons. It is personal and subjective. Experiments, by contrast, are objective tests of whether our suppositions are factually valid, not just intuitionally plausible or logically cogent. Experience makes us assume and expect relations between things in nature, but it remains for the experiment to verify the assumptions and expectations. Experience prompts and guides experiments, and the experiments, in turn, confirm or amplify or modify the content of experience. In short, experience, experiment, and logic play back and forth upon each other in mutual enhancement; it takes this triple interplay to promote knowledge:

However, in biology the experiment has long been but a junior member in this partnership. It is fitting, therefore, to pay tribute to the period of Vallisneri, which we commemorate, for having raised experimentation to senior rank and status. It seems that during that epoch the number of converts from speculation to the discipline of the experimental method reached, in the terms of physics, the "critical mass" necessary to generate a carrier wave of telling force and sweep, whose mounting swell, washing away old rocks of idle supposition and contention, has brought on the stupendous growth of our understanding of living systems. So we may date from that period the systematic ascent of biological experimentation to its present culmination as the powerful tool for sorting fact from belief, for testing the pertinence of logical premises and conclusions, for settling ambiguous

*Address delivered at the Symposium held by the University and Academy of Padua in celebration of the 300th anniversary of the birth of Antonio Vallisneri, September 29-30, 1961.

Reprinted from SCIENCE, Vol. 136, pp. 468-471, 1962.

issues, for removing inconsistencies among conflicting data, and, in general, for aiding the human mind in getting to understand living nature by manipulating natural events and tricking them into revealing crucial information.

The point is that experiments have been done, and ought to be done, for a purpose—a purpose other than just to do another experiment. Experimentation used to be deliberate, not improvised; planned to reduce confusion, not just to add profusion; it was meant to be relevant and incisive, not just trifling and redundant. Or, to put it succinctly, in the tradition of those past centuries, designing an experiment has been like training a gun at a target, rather than like spattering buckshot all around at random in the hope that somewhere something might be hit. The targets, in turn, were products of experience, including those extrapolations from experience by logic and imagination which generate hypotheses and theories. Throughout, deliberate orientation of experiments toward visible or envisioned goals has been the practice and tacitly accepted work rule.

Yet work rules have a way of changing imperceptibly as time goes on and as conditions change. Much as in evolution, such trends of change may be for the better or the worse, ending, respectively, in progress or disaster. But unlike evolution, intelligence ought to be able to recognize turns into disastrous courses in advance and thus prevent potentially monstrous products. For instance, let us take a complex system—an organism or a community or any social enterprise—whose proper functioning requires that all its vital parts maintain harmonious proportions; let one set of parts defy this harmony and go off on its own, with no regard to the others and the total pattern, and the result will be monstrosities. The dinosaurs, extravaganzas in size and mass beyond the power of a nervous system to manage and coordinate, were such monstrosities. Now, consider that the body of knowledge likewise is a cohesive, consistent, integrated system (*1*), not just a hodge-podge of miscellaneous information, which therefore likewise requires for its healthy growth a sound balance among its tributaries—experience, experiment, and logic. So, if biological research were to allow the share of experience to dwindle and let experimentation gain in volume, while losing in purpose and direction, biology might yet meet the fate of the dinosaurs. This is a fate which we can forestall if we heed signs, or even mere forebodings, that such a trend is in the offing.

Bulk Replaces Brains

Now, I submit that such warning signals have indeed appeared; that biological experimentation, at the height of success, is beginning to drift from the rigorous work maxim of its preceptors into habits that threaten to place bulk ahead of brains, and routine exercises ahead of thought.

I said experiments should be purposeful and meaningful. To be concrete, let me illustrate briefly some of those purposes and meanings. Organic nature confronts us with a host of puzzling questions, which we then try to answer by experiments. But the major class of experiments is that which boldly tosses questions back at nature and tricks nature into answering them by confronting her with combinations and constellations of conditions unprecedented in her standard repertory. To mention some examples at random: the taking of living cells out of the body and growing them in an extraneous medium—the ingenious experiment of Harrison that started tissue culture; or the surgical removal by Lashley of arbitrary fractions of the visual brain cortex in rats that had been trained to discriminate visual patterns, with the result that the learned patterns persisted in the defective brains as proof that visual memory is not a fractionable mosaic; or the first injection of foreign molecules into a rabbit, which then formed antibodies matching the alien agent, proving that immune responses are truly adaptive; or the transfer of the perfusion fluid of an excited frog heart into another heart, which thereby got excited, proving the humoral character of the transmission from nerve to muscle; and so forth.

What really distinguishes such experiments is not their novelty, but rather their originality and pertinence. Without imagination one can contrive infinite variations of experimental set-ups, all of them novel, yet utterly uninteresting, inconsequential, insignificant. The mere fact that something has not been done or tried before is not sufficient reason for doing or trying it. It takes originality to conceive innovations of true significance or of relevance to the solution of a problem or to the assessment of a theory. When Harrison removed nerve cells from the body to prove that they can sprout nerve fibers with no help from the body, he had expected the outcome. Experience had shaped his expectation, and the expectation dictated the experiment. When

Lashley inflicted brain lesions in trained rats, his thinking was guided by clinical reports of functional integrity in human patients with brain injuries. The experiments were designed to settle problems. If they were gambles, the stakes were high. And incidentally, they all were done with rather elementary means—artfully. The crux is that they succeeded because these men had let their seasoned experience lead the way to critical experiments. This used to be the common practice. Is it still?

Accidental Discoveries

Or is my argument perhaps ill-founded? For instance, I have selected as examples star performers to the neglect of lesser lights. True, but stars of major brightness on the biological firmament used to be sufficiently distinctive to act as navigation guides for succeeding generations. The milky way is not well suited for this role. A crowd of mediocrity, however tolerable, if in the foreground, stands to becloud the guiding lights of excellence. There used to be, however, no such crowd.

Next, I intimated that experiments used to be designed in expectation of a relevant result and that this was good. But is not scientific history full of instances of the accidental discovery of the unexpected? True again, but he who does expect something will be on the alert even for the unexpected, while he who just ambles, looking for nothing in particular, is prone to miss even the obvious. And as for the saying that the blind hen, too, finds a grain, this certainly would not hold for a hen on a grainless desert, and at any rate, it does not suggest that blindness or deliberate blindfolding is superior to vision. Of course, we frequently end up with answers to questions other than the ones we asked, or even with a lesson on how to phrase our questions better. But the historic successes of our predecessors still argue for the virtue of taking off for the exploration of the unknown from clearcut questions born from expectations, not just from vague expectancy of who knows what.

Experiments are also checks of whether what experience presents as obvious or plausible is true or false. The linkage of events in nature is a matter of experience; to decide the nature of the linkage remains a matter of experimental tests. The remarkably observant Leonardo da Vinci noticed that castrated animals lose their fighting spirit, which led him to infer that there is a direct linkage between the testicles and behavior. It so happens that modern experiments have proved him right, but what if the behavorial change had been an unspecific by-product of the trauma of removing an organ—any organ—rather than specifically the testicles?

Plausibility alone is quite untrustworthy. Remember the case of the eruption of the forelimbs of the metamorphosing frog larva. These limbs develop inside a deep subcutaneous pocket; to become useful, they must break through the covering layer of skin, and indeed, when they have grown to size, perforations form in the skin where the limbs chafe against it, letting the limbs emerge. What would be more plausible than to assume that the pressure of the limb itself causes the perforation? Distrusting plausibility, the skeptical biologist—in this case, Braus—put the assumption to an experimental test by suppressing the development of the fore limb altogether; surprisingly, at the appointed stage, an opening formed in the skin nevertheless, in readiness for the delivery of a limb that was not there. The puncture has since been traced to a coincidental autolytic process in the skin, quite unrelated to the limb.

Biological research has uncovered a distressing multitude of such surprises. Take for example, the story of the development of the lens of the eye. The eyeball forms as a cup-shaped outpocketing of the embryonic brain; whereas the lens starts as an inpocketing from the outer skin, fitting snugly into the cup. Thus, faced with this composite origin, one had to wonder how the lens could always form precisely where the eye is later to look out. The question seemed comfortably answered for a while when Lewis and Spemann both demonstrated that in some amphibians the lens would not form if the eye were absent, hence that the eye itself induced the lens. The comfort of this simple answer, however, did not last. When the experiments were repeated in some other amphibian forms, the lens formed independently, whether or not the eye was there. Therefore, not only can sheer plausibility not be trusted, but, even if experimentally confirmed for one set of circumstances, the confirmation need not be valid for another set.

Another instance is chromatophore reaction: experimental studies on its control again brought widely disparate results, submitting to no unifying formula. In some forms, the control turned out to be neural, in others hormonal, and, in still others, shared by both the nervous and the hormonal systems, the one causing contraction, the other expansion. To come to this conclusion, a fair variety of forms had to be sampled. Doubtless a more limited sample would have led to the false generalization that the control is exclusively either nervous or hormonal. Thus, to test a certain variety of species proved to have been an absolute necessity. Yet, once having established the salient point that evolution has made promiscuous use of all possible combinations between the agents and effects at its disposal, all further experimental repetition, except for training purposes, would only serve a cataloging function—expansion in bulk, rather than penetration in depth. But, we may ask, how large a catalog of data can we afford and justify?

Where Does Necessity End and Redundancy Start?

In fact, any set of examples of biological experiments that I could cite would make us ponder certain questions. What is the minimum range of variables that must be tested before we can certify a given biological proposition or conclusion as reasonably safe? How much additional variation and repetition beyond this range is essential and justifiable on scientific grounds, considering the finite bounds of social and economic reality? Where does necessity end and redundancy start?

In trying for answers, the biological sciences find themselves somewhere on middle ground between the one extreme of physics, which concentrates its interest on general principles, with less concern for specific mechanisms (except in meteorology and the like and, of course, engineering), and the other extreme of the historical branches of learning with their preoccupation with the particular, specific, and often unique shape of events. At the physical end of this scale, a maximum number of phenomena can be condensed into a minimum number of general formulas, but as one proceeds toward the other end, this ratio becomes progressively inverted, as itemized fact-finding and data-recording become more and more ends in themselves, rather than way stations to the formation of theories.

The center of gravity of the life sciences has steadily shifted on this scale from the descriptive and normative end of natural history toward the analytical and formulative end of the exact sciences. Of course, the assumption that biology could ever reach the physical end completely is a delusion, based either on lack of realistic acquaintance with living systems and their true nature or unawareness of the conceptual limitations of physical reductionism. This is not to question our success in reducing cellular phenomena to molecular terms. However, to pretend that the process can be reversed, that the molecular shambles can reassemble themselves into a functional living system without the cheating intervention of another living system, is a conceptual perversion, whatever one may think of the primordial origin of life (2).

Biology, therefore, is destined to retain its autonomy, which means that to be known and understood, biological mechanisms will still have to be studied and formulated in their own right and full diversity. And this explains why in biology so many generalizations must stop far short of the vast inclusiveness of laws of physics, hence, why the range of validity of each must be determined empirically. It is this inherent feature of biological nature, rather than backwardness or extravagance, then, which necessitates testing over a far wider spectrum of variables, such as species, cell types, stages, environments, and so forth, than would seem necessary or even pardonable in most of physics. It sanctions the usage of repeating biological experiments with appropriate variations: with change of objects, agents, dosage, timing, methods of observation, measurement, recording, and the like. But when does usage turn into abuse? When is one to terminate potentially infinite series of variations? Or is it still legitimate, in the name of scientific freedom, to go on interminably?

This brings me to the crux of my argument. Throughout the phase of history which we have come to survey, till very recently, to be a scientist was a calling, not a job. Scientists were men of science, not just men in science. They had come to science driven by an inner urge, curiosity, a quest for knowledge, and they knew, or learned, what it was all about. They were not drawn or lured into science in masses by fascinating gadgets, public acclaim, manpower needs of industries and governments, or job security; nor did they just drift in for no good reason. The scene, however, is now changing rapidly. The popularity and needs of an expanding science bring in more drifters and followers than pioneers. While the first signs of this change are perhaps a little more conspicuous in our country, the growth of interest and investment in science, with mounting opportunities and recruitment, is bound to sweep across the globe. The carrier wave of experimental research set off in the pioneering days is suddenly swelling into a gigantic tidal wave. Having barely begun, we cannot foretell its ultimate dimensions, but it is already bursting the narrow frame of current scientific facilities and practices, which have essentially been fashioned by and for traditional science, the small-scale enterprise of yesteryear. This growth will keep right on. Now, as biologists, we know that sheer expansive growth, unrestrained by differentiation and functional adjustments, breeds tumors. Shall we let the oncoming scientific expansion likewise become a tumorous inflation? Shall we let brain-power be overgrown by manpower and mechanical rote performance?

Growth in a healthy organism is self-limiting, restrained by inner balances, not by external strait jackets. In the growth of biological research, likewise, lest we conjure the horrible specter of some administrative authority prescribing to our scientists what to do, and what not, and how much, when, and how, we must by all means strive to keep alive, or else revive, the old spirit of self-restraint of the experimenter, exercised by being most circumspect in the selection of his research targets in terms of relevance, and being most disciplined, responsible, and parsimonious in his attack on them. Research morality is even more important than research morale.

I had intended to cite specific evidence that as research has grown in volume it also has grown softer by loss of self-restraint, lowered selectivity, blurring of research targets, and, consequently, lack of self-direction. But then I decided not to quote because, after all, contemporary biology has such a superb record of truly outstanding achievements that it would gravely distort the total picture if only some flaws were drawn in magnified detail.

Nevertheless, the general conclusion stands: it is that however vigorously biological research has been growing, the diluent has begun to grow faster than the solid substance, and this bears watching. The symptoms are many. We see instruments turning from servants into tyrants, forcing the captive scientist to mass-produce and market senseless data beyond the point of conceivable usefulness—a modern version of the Sorcerer's Apprentice. We see bewildered youngsters composing research projects like abstract paintings: picking some colorful and fashionable words from recent literature, and then reshuffling and recombining them into another conglomerate, yielding a stew of data, both undigested and indigestible. We see narrow specialists lavishing their pet technique on reconfirming in yet another dozen ways what has already been superabundantly established to everybody's satisfaction. But why go on? Most of you will know the hallmarks of this growing dilution of our research effectiveness. They are irrelevance, triviality, redundancy, lack of perspective, and an unbounded flair for proliferation.

Now, granting the fact, why be alarmed? All right, there is some waste; but wastefulness can never be wholly banned from science. Yet, what is serious is that the volume production of trifles is not just waste. It actively competes with the pursuits of worthier objectives. The map of biological knowledge is still so full of major blanks and gaps that our elementary sense of proportions cries for an equitable distribution of our research potential over the whole field. Carl Hartmann (3) has recently published a list of major unsolved problems in the physiology of mammalian conception alone: it added up to 154, only a fraction of them under study. Imagine the size of such a catalog of ignorance for the whole of the life sciences. Yet dull, routine mass production in research only swells the traffic along the well-traveled familiar highways of activity, rather than branching out into the unfamiliar wilderness that needs to be explored.

Experience

These are just some of the symptoms of "Big Science." Well, Big Science is on the way and will remain here for good. The time to think how to adjust to it is now. This is a matter for all of those concerned with the future of our culture—research men, teachers, administrators, historians, philosophers, publishers, editors and statesmen. The growth of science can be the greatest blessing for humanity, but only if we resist the easy coasting downhill carried by the inflationary momentum. Ever more men of special technical competence will be needed in science to elaborate and apply that which we have come to know. They are not the ones I am concerned about. They are well taken care of. It is those others, able and destined to contribute significantly to the advance of knowledge, whom we must salvage from being either crushed or swept down with the current. They are those young men and women full of curiosity, imagination, and sharp intellects whose mental powers can find full realization only by exertion, but would be doomed to atrophy in the dull and effortless game of routine mass procedures.

To them, the scientists of the future, we ought to pass on the lessons of our glimpses of the past. So, let them look at the old masters. Outmoded? Technically, of course; but not so much in method, and not at all in the spirit which guided their experiments. What were their guides; Ideas, not gadgets, not the need to publish. Ideas, in turn, sprout from the fertile soil of experience. So, then, at last, what is this potent nostrum, experience?

It is that subtly discriminating, screening, sorting, evaluating, and integrating faculty of our minds which we elaborate and perfect continuously throughout life, more subconsciously than in awareness. Its potency stems from the extraordinary innate acuity and sensitivity of our nervous system, sharpened and polished ever more by use and training. Our retina can perceive a few quanta of light, our nasal organ, molecules in concentrations below the detecting power of the finest tests. Why not concede, then, similarly high efficiency to the brain and give it free rein in its incessant activity of selecting, comparing, rating, judging, and creating, which is the mainspring of our concepts and ideas? The experimental discipline has rightly eradicated faith in any a priori truth of such ideas, but let us guard the young generation against seduction by the opposite extreme, no less pernicious—undisciplined experiments, unguided by ideas.

REFERENCES AND NOTES

1. P. Weiss, "Knowledge: a growth process," *Science* 131, 1716-1719. 1960. (see Chapter 9).

2. —————————, "From cell to molecule," in *The Molecular Control of Cellular Activity*, J. M. Allen, Ed. (McGraw-Hill, New York, 1961), pp. 1-72

3. C. Hartmann, "Physiological mechanisms of conception—an inventory of unanswered questions," *Perspectives in Biol. and Med.* 4, 77 1960.

Publication: Tool of Research*

The difficulties in the field of biological publication are only partly of a technical and administrative nature and therefore can only partly be overcome by technical and organizational measures. The roots of the problem lie much deeper and concern the whole future of biology.

As publication is merely crystallized research, publication ills are largely an outcome of defective research, and bad research, in turn, may be blamed on bad training for research. The publication problem thus appears as just one aspect of a much broader problem; namely, that of teaching and research in biology in general.

If the volume of publication threatens to surpass what is technically and economically manageable, we must decide on how to meet the threat without hampering scientific progress. Our capacity to process, finance, store, and utilize scientific literature is certainly not unlimited. Yet, in the past, we have often behaved as if it were. We now realize that we are approaching the critical limit at an ominous pace, and we want to be prepared.

Logically, there are several ways of keeping the volume of publication within reasonable bounds. We might reduce research production, or we might continue to produce at full capacity but publish only part of it. Above all, we might increase the efficiency of both production and publication; that is, the yield, per unit of time, of scientifically useful results, and the yield, per printed page, of scientifically useful statements. In deciding just what course to follow in practice, the long-range interests of biological science as a whole should prevail. However, since biology lacks unity of purpose and has never developed a deliberate and consistent research policy, we simply do not possess valid criteria by which to judge what would, and what would not, serve the interests of biology as a whole. Our opinions on the subject are diverse and often conflicting, and by their very diversity

---

*Address before the Conference on Publication Problems in Biology, held at the Cleveland meeting of the American Association for the Advancement of Science on September 11, 1944.

Reprinted from SCIENCE, Vol. 101, pages 101-104, 1945.

reveal the part which fashions, local traditions, personal predilection, and expediency have played in their molding.

Opinion is too casual and unstable a basis for any science worth its name to rest upon, and if we are really concerned about the future of biological research, the thing to do is to provide it with a firm foundation of principles defining the purpose of research and the methods that have proved most successful in attaining it. The time has come for changing from a drifting to a charted course, not only in the field of publication, but in biological research. This study of the publication problem might, therefore, profitably be made the occasion for initiating a much broader enterprise: a concerted reexamination, reevaluation and restatement of the goals, ways and means of biological research. I shall try to illustrate in the following very sketchy outline how the field of publication would benefit from such a more comprehensive action.

It has become perfectly plain that with the increase of workers flocking into research, the cherished doctrine of freedom for random movements must gradually be abandoned. This is not the place to go into a detailed discussion of these matters. All I mean to indicate is that, while the shelling of every new walnut promises to reveal some new configuration on the inside, we shall have to consider how long it is scientifically proficient and economically feasible to continue to shell walnuts in the hope that something worthwhile will come of it.

There are some basic fallacies current among biological workers. They are: (a) that every as-yet-unrecorded item is worth recording; (b) that every recorded item is worth reporting; (c) that every fact worth reporting is worth publishing in print.

There are those who contend—I am sure, quite sincerely—that in science anything at all that has not yet been done is worth doing, and that one fact is as good as any other fact. I respect their viewpoint, but can not share it, because it seems to me to be based on an utter misconception of the aim and function of research. It is a perversion of the teachings of the history and philosophy of science to claim that the aim of research is fact-finding. The aim of research is knowledge, and as knowledge is not a mere collection of data, research cannot consist merely of a compilation of facts. Information does not constitute knowledge. It merely furnishes the food on which knowledge grows (see the following chapter). To expect that a hodge-podge of miscellaneous data is going to sort and order itself automatically into knowledge is like the illusion of the medieval magician who expected a mixture of chemicals in a retort to organize itself into a homunculus.

Now, if facts are but the food on which knowledge grows, is it not about time that we concern ourselves a little with the dietetics of knowledge to find out which foods are healthy, how they are to be prepared and what constitutes a balanced diet? Certainly as bulk is no criterion of nutritive value, so the volume of data being piled up can be no measure of the progress of science. The primary aim of research must not be just more facts, but more facts of strategic value.

By strategic value I mean that property of an observation or experiment that leads to the clarification or solution of a problem, to deeper insight into a phenomenon, to the linking of previously unrelated facts and ideas, or simply to the birth of a new problem; at any rate, leads to some end other than the bewildered question, "So, what?"

The crux of the problem, therefore, is to make research workers more strategy-conscious. How? Most of us are vaguely conscious of an unwritten code of scientific strategy, which has been passed down through the medium of example and personal contact from teacher to student. But now that scientific research is assuming mass-production dimensions, this mode of transmission is breaking down. More and more students leave our classrooms for so-called independent research, with barely the faintest notion of what science is all about and of how best to promote it. While they are learning tactical tricks, they rarely come to know those rules of scientific strategy which could give aimfulness to their future research.

Now, if the patriarchal system of instruction, which could give a student perspective, is forced out of operation by sheer pressure of numbers, then we shall have to do what all communities and tribes had to do when they outgrew the patriarchal state in which unwritten convention could pass for law: they had to codify the law. So we may likewise have to formulate and codify the rules of scientific research. Unless we do, we cannot expect an uninitiated generation of tomorrow to observe these rules, for they will not know them.

Yes, I am envisaging a written code of scientific research to serve as a manual of scientific strategy and as a standard frame of reference for the rating of scientific products, for the guidance of research workers, editors, and administrators alike. However, in contrast to a code of law, with its powers of enforcement, the implementation of this scientific code must be left to the conscience of the research man himself. Conformance must be a matter of his sense of responsibility and judgment, which we, as teachers, must strive to develop, and there must be no coercion. Some will continue to waste their time and somebody's funds on petty tasks, but this will still be much less costly to science than would be any attempt to prescribe certain ways of research and proscribe others. On the other hand, unless we do exercise and teach self-discipline, restraints may be forced upon us from the outside by agencies of much less vision and competence. And this we want to avoid.

The suspicion that I am here advocating a subtle scheme to deprive the scientist of his freedom of decision may be allayed by reiterating that, quite to the contrary, I want us to provide him with a more rational basis on which to make intelligent and responsible decisions. Even now freedom of choice in research is restricted by such factors as pressure of opinion or authority, accidents of training and circumstances, subsidizing policies of institutions and foundations, practical needs, and others. These are extraneous influences. How, then, could anyone object to letting biology develop a directive from its own inner resources—the envisaged articles of the strategy of scientific research? The quality of both research and publication could only gain from such an educational campaign, which would reduce the aimlessness of thousands of sorcerer's apprentices now busily engaged in swelling the flood of literature. So much for long-range policy.

Of immediate benefit would be the incorporation in our educational program of some instruction to graduate students on how to organize their material for publication. We teach our students to use only clean instruments and glassware, but we do not always insist on similar cleanliness of their mental and verbal tools. We expect them to be meticulous in their observations, manipulations, and measurements, but we often let them get away with a muddled presentation of their results. Would it not be wise to develop their sense of proportion and, for instance, call their attention to the fact that they only hurt themselves and irritate the reader by such common practices as camouflaging important results by setting them down in an underbrush of irrelevant trifles?

We must also help the student to steer clear of two extreme and opposite attitudes that he is prone to adopt. On the one hand, there are those who feel that the main thing is to do the work and that publishing it is a side issue. On the other half of the picture, there is the understandable tendency of some to recite for the reader all the little incidents of their research, which have no scientific interest. Add to this the tendency of "padding" for the mere sake of attaining impressive volume, and it can be seen that a lot of improvement might come from proper education at the research end, long before a manuscript reaches the editor.

I have been talking of the student, but the student of today is the research worker of tomorrow. If there is nothing we can do about the past, we can at least provide for the future.

Cleanliness of mental tools and mental operations in the description of scientific results would go a long way in saving publication space. A concrete step in this direction could be made by insisting on more uniform and consistent terminology. If one compares the care with which terminology is treated in physics and nomenclature in taxonomy with the terminological carelessness in some other biological fields, the contrast is appalling. Three improvements could be made with little effort.

(a) The creation of new terms or symbols, even if only for temporary use, to designate complex phenomena or situations that otherwise would have to be circumscribed at each mention by long-winded phrases, should be encouraged. Authors should acquire the habit of giving a vocabulary of their main terms in the first part of their paper, and then sticking to it.

(b) The creation of new terms for phenomena for which there is already a good old term should be discouraged.

(c) Use of the same term in different meanings by different authors is a common source of controversy that leads to polemics, and should be eliminated.

The time seems ripe for various biological disciplines to attempt some terminological house cleaning, and it might be profitable to encourage the setting up of commissions in each field to attempt a standardization of terms in that field, possibly to be incorporated in sectional dictionaries to which reference could be made whenever the terms are being used in publications.

More serious consideration should be given to the state of digestion at which research results or theories are deemed ready for presentation. This is one of the knottiest problems, because it involves so many considerations other than the sheer interest of science—for instance, competition, priority, baiting of funds, institutional publication pressure, etc. This problem reaches over into that of the technique of publication, and the solution may lie in giving factual data that deserve quick diffusion a different treatment from other materials in which the advantage of maturation outweighs the disadvantage of delay.

One could envisage a bulletin service through which raw research data would be communicated only to those research workers known to be engaged in related work or specifically requesting them. Routed through a central clearing agency and reproduced by cheap processes, such bulletins would not only speed the dissemination of information, but would make available information that otherwise would have to remain unreported. Some specialized and highly active branches of biology have already adopted such a scheme, unofficially, as it were. There is no reason why it should not be made universal and be given bibliographic recognition. Lack of editorial screening is counter-balanced by the author's awareness that his information will reach the most critical judges—his peers in the same field.

Relieved thus of the congestion caused by the growing tendency of authors to present their work in installments, publication in print would return to its original function of reporting work which has been brought to some sort of conclusion. Printed publication would be reserved for results and thoughts worthy of more general circulation and of permanent preservation, and would no longer dignify the ephemeral.

Let us now turn to some further aspects of the publication problem which would be materially affected by whatever policy biological research chooses to follow.

(1) Biological disciplines have gradually and imperceptibly changed their content and methods so that many of the historical designations which now delimit fields have lost their former meanings. Other fields have not changed in content, but in emphasis. While there has been a tendency to accommodate new trends by establishing new journals, there has been less evidence of reorientation among the existing journals to adapt themselves to the changes that have occurred. No

satisfactory solution of this problem will be reached unless biologists get together and rearrange and reallocate their various disciplines. This could, of course, come only from free, wise, and cooperative planning.

(2) Many existing journals are distinguished by their histories. It would be deplorable if attempts at standardization and uniformity were driven to the point at which individual organs of publication would lose their personal character. However, with all due reverence for historical tradition, certain incongruities of the past are in need of correction. Most serious among these are the duplication of effort and the overlap of domain between journals covering nearly identical fields in a spirit of rivalry. We shall not be able to change the weaknesses of human nature, but we do not have to accord them a prominent place in the determination of our scientific policies.

(3) Institutional administrators, government bureaus, etc., will have to be persuaded that the number of printed pages or articles is no valid measure of a man's productivity and usefulness. That some waste of print can be ascribed to institutional publication pressure is generally recognized. What is not usually pointed out in this connection is that we cannot expect administrators to give up the convenience of counter and yardstick as long as many of our scientific societies apply this criterion in ruling on admission to membership. The question of what other criteria to substitute for volume of puplication involves the fundamental problem of how to appraise research efforts and assess research achievements and this, again, cannot be answered otherwise than in terms of certain agreed-upon standards of the goals, ways, and means of biological research.

(4) Universal adoption of the policy of making publication an integral part of a research project, so that at least part of the publication costs would naturally be carried by the institutional, foundational, or private funds supporting the research might cure some of the ills. Psychologically, it would make for greater care in publication. Economically, it would discourage expansiveness. Publication is as inseparable and as legitimate a part of research as is the developing of an exposed plate in photography. The objection that funds would thus be deflected that otherwise might be used for productive research is not really serious, for anybody who takes the trouble to look into the concrete figures will soon convince himself that publication costs, by and large, amount to only an insignificant fraction of the total cost of a research project.

In conclusion, our present system of publication in biology, while perhaps capable of temporizing a little longer with the aid of technical improvements, subsidies, stronger editorial control, and similar expedients, is admittedly unprepared and unsuited to serve the needs of a science which grows as rapidly and vigorously as does biology. Our collective responsibility for the future of biology forces us to take notice. To take appropriate action will require much wisdom and experience, but, above all, vision.

It is my plea that whenever such action is taken, the publication problem be dealt with not separately, but as part of the larger problem of biological research, of which it is a natural branch. I feel that education for research, planning of research, prosecution of research, financing of research, and publication of research should each be viewed from the perspective of the whole complex. To be able to do this, we need a more explicit and consistent research policy than we now possess, and it might be a timely undertaking to formulate and codify the unwritten rules of scientific—more particularly, biological—research strategy, for the good of research workers, teachers, students, administrators, legislators, publishers, editors, donors, and all others whose action or inaction may affect the future of our science.

Postscript 1970: It may seem worth pondering that this address was given more than a quarter of a century ago. In the meantime, many of the predictions made then have come true and several of the corrective measures tentatively proposed above have actually been instituted, particularly those formulated in points 1, 2 and 4. Without presuming that there has been any direct instrumental connection between these improvements and my proposals, the concurrence still indicates to me that the latter must have been at least aimed in the right direction. Should one not feel encouraged then to call for a second look also at those defects that have failed to receive proper attention, especially those summarized in recommendation (3), i.e., the decline of value judgements?

Knowledge: A Growth Process*

In our day, promotion of knowledge has become a public trust. Its managers and practitioners must see and keep the object—knowledge—in sharpest focus; lest it get blurred in the excitement of a mass-production boom, or get disjointed by progressive parcelling among producers, sponsors, distributors, interpreters, administrators, and consumers.

Promoting knowledge can only mean the fostering of its intrinsic growth. To do this rationally requires insight into the nature of the growth process. I wish to show that fundamentally, our knowledge grows the way a living body does. The kind of knowledge I shall deal with is scientific knowledge; implying no inference to other forms. And even this limited perspective is slanted from the angle of my specialty, the life sciences. Yet, it takes the vantage point of a biologist to recognize the growth of knowledge as truly a mirror image of the growth of organisms. Scientific knowledge grows like an organic tree, not as a compilation of collector's items. Facts, observations, discoveries, as items, are but the nutrients on which the tree of knowledge feeds, and not until they have been thoroughly absorbed and assimilated, have they truly enlarged the body of knowledge. This thesis I shall now try to expound further.

My model is a higher animal. The main steps of its growth process are diagrammed in Figure 1A. (Boxes indicate material entities; arrows, the flow of processes connecting them.) Growth converts food from the environment into body substance in a sequence of four major steps: intake, digestion, assimilation, and final utilization. The raw materials

*Reprinted from PROCEEDINGS OF THE AMERICAN PHILOSOPHICAL SOCIETY, Vol. 104, pp. 242-247, 1960

are gathered from the environment and either stored or passed on directly for alimentary processing. Digestible items are broken down chemically to more manageable compounds, which are then screened and sorted into useful and useless varieties. The wastes, together with undigestible residues, are eliminated, sharing the fate of spoilage from protracted storage. The useful fraction, the true nutrients, are circulated to the tissues, whose cells pick what they need, then recombine and modify it to form intermediary products, already bearing specific earmarks of that organism, some to be recirculated for use by other cells, some still to be discharged as waste. Finally, culminating the

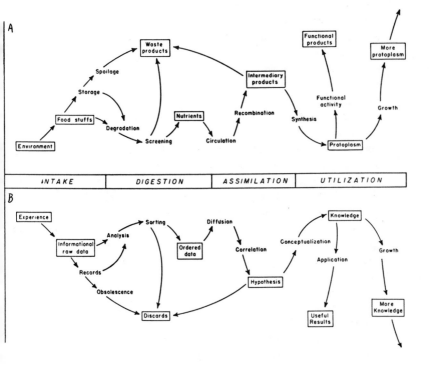

Figure 1

synthesis, each cell constructs from this supply pool selectively the substances and structures uniquely characteristic of its own kind. In this last step, cells branch in two directions. They either reproduce, that is, add more cells to the body; or they turn to the manufacture of special products, like fibers, hair, secretions, bone, and such.

This model is abridged and oversimplified. However, it illustrates the essence of the growth process, which is that in its growth an organism never adopts foreign matter outright, but reorganizes and assimilates it to fit its own peculiar pattern. Even a leech must first dissolve the hemoglobin of its meal of blood and then compose its own brand from the fragments. Organic growth is by assimilation, not accretion. Food items are not simply stuck on to the body, but, on the contrary, lose their identity, become anonymous and indistinguishably blended into the body's very own type of constituents by the processing chain of extraction, screening, sorting, fitting, and recasting.

How closely this course is mirrored in the growth of knowledge, is symbolized in the whole figure 1. The upper half is the organismic cycle, the lower half deals with knowledge, beginning from its source—experience, still unprocessed. Probing of the environment furnishes the raw data of information, which are either stored as records for future use or analyzed forthwith. The products of analysis are then screened and sorted according to relevance. Irrelevant ones go into discard, sharing the fate of records that have become obsolete. And, from this sorting, the pile of data emerges as an ordered system, catalogued and classified, yet each item still revealing its erstwhile identity. The grandest examples of such ordered sets of data are perhaps the Linnaean system of species prior to the theory of evolution, or the Mendelyeev Atomic tables prior to modern physics. In various stages of evaluation, such packaged information is then widely circulated, leading to confluence and critical correlation with countless contributions from other sources. From this synthetic process hypotheses emerge, which, upon further verification, turn into integral parts of the body of knowledge—theorems, principles, rules, and laws—general formulae which not only supersede the itemized accounts of the very data from which they were derived, but can dispense with the further search for items of information, which they subsume.

At this stage, data have become assimilated, have lost their individual identities in merging with that higher entity—the body of organized knowledge. Sheer listing has given way to understanding. A patchwork of unrelated facts has been transformed into a rationally connected thought structure of inner consistency, viable and durable, subject to the tests of survival and the adaptive improvements of evolution—a veritable model of an organism. As in the organism, the culminating phase is branched. As basic knowledge grows, part of the increment accrues to its own body, yielding more basic knowledge, while another part is converted into differentiated products—all that is commonly lumped under the attribute "applied."

Note that no separate express tracks connect either food stuffs directly with functional products in the organism, or informational data with practical results in human affairs, but that both must be routed through the common machinery for growth. In knowledge, as in nature, fruit grows on trees and cannot be raised directly on the soil by short cuts, by-passing the tree.

Our growth analogy could be expanded – tradition standing for heredity; novel ideas, for mutations; the "team" approach, for symbiosis—but the general parallelism will have become clear enough for us now to examine its implications.

In the first place, it shows that information is not tantamount to knowledge. Information is but the raw material, the precursor, of knowledge. To hoard a store of unrelated items of information in a mental gullet by rote memory and without sense of relevance— including the ability to regurgitate the data on a quiz master's prompting—should pass for knowledge no more than the stuffing of a hamster's pouch can be regarded as growth. Knowledge emerges from the distilling, shaping, and integrating of the raw material into concepts and rules; and, in this process of condensation and generalization, the number of bits of detailed information dwindles, rather than mounts: a piling up of raw data signals glut rather than growth.

Accordingly, if knowledge grows like organisms, we ought to observe sound dietetics and avoid unhealthy overstuffing; the symptoms of glut—redundancy, superdetermination, oversophistication, and just plain bulk—are already noticeable in current research practices. Part of the syndrome carries rather undignified names, such as "soft money" or "projectitis." But the crucial ailment is myopic vision, which fails to recognize the true character of knowledge. Once out of sight, the body of concepts to which data collection should be related no longer guides the search for data. The sense of relevance and selectivity becomes atrophic, composing stops at sheer compiling, search becomes pointless, and freedom of investigation degenerates into license for random movements.

The diagnosis calls for preventive therapy. One nostrum proposes that research be governed, with social utility as beacon. Unfortunately, the diet this prescribes for knowledge is of the sort that social insects feed to their larvae to mold them to preordained stations in life—mostly soldiers and sterile workers, instead of versatile and reproductive specimens. By contrast, I submit that knowledge grows best on a liberal, balanced diet based on variety and wide freedom of choice, free of excessive roughage.

Now, who is there to write the formula? We all abhor the notion of an all-wise potentate of knowledge, whether person, institution or society, to rule on what will, and what will not, promote the growth of knowledge. But there is one wizard who has the formula and gladly hands it over for the asking—history, which has watched knowledge grow from infancy. It tells us that the key agent in the growth of knowledge has always been the human mind, imaginative, critical, and integrative; devising robots, tools, techniques, merely as aids to extend the limited reach of man's perception and control, but never abdicating the functions of evaluation and invention. Promoting knowledge, therefore, implies giving full scope to the exercise of the faculty for assimilation and synthesis by which the mind converts facts to knowledge. The history of knowledge contains the rules to give those bent on promoting knowledge by either doing or supporting research the necessary cues for intelligent and responsible self-direction. The stress here lies on "self"; there is no need for forcible external steering. But how could the uninitiated self orient itself purposefully if we hide or blur the goal? Or do we expect each self to rediscover the goal for himself by trial-and-error, fumbling and floundering in semi-darkness, when we could readily draw on the lessons of the past to illuminate both goal and path?

You realize what I am driving at. As educators we mold tomorrow's promoters of knowledge. We must be far more explicit than we have been lately in teaching them not just the present state of knowledge, but the way in which it has grown; this is the only way in which it can grow further. Inspired teachers teach and practice it, but they are too few. Some students find it by themselves, but not enough of them. So, let us restore to education some fundamentalism—making explicit to the student the basic bearings he needs to chart his own course in clear view of what furthers knowledge, and what does not, instead of letting him drift in the cross-currents of traditional momenta and alluring fashions. Ideas—yes, even well-founded speculation—should find a respectful place again among the shining gadgets. And his critical mind, rather than the board room of a fellowship or grants committee, should become again the primary testing and screening ground for relevance. If he finds data, let him explain their meaning. And if he can't, he should feel a sense of void rather than of glee over having abstained from intellectual contamination of data. Let editors encourage, rather than blue-pencil, an author's interpretive excursions. And let the whole process of fostering knowledge become refocused on penetration and concentration, instead of sheer expansion and bulk. Otherwise, knowledge—an organism—might come to share the fate of the dinosaurs.

Yet, notwithstanding this plea for more thorough digestion and mental processing of data, there is another side of nature which is refractory to this treatment and does not fit our analogue at all. I am referring to those phenomena whose constellation in space or seriation in time is so unique that generalization would obliterate their most relevant features. We can establish general principles of parasitism, but each species of parasite has its own peculiar life history, which must be known as such. Chemical chain reactions must conform to thermodynamic law. But just what sequence of steps constitutes a given metabolic cycle must still be determined separately in each instance. Despite their common name, each hormone has its own special way of operating, and each disease has its specific course. In other words, the information which in the search for basic knowledge would merely be a way station, becomes a terminal; to remain useful, its itemized character must be preserved.

This seems the proper province of automation, relegating increasingly to technological devices the jobs of recording, scanning, sorting, reducing, storing, and retrieving data. But even here human intelligence will have to judge what to explore and to record. Every single walnut is unique; can we afford to go on indefinitely shelling walnuts and loading down our libraries with records of their physiognomies? Certainly not, unless there is a point to it. To make the point, is up to the investigator. But it is up to educators to imbue

investigators with a sufficient sense of relevance and responsibility to
make them shun pointless tasks. Self-direction must not be allowed to
lapse into self-indulgence. But how draw the line? Whether to stop at
pragmatism or to go on to generalize, varies, of course, with subject
matter, need, and interest; above all, with perspective.

To gain perspective, let us again turn to history. What is—so we may
ask—the real fate of plain recorded data? What is their life expectancy,
and does it differ substantially for data that can be generalized and
those that cannot? Since mere occupancy of library space is no
criterion of life as against mummification, I made a little actuarial
study, using as gauge of relative vitality of data the frequency with
which they are referred to in the literature.

For comparison, I chose two biological journals: *Experimental Cell
Research*, with a strongly analytical emphasis, and the *Biological
Bulletin*, with a larger descriptive bias. I tallied all references, except
self-citations, by all authors year by year over a 10-year period and
plotted the percentage frequency with which publications were cited
dating back 5, 10, 15, 20, and so forth, years. The graph in Figure 2
shows the results, which are quite striking.

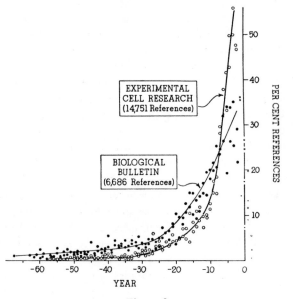

Figure 2

For each of the two journals, the annual percentage frequencies define with remarkable consistency a single curve, whose course expresses the rate of obsolescence of publications. The steepness of its slope should give us pause. No more than 50 per cent of the annual references in *Experimental Cell Research* date back farther than five years, and still older literature is rapidly lost sight of. By contrast, the flatter curve for *Biological Bulletin* reveals a much greater dependence on older records. The difference is highly significant. To validate it further, I plotted the chronological frequencies of back citations during 1952-1954 in the major journals in physiology and in zoology and entomology (Figure 3) from a report by C. H. Brown on "Scientific Serials," and obtained an essentially similar pair of curves, both of which dropped off sharply; but the drop was much steeper in analytical physiology than in its more descriptive biological sister sciences.

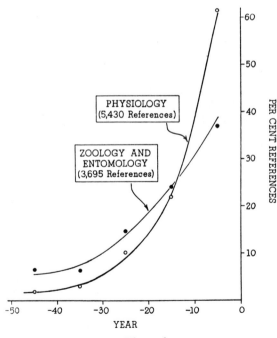

Figure 3

The lessons of this actuarial census of literature thus are twofold. In the first place, the active life span of pure data is at any rate amazingly short: they die of either assimilation or oblivion. Second, the less they lend themselves to assimilation, the longer they remain useful individually.

This leads me to conclude that each field of knowledge must be accorded its own merit ratio between generalization and particularization, taking for granted that assimilation will be driven to the utmost limits compatible with the nature of the field. Yet, in view of the rapid attrition of *all* unassimilated information, a radical reorientation of our publication policies would seem warranted, based on introducing the principle of actuarial tables, about as follows. In each discipline separate media of publication would be established for classes of communications of different life expectancies. Each author of a manuscript would assess its prospective useful life span—presumably with the benevolent advice of editors—on a rating scale extending from the ephemeral technical note at the low end to the great synthetic opus at the other. The paper would then be allocated to the corresponding fast-aging or slow-aging class of serial. Each serial volume would be kept on library shelves only for the time span allotted to its class, and then discarded, except for a few libraries specifically designated as permanent historical repositories. Some such deliberate scheme would go far in restoring and preserving a reasonable ratio of payload to ballast in our records of knowledge.

Graded in terms of relevance, not every observation is worth recording; not every record is worth reporting; not every report is worth publishing; and not every publication is worth preserving for eternity, except in sample specimens as in Noah's Ark. I submit that this grading can still be left to the investigators and their peers, as long as they are cognizant of the true nature of knowledge as a growth process, of which assembling facts—of food for thought—is but the first preliminary step. It is a growth process, moreover, which often thrives better on a spare, than on an overly rich, diet and in which self-restraint can readily ward off obesity.

So in conclusion, and dropping parabolic language, the effective pursuit of knowledge is intimately linked to the old virtue of disciplined research morale, which will not countenance the substitution of bigness for greatness, gadgets for intellect, projects for ideas, and man-hours for thought, although it must rely to the fullest on technical relief by gadgets and man-hours in those auxilliary services which do not require the intervention of a constructive mind.

As I said at the outset, my comments are confined to *scientific* knowledge. Its steady, long-range growth has still immense potential scope. We should not let it get diverted, inflated, and unbalanced by pressures for short-range crash spectaculars. More than ever, our key words should be "balance" and "perspective."

The Growth of Science:
Knowledge Explosion?*

Is the explosive growth of science tantamount to a knowledge explosion? If science is supposed to have furnished the main explosive force for the growth of knowledge, one might expect it also, through spirit and techniques, to be able to ameliorate its social consequences. Any excessive speed-up of evolutionary progress places a heavy strain on the adaptive faculties of living groups. Left unopposed, such strains are apt to entail disruption and extinction. Therefore, it appears pertinent to ask whether the rate of growth of knowledge has become too fast for man to adjust to its progress. And, if knowledge were really growing and, let me add, "maturing" at such a stupendous rate as both the overoptimistic devotees and the prophets of doom would make us believe, there would indeed be cause for worry. But is it?

I submit that knowledge is not growing at anywhere near the rate that is intimated by the deluge of so-called innovations, discoveries, inventions, observations, research data, and so forth, showered upon our public. I refuse to be overawed by the current inflationary mass production in so-called research. I reject sheer volume increments as valid standard of growth, just as the amount of junk mail is no true reflection of economic growth. Thus, a first issue for debate centers on the widespread and pernicious identification of *knowledge* with *information*, hence of the growth of knowledge with the sheer piling up of data (see the preceding chapter).

The kind of knowledge I have reference to is the one formulated in concepts, theories, generalizations, rules of order, systems of thought, and principles, which, through insight and understanding, reduce to common denominators the immense diversity of the phenomena of our experience with the universe and with ourselves, and thus enable us to derive from them reasonable extrapolations and expectations as to future events not yet experienced. In other words, these are devices

*Reprinted from THE KNOWLEDGE EXPLOSION, Liberation and Limitation, (The 1963 Centennial Colloquy at Boston College), Ed. Francis Sweeney, New York, Farrar, Straus & Giroux, 1966, pp. 60-69

which yield infinitely more information than went into their making, in sharpest contrast to a sheer filing system of data, however well-ordered and retrievable. If one accepts this distinction, one readily perceives that the purported explosion is merely a glut of unassimilated data, rather than a spectacular breakthrough of deep insight and understanding. This is not to belittle modern scientific progress, which has been most spectacular in retrospect, but rather to point out that in prospecting over the immense wasteland of the unknown yet to be conquered, current progress seems less impressive, and certainly short of explosive. On the other hand, the sheer piling up of data unquestionably is building up explosive pressures which call for safety valves. This brings me to my second point.

Considering how much human folly can be traced to uninformed opinion, the importance of replacing vague notions by accurate information cannot be overemphasized. This is the rationale behind much of the current mushrooming of research, data collection, fact-finding and what has aptly been called "pebble picking." The problem of how to deal with this mounting flood has stimulated a host of imaginative and effective innovations in the techniques of documentation, communication, and publication, including the listing, ordering, storage, and retrieval of data that must be preserved as such for their uniqueness, such as chemical formulae, descriptions of organisms, geographical data, historic events, geological maps, and the like. Admirable as these efforts to handle the tide are, the question remains as to whether all that flood is necessary and justifiable, or whether some of it is not the product of a sorcerer's apprentice's obedient, but thoughtless, broom being on the loose. Again I find myself fully in agreement with those who deplore the omission of value scales in all this clutter. I have listed in Chapter 9 as basic fallacies the assumptions that "every as yet unrecorded item is worth recording, that every recorded item is worth reporting, and that every fact worth reporting is worth publishing in print," for this would give the relevant and the trivial equal status.

Now, who is to decide between them? I submit that well-oriented and responsible scientists and scholars would be quite competent to decide for themselves, provided value judgements were made respectable again, and furthermore, provided they could afford acting in accordance with their conscience as long as the administrative technicians, who frequently manage our academic lives, continue to bribe them into senseless literary profligacy. It would clear the air if we replaced the fetish of unfettered—meaning haphazard—research by the maxim that research should have a purpose and be selected with a sense of relevance. The curious mind asks questions and then strikes out for the answers, the search being given orientation by the pursuit of an idea or by a practical objective. The incurious mind, by contrast, just amasses data which he hopes will provide him with questions. As long as education treats them at par and as long as public funds sustain this parity, the flood of information, unscreened, undigested and unassessed, will keep on swelling—a matter of concern, to be sure, for the storekeepers, but really not of too much public concern, which is at issue here, except perhaps in its moral and economic implications.

The stemming of this tide before it has reached unmanageable proportions is an internal matter of the academic community. Besides educating students for more rigorous self-criticism, selectivity, and responsibility for self-direction, I can see at least one other practical therapeutic. If we bear in mind that items of information often are, or ought to be, just clues to some general conclusion, stepping stones of transitory value in finding a result, then it would seem as unwarranted, and indeed negligent, to leave them permanently on display, as it would be to leave a scaffolding standing after a building has been completed. In a census of the rate of obsolescence of biological articles, as gauged by the decline of references to them in the literature, I found (see the preceding chapter) that the half-life time of unassimilated data was less than five years. After that they have either been usefully assimilated or fallen into oblivion. For a great many such data, their provisional character and short life expectancy could have been predicted by any author with an average admixture of responsibility to vanity. I therefore believe that built-in obsolescence by publication graduated for varying life spans according to predictable needs and potential usefulness, as in book publishing, would be just and practicable. Just where an author wants to rank his product on such a literary actuarial scale, must, of course, be left to his judicious self-appraisal.

Perhaps I have spent too much time here on toning down the premise of our discussion, that is, the purported "*knowledge explosion.*" Undoubtedly, we do have a publication explosion, but if pruned of its trivial irrelevancies and redundancies, the actual growth of valid information would appear far more moderate. In turn, the growth of our solid stock of knowledge is far less conspicuous than is the accumulation of valid information. But turning now to the more urgent task, namely to evaluate what effect the growth of knowledge, whether explosive or not, has had, and is apt to keep on having, on the affairs of man, I find that the question which really strikes at the heart of the problem is this: Whatever the rate of growth of knowledge be, has man's wisdom and willingness to use it been growing commensurately? Perhaps the question should be rephrased. To serve man as guide, knowledge must first be known, accepted, and respected. And here, I sense, lie the major bottlenecks to the flow of benefits from knowledge to the advancement of culture and human welfare. The stock of acquired and consolidated knowledge that is already available and could serve man as a guide is vastly greater than what is actually being utilized either by individuals in their self-direction or by groups in their decision-making processes.

In the past, part of this disparity has been due to severe restrictions in the accessibility of existing knowledge, but a much larger factor has undoubtedly been man's resentment that knowledge is impartial and does not always cater to his self-interests. Many times it is not that he does not know, but rather that he knows but chooses to ignore. This attitude is made even more critical because far more rapid than the acquisition of new information has been the growth of our methods and facilities for its communication and dissemination, which obviously applies to the old as well as to the new. I believe this spilling forth of formerly bottled-up content is a far more dramatic development of the modern age than is the growth of content.

Now, has this had a beneficial impact on man's conduct? Knowledge appeals to reason, but man tends to shun rational solutions if he stands to be hurt by their acceptance. To that extent, his biological past asserts itself. Man picks from the available stock of knowledge just that which becomes him, quite satisfied with half-truths that suit him. But who is man? Is there as yet such community and universality of thinking as to set a common master rule of fitness to suit all men and nations, creeds and classes? There is with regard to certain fundamentals. But for the rest, each different group still behaves, as the product of its specific nature, history and tradition, adapted to the particular circumstances of its existence. No wonder, therefore, that each chooses and uses from the same pool of knowledge just those fragments best adapted to its needs, often incongruous and conflicting with those of others.

This is the great bottleneck that science has as yet no magic formula to break. For even though the recent rise of the social and behavioral sciences has improved enormously the diagnostic tests for the ills that plague human nature across the globe, they have not yet, to my mind, been spectacularly successful in making the suggested therapeutical procedures palatable.

This, then, is the situation. Science does reveal the laws of nature, which circumscribe both the measure of conservatism and the latitude for change within the universe. But man resents that, by those very laws, nature exacts a price for every delivery. So, throughout history he has tried to cheat on nature, mortgage his future, and thrive at the expense of others as long as he can get away with it. Men just are not of one mind. If science succeeds in making or dispelling rain to order, who is to reconcile the conflicting interests of wheat and fruit growers, the former's blessing meaning the latter's plight, and vice versa? If science proves the risks to his health that man is taking by overeating or excessive smoking, is not the conduct from then on still left to one's own choice, and is risk-taking not a privilege of man, as contrasted with a machine? Indeed, the increase in highway accidents has not deterred people from taking to the road, nor would a life free from risk be biologically feasible or humanly desirable. For where there is no risk, there is no choice, and where there is no choice, freedom is meaningless; which brings me to my concluding point.

Science has taught us that in a complex system of interrelated and interdependent components, the same ends can be attained by countless different routes. No cell in an organism, no organism in its group, and no group of organisms, could function and survive amidst the incessant unpredictable fluctuations of its environment, which includes other cells, organisms, and groups, respectively, unless there is latitude to change course appropriately without losing the goal from sight. Freedom of choice is therefore a vital corollary of the indeterminacy of the micro-events of life. Deprived of this self-adjusting faculty, a cell, an organism, a species, a society must perish, for rigid predetermination for a fixed frame of existence is of no avail once the frame for which it has been designed changes. Encouragingly, even in societies in which the exercise of freedom of choice has been alarmingly restrained, human individuals still tend to reassert their urge to freedom.

I believe the loss of freedom in the manner of pursuing given objectives has added less to the alarming instability of our modern world than has the diversity and disparity of those very objectives, each one slanted to suit a certain group, rather than all of mankind. Surely, scientific knowledge and the repression of ignorance and superstition have a major role in raising the sights of all men from the reckless pursuit of self-interest to objectives of universal interest. But science can give man only tools for acting rationally, it cannot act on his behalf. Man's purposes are beyond its reach. A knife is an instrument and as such is neither good nor bad. Its choice for better or for worse, by surgeon or assassin, should be of concern to the individual scientist as the human being and citizen that he is, but one could argue whether science as such should be involved. Scientists should take sides, but science should be impartial.

So, in conclusion, increasing knowledge is bound to bring man from the realm of day dreams and wishful thinking down to earth to face reality. Is this a gain or a loss? Liberation or limitation? What is our rating scale? Happiness? Whose happiness? Mine? Yours? Ours? All peoples'? If satisfaction is our criterion, let us not overlook that as our knowledge grows, the realization of our remaining ignorance grows even faster. If this arouses dissatisfaction, we sense a loss. Yet, this is offset by the joy of reinvigorated driving for further knowledge thus instigated—an indisputable net gain in satisfaction. And all that we can do in this game is strive to improve our score. No doubt, the odds are mounting. We are teetering in a precariously labile balance between a mounting mass of codes and institutionalized restraints for the enforcement of the rule of order, vital in a complex system of interdependent members, on the one hand, and freedom for adjustive and creative activity of each individual member within those codes, on the other. From the one end, we face incessant pressures to expand rule to regimentation; from the other, to pervert freedom into anarchic license. Science can only document the threat to survival from letting either course get the upper hand. People will have to watch out for themselves; as knowledge and reason grow and lead to limitations and restraints for members of society, the will and power and freedom of those members to exercise their faculties for knowledgeable and rational behavior will have to be made to grow commensurately. This is a prime task for education: not just to cope with expanding and changing knowledge, but to bring up people able to face it, to live with it, and to live by it.

Renewable Resources*

This summary represents my general conclusions arrived at as a result of evaluations of (1) the conference of experts held at Woods Hole, Massachusetts, August 15-18, 1961; (2) a sampling of the extensive literature on the subject; and (3) briefing sessions held with selected groups and individuals from industry, academic institutions, and governmental agencies.

The area of concern of the study on renewable natural resources was the total range of living organisms providing man with food, fibers, drugs, etc., for his needs (save for marine resources dealt with in a special study), but also including hazards to his health and welfare. The consideration of man himself as the focal point of the resources problem is left partly to consideration by other panels, but mostly for the integrative consideration by the Committee as a whole. The non-utilitarian aspects of organic nature, as in recreation and esthetic pleasure, will likewise not be dealt with here. It will become obvious that such a sharp delineation of the topic is purely artificial and provisional, although a practical necessity, and calls for the eventual restitution of the temporarily isolated segment into the integral fabric of the total problem of man in his relations to his environment ("Human Ecology").

Similar arbitrariness attaches to the geographic and chronological frame within which the resources problem is to be treated; (Resources for whom and for how long?). In line with the decided policy of the Committee, the geographic unit of prime concern in this report is the United States, with a proviso, however, that the self-interest of the

*The Study of Natural Resources was conducted by the National Academy of Sciences—National Research Council at the request of the President of the United States, John Kennedy. It was carried out by seven task forces (Renewable Resources; Water; Minerals; Energy; Marine Resources; Environment; Social and Economic Aspects). The present chapter contains the Summary and Propositions of the Chairman of the Renewable Resources Study, Paul Weiss. It is reprinted from Publication 1000-A of the National Academy of Sciences—National Research Council, Washington, D.C., 1962.

nation, as well as its cultural mission, demand increasing attention to our interrelationships with the rest of the world and to the essential indivisibility of this global interdependency. Chronologically, realistic considerations dictate a forward projection of both resource needs and provisions for their satisfaction for at least the life span of the current generation of children or the time to grow a stand of timber; that is, between one-half and a whole century.

The problems of renewable natural resources have been approached by two essentially different types of operations, one going on continuously, the other occurring in sporadic episodes. The former is carried on systematically as part of the mission of government departments or agencies (e.g., Department of Agriculture, Fish and Wildlife Service, Forest Service), certain foundations (e.g., Resources For the Future, Inc., Conservation Foundation, Nature Conservancy), and a few academic institutions. The latter is represented by individual conferences, surveys, and reports. These are mutually supplementary. The former suffers from preoccupation with narrow, segmental views of the total problem, but has the advantage of continuity and operational effectiveness in action programs, while the latter is essentially confined to evaluating and advisory functions, without power of implementation, but giving more balanced attention to the total perspective.

The combined record of these activities in the United States over the last half-century has been one of admirable achievement in providing necessary data of information and interpretation as guides for practical actions. There have been shortcomings in the cross-correlation and mutual reconciliation between different and separate sectors, but, on the whole, the growth of pertinent information has been about as steady as could be expected in view of the general state of scientific advance and existing limitations of manpower, funds, facilities, and public interest. At any rate, so vast is the store of available knowledge residing in the printed records, as well as in the aggregate experience of experts actively engaged in this field, that it would be utterly presumptuous for a sampling examination, such as the one underlying this report, to make any pretense at comprehensiveness or depth of penetration. Even so, certain common denominators have emerged with such regularity and clarity that they can be put forward as general conclusions with a high degree of confidence. These are listed in the following as separate propositions.

Proposition I

There is no prospect of critical shortages in United States renewable resources in the foreseeable future, as long as prospective needs and supplies are tallied and compared in purely algebraic terms, i.e., total amounts. However, taking into account differential patterns of distribution engenders a greater sense of urgency, though not of alarm.

Some degree of uncertainty, of course, adheres to any forward projection of needs. Even if population growth could be more safely forecast, per capita consumption would be less predictable because of its dependence on such indeterminably variable factors as general economic growth, education, public health practices, increased leisure time, etc. It must be borne in mind that the trend to sedentary habits and the replacement of physical labor by automation, as well as medical considerations, will influence both caloric intake and selection of foods, while higher living standards and growing concern with social welfare will increase the per capita demand for fibers as used in textiles, building materials, paper, etc.; both food and fibers derived in last analysis from the same stock of renewable resources, as well as from some nonrenewable deposits of carboniferous materials.

The estimation of available supplies to satisfy the growing needs is likewise subject to great uncertainties. Improvements in the rate and efficiency of growing living things and of processing them for human use, coupled with steady reduction of losses incurred by waste and spoilage, assure us of the fact that the supply side of the account will keep on growing, but no safe prediction is possible as to the *rate* of the increments. If basic research is adequately supported, human ingenuity is bound to produce unforeseen innovations in steps of major magnitude, which cannot be extrapolated from curves of slow and gradual development.

Granting these uncertainties, it is generally assumed, however, that within the next two decades the current surpluses in agricultural produce will have disappeared, followed possibly even by a reversal of the trend, particularly if by that time political and economic reasons for large-scale exports should not have subsided. As for forest products, no serious imbalances between supply and demand are at present prognosticated for the contemplated period, provided measures in the sense of the propositions stated below are taken.

In all of these considerations, however, supplies and demands are commonly compared in terms of total numbers or amounts, regardless of the fact that both occur in incongruous and highly specific patterns of *differential distribution*. To be useful, supplies must ultimately be available where and when they are needed, which implies that a purely algebraic tallying of the accounts is of no more than academic value. A realistic assessment of the adequacy of available supplies for the satisfaction of prospective needs requires knowledge of the patterns of distribution of both. Consequently, optimum utilization of resources presupposes not only that production quantity and efficiency will be maximized and losses minimized, but, above all, that the correspondence between patterns of distribution of needs, on the one hand, and of supplies, on the other, will be optimized.

It is on this score that current resource practices give rise to apprehensions. Many of the current practices and the underlying guiding policies in the various sectors of the field have proved themselves by their past successes and, therefore, are becoming rather firmly established, formalized, and institutionalized. But their tested adequacy pertains to current conditions only. If these patterns were to be frozen and mechanically continued into the future, the whole system would lose its flexibility and become unfit to respond and adapt itself to the unpredictable evolutionary changes which the current conditions will undergo. Today's successes can thus become the very sources of the failures of tomorrow. The risks become even greater where the rigidity of established patterns is not only based on usage but is incorporated in law. The violent repercussions of economic and even sociological nature upon agriculture and food processing, which we have witnessed recently as a result of campaigns of fear about health hazards in different foods and food additives, presage far greater strains and stresses in the future if production and utilization systems were to become even more rigidly locked into established tracks.

In conclusion, lest the cohesion of socioeconomic structure suffer irreparably, it is evident that the more rapid the tempo of change is becoming, the more sensitive and responsive the whole system of resource supply must become in order to cope with the greater rapidity and severity with which inconsistencies, conflicts, and stresses from independent innovations will arise. The lead time for corrective measures must be progressively reduced, which obviously runs counter to the inertial momentums of established courses; and recognizing these opposing tendencies, it is plain that corrective attempts by sheer trial and error, as of old, would be far too slow to avert the indicated perils of disruption and breakdown.

Since this prospect seems a safe extrapolation from current trends, it calls for immediate attention and action, thus introducing a note of urgency into the whole matter. If divergent lines of progress are seen to give rise to ever-greater stresses and strains too fast to be resolved *after* they have arisen and been perceived, then obviously the intelligent and rational thing to do is to learn to anticipate those untoward developments *before* they arise. No adequate machinery for this task is at present in existence. In view of the irreversibility of many actions that will be taken in our time (for instance, in the reallocation of land from forest to agriculture or from agriculture to industrial uses), it seems vital to establish without delay a broad-gauged agency charged with the continuing examination, identification, and assessment of changes in the natural resources picture, and of their potential effects upon each other and on the material and spiritual welfare of man in a free society. The need for such an operation will become more obvious from the subsequent theses and will be reiterated in the concluding statement.

Proposition II

Organic nature, furnishing renewable resources, constitutes a complex dynamic system of interacting components most subtly equilibrated and interrelated in such mutual dependency that any change in any one component is bound to entail changes throughout the rest of the system.

Such systems can have no truly "isolated" parts. Alterations of any part may have repercussions that might stabilize the total system or, more commonly, on the contrary, jeopardize its effective operation and even survival. Whether the direction of the resulting net effect will be toward improvement or impairment can be inferred only from a thorough knowledge and understanding of the intricate web of diverse interactions among the component parts through which the system is maintained in its integral operation. Accordingly, the isolated analytical study of the separate components individually cannot yield the desired insight; nor would it be feasible, lacking such insight, or indeed ever, to build up complex viable systems artificially by piecemeal synthesis, putting together their isolated components step by step.

This ecological principle is a basic law of living nature applying to all levels, from the cell, through organs, organisms, communities, to species, as well as to societies. Not only must the constituent parts within any of these ecosystems, including human society, operate in mutual harmony and adaptation, but also microbes, plants, and animals, upon which man subsists, in turn, depend on water, soil, and climate, as well as upon one another. Thus, one of the major lessons that has emerged from our studies has been that, in order to find the solutions to problems of hydrology, waste disposal, plant growth, climatology, animal nutrition, pest control, soil depletion, food habits, etc., which would be truly relevant to the optimization of natural resources, we must assess the impact of every one of these factors upon the others and ascertain its relative weight in the total account. In such decisions, again, prime consideration must be given to the "structure," that is, the unequal distribution in space and time, of biological requirements, rather than to sheer bulk accounts. Plant growth, for instance, does not depend locally on the *average* amount of water available, but on the availability at the proper soil depth at the right season within a tolerable margin between drought and flooding; not on the *total* amount of light, but on the proper ratio and timing between light and darkness; not on the *total* freedom from admixtures of other (not directly needed) forms of life, but on the presence of the right proportions of particular populations of microbes, other plants and animals of indirect benefit in their complex contributions to more immediate environmental prerequisites for optimal growth.

Technological control and corrective measures based on thorough understanding of such ecological requirements can greatly improve upon conditions found in raw nature, in the sense of increasing yield and reducing waste. But they will fail in a purely compartmentalized approach, without due regard to the cohesiveness of the total network of interrelations. The treatment of such complex multifactorial and multivariant systems requires suitable new methodologies, the development of which ought to be given high priority.

Besides the techniques of dealing with such relational networks, however, serious attention ought to be focused on the development of public understanding and acceptance of the underlying principle of interrelatedness and interdependence, and the consequent impossibility of reaching decisions by confining considerations to limited aspects or sectors of ecological systems. It is always possible to find a categorical solution to a problem if one is free to circumscribe the problem as narrowly as is necessary to find a solution. The artificiality of such a procedure should be impressed upon the public mind early in the educational process, to which reference will be made in a later section.

Proposition III

The artificiality of singling out for study individual components or aspects of a complex ecological network, as if these component members could actually exist in isolation, finds its counterpart in practical applications in the field of renewable natural resources in the no less fallacious tendency to concentrate more and more on purity, uniformity, and single-track standardization of isolated measures and practices.

Since the survival of any ecological system is based on the coexistence of interdependent mixtures of components and environmental conditions in requisite proportions, the omission of any one often leads to wholly unnatural and self-defeating results. And, as stated above, their significance or insignificance cannot be judged from sheer data on bulk or averages. As examples, we may cite the detrimental effect on plant growth of the lack of trace elements in the soil; the reduction of viability in animals raised germ-free; the self-sterility of highly inbred lines; the epidemic over-growth of species of prey after the artificial elimination of their predators; and, in general, the often fatal disruption of organic equilibria by the disturbance of the equilibrated fabric of competitive, as well as cooperative, relations.

Again, however, existing equilibria are not necessarily optimal. By moderate alterations of the mixture of components, on a scale short of endangering the vital integrity of the whole system, improved combinations could be discovered which would come closer to maximizing the total yield than do the current ones. Some such practices have already been introduced into animal and plant breeding, where past trends toward specialized breeding for weight or composition or growth rate or reproductive capacity or palatability or disease-resistance or climatic tolerance or food economy or longevity, and so on, are being increasingly paralleled by tendencies to breed for the optimum common denominator of all of these. *Optimizing* the *total* result should become more generally an objective at par with maximizing a specific *partial* result at the sacrifice of other interrelated parts. This requires the introduction into the total perspective of the field of natural resources of the basic principle of "sense of proportions." It requires, for instance, that one not only investigate how to eradicate a given pest or wastage, but also determine the lower limit to which such reduction could be carried and still remain harmless for the continued survival and thriving of the afflicted system. In other words, a certain minimum of impurities, contaminants, and admixtures of organisms and inorganic items is often not only compatible with, but essential for, optimum results.

Clear recognition of this fact will open numerous new and important lines of research. Where such research can be carried out by first identifying, then analytically separating, and eventually recombining in steps the several components of a complex ecological system, this would be the investigative course of choice. In most cases, however, the network of conditions is too intricate and many of the factors involved are too intangible to be isolated or too far removed from experimental control (e.g., in the case of climatic, geographic, and economic factors) to be amenable to this analytic and recombinative procedure; in that case, recourse to statistical studies will have to be taken. Either way, however, the opportunities for potential major progress by trying a *much wider variety of heretofore untried novel combinations for the production of unprecedented major advances* are not yet being explored and exploited as fully as current research technology would permit.

By way of example, one may point to three areas of great promise in this regard. In microbiology, deliberate induction of mutations by radiation and by exposure to chemical compounds and environmental extremes, followed by careful selection of viable strains with new useful properties, promises to lead to breakthroughs in the cheap supplementation of deficient diets (for instance, amino acid additives to plant proteins of inferior dietary composition); in the chemical decomposition for industrial use of organic fibers, including, perhaps, the processing of lignin; in the biological control of pests; and in the biological solution to problems of organic waste disposal and environmental pollution. Although still largely on an empirical basis, rational courses for methodical progress are beginning to emerge from the results of basic research in microbial systematics, genetics, biophysics, and biochemistry, and intensified investment in this area is indicated. In the macroorganismic field, probing for new combinations between animals and plants, on the one hand, and between them and their environments, on the other, has been undertaken so far only on a scale incommensurate with its potential successes. Such explorations can proceed along two different lines. The growing knowledge of genetics can be used to accelerate the production and appropriate selection of improved animal and plant races within given environments, with the concomitant development of proper techniques for the preservation and storage of seeds, sperm, and perhaps ova in germ-plasm banks. The other approach is to test existing species in new environments to which they have been transported and transplanted. Thus far, for instance, only a small number of wild species of plants have been domesticated, although the recent upsurge in the raising of industrially or dietarily desirable crops (soybean, castor bean, sesame seeds, safflower, etc.,) documents well the feasibility and merits of such an approach. A much wider search, particularly of the lesser-known vegetation and fauna of the more remote parts of the globe, followed by locating biologically and economically superior environments and culture conditions in more accessible regions, should receive increased emphasis. The use of phytotrons, in which the testing, sorting, and evaluation process can be greatly accelerated and optimum constellation of conditions can be established much more rapidly than in tests in nature, would serve an important auxiliary function in this effort, with the understanding, according to the earlier statements of this proposition, that the ultimate verdict of success or failure will still rest with conclusive tests in nature.

The ecological argument against excessive one-sided preoccupation with standards of absolute purity applies to the level of human affairs and industrial uses as well. For instance, it suggests greater emphasis on multiple land use of somewhat flexible proportions, as contrasted with the current trend to rigorous single-use parcellation. That is to say, in many areas the same forest land could serve at the same time for timber production, wildlife preservation, and human recreational use (provided a correlated educational program is undertaken to minimize the attendant hazards, like fire hazard, traffic volume, etc.). On the industrial side, likewise, the use of different resources in combination could lead to major innovations over the separate use of the pure component items. To give an example, wool fibers coated with plastics have already given fabrics with properties superior to those attainable from either component alone. Similarly, a mixture of wood fibers and plastics in laminated or dispersed form promises to yield building materials of greater total utility (strength, durability, temperature and humidity resistance, molding capacity, etc.) than would reside in either the pure lumber or the pure plastic product.

To reduce steadily the role of blind empiricism in the search for such new combinations, it is absolutely essential to give maximum support to any line in the basic sciences that promises relevant and major advances of knowledge in the following areas: cellular biology (including biochemistry and biophysics); developmental biology (including growth, differentiation, and nutrition) ecologic biology (the mutual interaction, beneficial or harmful, between organisms and their environment, including other organisms, particularly, also, the problems of parasitism); soil biology (including the physical chemistry of polydisperse systems in colloidal dimensions); and bioclimatology (the interactions between meteorological factors and organisms). It is particularly important, however, to emphasize that in line with the conclusions of Proposition III, undue preponderance of research support in so-called molecular biology, which deals with isolated components of biological entities, however valuable in itself, cannot provide the knowledge of the behavior of the organized complex networks needed for both fundamental and practical purposes; hence, that in research support of the biological sciences, likewise, a "sense of proportions" must be maintained and one-sided distortions prevented.

In conclusion, it is imperative that in dealing with problems of renewable natural resources, whether in study or application, one clearly recognize that viable ecological systems are composed of mixtures of heterogeneous member units and that this heterogeneity be fully taken into account as vital for the existence and equilibrium of each system. Such equilibria are by no means yet the optimal states attainable; hence they permit of continued evolutionary improvements. Yet, steps aiming at improvement must not be of a rate and magnitude that would exceed what is compatible with the conservation of the system as a whole. In view of the nature of ecological systems, *matching combinations* of steps for groups of components are apt to be less disruptive than would be isolated steps taken separately for individual components. Moreover, by the same token, equivalent improvements, that is, the same degree of optimization of the total result, can be achieved by a variety of combinations of steps involving different parts of the system. It is a scientific task to circumscribe the degrees of recombinative freedom within such systems and eventually to define precisely the margins of tolerable adaptive flexibility within a given ecosystem between complete and lethal solidification at one extreme, and perilous distortions to the point of disintegration at the other.

Proposition IV

The net-like character of the natural resources problem calls for the replacement of linear chain-reaction determinism by principles of thought and action which are based on the fact that in such network systems there can be many equivalent, multi-pathway, multiple-choice approaches to the same goals—in the present case, the common objective of optimization.

The older concept of single rigid linear cause-to-effect chains of natural events has given rise to legalistic, organically unreal, and practically untenable conclusions, according to which any deviation of any link along such a chain would inevitably and irrevocably lead to a correspondingly deviant result. By contrast, the network type of causal relations in an integrated system, with its branched and reanastomosing lines of interdependencies, establishes a multiplicity of alternative routes toward a given end. Deflection, reduction, or even complete obliteration of one of the multiple communicating channels in such a system in no way need interfere with the attainment of the end or goal, and the collateral channels can automatically act as substitutes. Historically, in human affairs such substitutive collaterals have usually been looked for and set in operation only after an emergency had changed or occluded some established conventional channels. This has been as true of agricultural practices as of industrial production lines. Our growing knowledge and experience, however, makes it incumbent on us to lay out patterns of alternative and substitutive practices *in advance* so as to have acceptable and feasible schemes for vicariation ready for immediate activation, if and when the unforeseen necessity for bypassing conventional channels should arise.

While this is commonplace in military planning, and partly also in economic planning, the resources field has not yet adopted the forward projection of versatility as a major principle and task. And, consequently, it is not properly prepared for sudden emergencies or, what is more important, for the continual adjustive shifts in volume and direction between different production channels for which there is a ceaseless call in the interest of optimal total results. For example, a sudden shift, because of a probable or just rumored effect on health, from animal to vegetable fats finds the dairy industry essentially unprepared for alternative uses for its products on a scale that could compensate for the sudden loss. Evidently, the singular over-emphasis on the fatty component of dairy products had deflected attention from the potential value of the non-fatty content, which, both as a dietary supplement to inadequate plant protein and as industrial raw material (e.g., in plastics, paints, glues, etc.), could fill the economic breach. Examples of this kind are too numerous to be cited in detail.

To cope with such situations effectively and without the temporary loss of efficiency, alternative pathways for production, processing and usage should be laid out in advance on scientific grounds so as to be ready to open the appropriate valves in response to any changes in the pressure distribution within the total network. Ideally, one should aim at the construction of a complete flow-chart of the channel system, leading from production sources, through distribution, conversion and processing, to utilization and consumption. As indicated before, the current pattern has a way of becoming stabilized as a result of the relative stability of social, economic and political conditions. The volume and rate of flow in any given channel are, therefore, determined not by their utility and efficiency rating alone, but these factors are weighted, in addition, by an inertia factor inherent in the status quo. Taking cognizance of this principle, it will be necessary, therefore, to make allowance in the design of alternative flow channels for potential

changes in social, economic, and political patterns which may significantly modify the practicability, efficiency, or acceptability of a given
channel. For instance, if dietary considerations should force a continued retreat from consumption of animal fat, the alternative diversion
of some such fat to more economical soap production would, in turn,
displace some of the detergents; this would result in a healthier
downstream ecology of microorganisms by reducing the harmful effects
of the accumulation of detergents in streams, which in turn, could be
instrumental in both waste disposal and industrial chemistry (see
above). Each link in this chain of consequences has certain sociological
and economical connotations, the momentum of which will weigh
heavily in the decisions of whether given existing practices will be
retained or allowed to be modified. Despite the uncertainties of the
task, however, it would seem imperative to try to assess these variables
in the design of alternative multiple-choice channels in a resource
master chart of the future, and to weigh the role of factors established
on purely objective, scientific grounds—biological, physical, and
technological—accordingly. In this manner, the prospective equivalence
or nonequivalence of alternative routes could be determined with at
least some degree of validity.

Proposition V

*The value of marginal resources should be assessed in the light
of the principle of multiple alternative pathways and the
equivalence considerations outlined in the preceding proposition.*

What taken by itself might amount only to an insignificantly
small contribution to the total resource structure might often, by its
singularly favorable position in the total network, assume strategic
significance way above its quantitative rating. Sea-water desalination
and solar-energy utilization are examples of this category. Even though
the energy requirements for pumping might make irrigation by
desalinated sea water economically prohibitive except for coastal strips
and depressions, the fact that this would liberate corresponding
amounts of fresh water from higher elevations for alternative uses might
mark a significant improvement for the total situation in the direction
of an overall social and economic gain. Similarly, the partial desalina-

tion of some rivers which have an agriculturally undesirable salt content could render wastelands, even though only of regional interest, productive. To give another example, if cheap devices for converting solar energy into refrigeration in small mobile units could be developed for transport and storage of perishable food, such as fish from the sea, in sparsely populated, undernourished regions, such a small scale improvement could be of crucial benefit. The more sensitive and responsive the resource network can be made, the more the distribution of flow from source to consumption among alternative equivalent channels will be regulated by relatively small changes of conditions. It would be unjustified, therefore, to let resource planning be dominated by gross bulk considerations.

Proposition VI

The abandonment of the outmoded linear, single-track, causal-chain model and its replacement by the systems concept require a major and profound reorientation of public thinking, for which the foundation must be laid in the educational process.

It is one thing to decide what course in natural resources planning would be the most desirable on objective scientific grounds in the sense of reducing inconsistencies to a minimum and optimizing the benefits to the public as a whole, but to obtain voluntary public acceptance of the necessary is another matter. Ideally, such acceptance should be based on insight into the nature of organic ecosystems and a thorough understanding of the interrelatedness among all components and aspects of such systems, as well as on the realization of the power and obligation of the human individual within such a system to use his understanding intelligently for the promotion of the common good. To cultivate both the necessary perspective and balanced attitude should become a major concern of our educational system. Since the field of natural resources offers a host of dramatic examples of the interconnectedness of individuals, groups, and environments, an elementary introduction to it early in the educational program could have a telling effect in preparing a citizenry fit to face resource problems realistically and judiciously. A few well-chosen lectures on the high school level, and certainly in all college curricula, could go far in promoting a general awareness and even appreciation of the "system" character of man's universe. To be truly effective, such lectures would have to be carefully purged of bias and propaganda.

Yet, the lead time to bring up a properly informed citizenry through regular schooling is too long to meet the need. Additional efforts must be directed to the adult population. This should be done by the insertion of natural resources discussions into adult education courses, and above all, by giving the topic far wider currency in the press. Moreover, the higher education programs will have to recognize their obligation to procure adequately trained expositors for the larger professional, educational, and publicity tasks to be performed. This would become part of a more general trend, already noticeable, of giving man's interest in his future a more central position in the educational spectrum. The miserly allocation of time and emphasis to nutritional science in medical schools is just as pertinent an example of educational deficiencies in need of correction as is the relatively low level of education in agriculture and veterinary medicine. Routine training perpetuates existing practices. To be able to meet the changing demands of the future will require an educational upgrading, including the attraction of high-grade manpower, in all areas bearing on the optimization of man's vital needs. In summary, it is doubtful whether efforts in the field of natural resources can ever become fully effective unless they are matched by educational measures of the required orientation and magnitude.

Proposition VII

In view of the principles set forth in the preceding six propositions, it is evident that optimization of natural resources for human use and welfare cannot be achieved by fragmentary and sporadic attention given to isolated parts of the problem, but that the issues involved must be made the subject of a permanent and systematic process of investigation, recording and evaluation, carried on continuously in reference to the total perspective. It would seem mandatory, therefore, to entrust an independent organization with this task.

Such a body would function in essence as an intelligence agency in matters of human ecology. It should keep itself constantly informed of all physical, biological, sociological, geographic, and economic events and developments of potential bearing on man's optimal adjustment to his environment, and attempt to evaluate in scientific terms the probable net effect of their mutual interactions on man's future—short-range and long-range—in national, regional, and global respects. In this pursuit, it should avail itself of the cooperation of the best talent of the country in the natural sciences and relevant branches of the social sciences. It should determine for any single alteration in the total scene—man-made or beyond man's control—the net balance between risk and benefit, not in absolute terms of the intrinsic properties of that particular change, but in relative terms of its putative consequences for the whole fabric of human affairs. In view of the ever-increasing rate of man-made alterations, with their ever-widening circle of sequelae, such an intelligence agency of broad scope would have to cultivate the highest degrees of perceptiveness and sensitivity so as to be able to feel the pulse of the ecosystem, as it were, and to register and assess incipient developments before they have reached critical dimensions. These diagnoses would then serve as guides for action programs, precautionary measures and the exploration of alternative courses. By its cultivation of a total integrative overview, such an organization would be in the most favorable position to detect signal gaps and incongruities in the map of existing knowledge in need of filling or reconciling by further research. And by its anticipatory point of view, it would be singularly qualified to identify what kinds of research might be undertaken or intensified in order to forestall, counteract or rectify predictable *future* disruptions and imbalances of the human ecosystem. The contemplated agency should not, however, be given powers of decision or enforcement and it should steer clear of the political arena.

To summarize:

1. No detailed problem bearing on renewable natural resources seems at present in critical need of remedial program research, whether in "crash" or more protracted form, beyond what is already underway or envisaged.

2. The detection and accommodation of future specific research needs should be made the concern of a separate agency to keep the field under continuous surveillance.

3. There are, however, two major and unchanging prerequisites for optimizing man's station in his environment by research which do deserve immediate and continuing attention: (1) The scientific concepts and methodology to deal with ecological "systems" of heterogeneous composition must be further developed and strengthened and made to penetrate educational practices and public thinking. (2) Vigorous general support should be given to *basic* research and education in the life sciences because of (a) their relatively immature state of development; (b) their newly acquired capability for greatly accelerated progress; and (c) their intimate bearing upon any future successes in improving the balance sheet of human ecology by rational procedures. Such promotion of the life sciences should be carried on along a broad front, with neither shortsighted concentration on "fashionable" sectors (e.g., molecular biology, radiobiology, and others) nor an equally unwise neglect of less popular ones (e.g., parasitology, bioclimatology, soil science, nutrition, and others).

A National Policy for the Environment

As Chairman of the Study on *Renewable Resources* by the National Academy of Sciences (see the preceding chapter), I formulated seven propositions for the guidance for future policy. They consisted essentially of practical examples for dealing with the problems of natural resources in terms of "systems operations" instead of in separate compartments. The growing concern in this country and abroad with the relations between man and his environment has led to many positive moves toward more concerted attention to the problems of human ecology from the broadest possible perspective. In line with these efforts, the *Senate Committee on Interior and Insular Affairs* (Senator Henry M. Jackson from the State of Washington, Chairman) and the *House Committee on Science and Astronautics* (Representative George P. Miller, California, Chairman) convoked a joint House-Senate colloquium to discuss a national policy for the environment. The proceedings of the meeting have been published by the U.S. Government Printing Office as Hearing of the respective committees of the Ninetieth Congress, Second Session, July 17, 1968, No. 8.

The letter of invitation to the Colloquium carried on Page 3 major quotations by Senator Jackson and Congressman Miller from the Introduction, as well as Proposition VII, of my Report on Renewable Resources, cited above and referred to in the following memorandum and therefore omitted in the present supplement. This supplement, representing a memorandum sent to the Congressional Committees after the meeting by request of the Chairmen and published on Pages 222-224 of the Proceedings of the House-Senate Hearing, is reprinted in full below.

I shall confine myself to adding some comments that seem to me pertinent in the light of the discussion at the Colloquium, taking for granted the consensus of the group that national planning and action in matters of environmental control require (a) the application of *systems methodology* to the man-environment continuum in its unitary totality, and (b) a corresponding organizational framework for the continual assessment from an unfractioned overall perspective of the totality of factors that influence the steadily evolving ecology of man in modern society.

(1) Taking the long-range view, emphasis in environmental control must shift progressively, like in medicine, from cure to prevention. This requires that there be kept on record in a single center a comprehensive running account of all diagnostic data relevant to the health of the system and that this record be continually scanned for signs of existing or incipient divergencies from an optimal course of development, so that forestalling anticipated error might increasingly supplant the need for correcting errors made.

(2) In order to keep both the collection and the continuous evaluation of the data for this diagnostic processing as objective and impartial as possible, it would seem indicated to separate the fact-finding, correlating, and evaluating procedures from the therapeutic decisions, which naturally lie in the political arena. The former could be carried out through a hierarchical system of clearing house operations integrated in an "intelligence" center, while the latter could operate through appropriate governmental agencies.

(3) Human ecology owes its "system" character to the confluence of many disparate component lines of human life and concern in a multi-dimensional unitary network of relations. The task of the "intelligence center" of point (2) should be to determine the net balance of the effects of developments in the various lines on the overall state of human ecology. As in all network systems, the same optimum effects can be reached through a variety of alternative pathways. The intelligence center should identify such existing and prospective alternatives as will insure the attainment of optimal stability of the total system.

(4) Examples of the different lines bearing conjointly on the well-being of man and his society (point 3) are: the natural sciences; the social sciences; education; the arts; law; technology; commerce; medicine; agriculture; demography; etc. Each of those diverse lines ought to have its own intelligence sub-center within its narrower range of competence and concern for the correlation, evaluation, and integration of the lessons from events within its own sector relevant to the total picture; the results would be communicated to the top intelligence center for guidance in its overall assessments. These

sectorial intelligence functions could be served by such existing organizations as the National Academy of Sciences-National Research Council, National Academy of Engineering, American Council of Education, Social Science Research Council, Smithsonian Institution, Brookings Institution, and similar bodies. Broadest intercommunication and close cooperation should be maintained wherever necessary among these various subcenters in the hierarchy, as well as between them and the appropriate agencies and task forces of the federal, state, and municipal governments.

(5) As the setting up of methodology and machinery for long-range prospecting and planning, indispensable for balanced progress, might be too slow to cope with currently existing predicaments, it might be indicated to start out on a dual course—a far-sighted one for planning for the future, as outlined, and a short-range one for dealing with emergent acute problems. The setting up of a Commission, recommended at the meeting, seems a realistic device for the latter task, while the former objective would require a more comprehensive and durable form of organization.

(6) No long-range planning can become fully effective unless there is a better preparation of the public mind for the acceptance of judicious middle-of-the-road solutions in terms of optima rather than of "either-or" decisions between extremes. Therefore, a broad program should be developed, drawing on education and the media of public communication and enlightenment (e.g., press, museums, radio, TV), to promote the understanding of the inner connectedness and inter-dependence—the systems character—of the natural, sociological and economic universe in which man lives.

(7) Some obstacles to rational conciliation of man-environment issues are not substantive, but due to mental blocks. Some of those can be reduced by omitting innuendo from our phraseology. A sample step in this direction of decontamination was taken by Senator Muskie at the meeting in substituting the term "enhancement" for "preservation". Similarly, "protection" of health should be upgraded to "promotion" of health. Such terms as "preservation", "conservation", "protection", carry a connotation of "status quo" philosophy, in that they stress only the prevention of decline rather than the raising of the positive balance of the whole production-consumption account which denotes the state of growth of a system, such as the affairs of man in a

growing society. "Enhancement" (or perhaps "amelioration") stresses excess of gains over losses. If man is to come to terms with nature (including his environment and other people), he will have to be deconditioned from his political habit of polarizing issues artificially around opposite extremes in the sense of "either-or" validity and become conditioned to accepting them as interconnected by graded scales, along which he must establish the points of optimum "ecological" balance between trends involved. Every change affecting the environment exacts a price; man must decide whether, on balance, the net benefit to the advancement of man's physical and cultural health is worth the price.

(8) The estimation of the optimum-cost-benefit ratio of a given trend, referred to in the preceding point, is a matter of evaluation; that is, it calls for value judgments not amenable to quantification. It would be incongruous to expect dollar equivalents for natural beauty or freedom of movement or other intangibles. Even so, a conciliatory depolarization of such conflicts as, for instance, that of economics vs. esthetic interests, would be easier to attain if the growing centrifugal polarization toward extreme attitudes, which focus on differences, could be deliberately counterbalanced, in education, press, publicity programs and the like, by greater stress on the basic community of interest of populations in self-development, let alone self-preservation. I question whether organizational measures from the top down could become fully effective without a collateral building up of increasing receptiveness and responsiveness of people on the ground floor. In conclusion, the language in which to deal with issues of man vs. environment, whether to speak in terms of one-sided dogmatism or of positive pointers to realistic conciliation, is in need of careful scrutiny.

(9) Most of the discussions of the man-environment problem complex deal with the reciprocal effects of man on his environment and vice versa, tacitly posing the environment as variable, while man is viewed as relatively constant, both physically and psychologically. This premise is false; for it leaves man's power of adaptability out of consideration. That faculty must be reintroduced in any serious attempt at arriving at a balanced standard of an "optimal environment." Whether it be a matter of pollution, drug hazard, carcinogenesis, food admixtures, traffic risks, pesticides, rain making, or what not, the simple verity remains that life cannot be made risk-free. Absolute

security is unattainable and the quest for it is not only illusory, but outright self-defeating for reasons which I have sketched in a statement inserted by Representative Rhodes (from the State of Arizona) in the Congressional Record of June 24, 1966. A stress-free environment, offering maximum comfort and minimum challenges, is not only not optimal, but is detrimental. To be exposed to moderate stress is a means of keeping the human faculty for adapting to stress alive and in practice; lacking the opportunity for such exercise, man loses that faculty and becomes a potential victim of any unforeseen, but inevitable, stressful occurrences. The optimum environment consists of a broad band of conditions bounded by an upper limit far short of the stress limit and by a lower limit considerably above an ideal zone of zero stress. Within those margins of reasonable safety or tolerance, man must navigate on his own responsibility. To tell him otherwise would mean to make him act against his own best interest. Realization of the considerable latitude of tolerable environmental stress can significantly reduce the host of conflict-breeding contentions conjured up by such unrealistically and unbiologically purist notions as "zero tolerances" or other "absolute" standards of safety.

(10) The Colloquium has given evidence of the superiority of balanced reasoning over fanatical one-sidedness. My comments here have been intended to strengthen, if only in a very modest measure, the arguments in favor of that trend.

Unity of Culture: A Program for a Program*

The barriers that have kept human groups of diverse ecologies and histories in a state of relative seclusion are rapidly breaking down in the wake of spreading trade, enlightenment, and communication—vertical sectorial barriers of geographic, national, and political groupings as well as horizontal sectarian interfaces dividing layers of philosophical, occupational, and educational distinctions within each group. As a result, there have sprung up, in many countries—polyphyletically, as it were—moves to articulate, give expression to, and translate into reality that mounting realization of a basic unitary core of human culture.

Some of those moves are motivated by fears about mankind's future, others more positively by the ethical postulate or sober extrapolation from scientific and historical fact that the trend of progress of the human race is, or at least ought to be, toward harmonization—the "brotherhood of man" glorified in Beethoven's Ninth. Some of the movements circle about professions of sometimes rather utopian ideals; others are more down-to-earth, sometimes overly pragmatic. And there are all kinds of intergrades. Yet, all of them tend to converge upon a common focus. One wonders whether they might not have a better prospect of getting there faster, with less meandering, if their community of purpose were matched by a concert of realistic programming and action. If so, claims or pretensions of primacy, priority, or sheer self-assertion would have to yield to an overriding call for co-operation; for no one can rightly claim to have all the answers—we hardly have as yet spelled out the questions, let alone weighed them.

It is frustrating to hear monopolistic calls for science to take leadership, while other quarters, no less vigorously, cheer for the humanities or religion or the law. This definitely is not the time to prejudge issues; what we must do is face and meet them in a broad and dispassionate perspective. This essay is an attempt to live up to that

*Reprinted from ZYGON/JOURNAL OF RELIGION AND SCIENCE
Vol. 2, No. 3, pp. 223-230, 1967.

temperate spirit; to bring the phrase "unity of culture" a little closer to our grasp; and then submit some thoughts on how one might approach the elusive task of bringing it about.

What Unity of Culture?

As a basic verity, "unity of culture" remains to be verified; as an ideal, it is an axiom; as a practical goal, it needs assertion; as a political slogan, it becomes perverted to the insidious question of: *Whose* "culture"? The scientist's, the humanist's, the spiritualist's, the fundamentalist's. the socialist's, the nationalist's, the globalist's, etc.?

The time has come when man must face the decision of either implementing the desideratum of unity or else reverting to jungle warfare of mutual extinction among conflicting doctrines, each claiming a monopoly for its particular brand of a dismembered culture. The time has come because rates of development and change in world affairs have become so steeply accelerated that the "lead time" for correcting errors of evolutionary mis-steps has been reduced to zero. Modern communication and growing universal responsiveness to communicated information have abolished the barriers that used to keep local events of conflict-generating potential confined long enough for the resulting strains and stresses to subside. This happy state no longer exists. Communication currents have broken through the former membranes and have brought the formerly isolated compartments into dynamic interaction, threatening to convert the potential energy of conflict into kinetic energy. The resulting turbulence precludes the calm and measured adjustments that were allowed to the formerly sluggishly interacting world; hence, in the new setting of our day, the slow way of *correction* of error by *hindsight* must give way to the anticipatory *avoidance* of error by *foresight*. Conflicts must be resolved before they erupt; and the conflicts in question are not just those of national, political, economic, or other group motives, but primarily those of ideas, which generate or rationalize those other motivations.

Such ideological conflict is as hazardous if raised as an antithesis between a *scientific*, or worse still, "technocratic" and a *humanistic* culture as it is between a "Western" and "Eastern" culture or a "capitalist" and "socialist" culture. Those are cults, not cultures. At best, they are different aspects of "culture"—singular. As man is global, there is, or ought to be, only *one* common culture, *a single undivided integrated continuum of culture.* To be sure, it has immensely diverse facets which make it appear under different aspects to people or groups of different character and traditions—none of them, of course, viewing it in its totality.

But by whose dictum "is there, or ought there to be, only *one* common culture"? This question is loaded with semantic and terminological traps. The answer, accordingly, will depend on whom you ask. One side will point to history and prove the pluralistic origin of culture, or rather of cultures—plural. The other side will confine the term "culture" to that inner core which all cultures have in common. The former, the particularist, viewpoint and the latter, the generalist one, are, of course, equally valid; indeed they are complementary, depending on preference of accent on either differences or common features among members of the same class of phenomena. Particularism, however, becomes outright ominous if it results in any one of the fractional cultures setting itself up as, first, the "true," presently the dominant, and eventually the sole, representative and spokesman of "human culture"—*pars pro toto.* To counter this perilous trend, abundantly reaffirmed by recent history, the generalists go to the opposite extreme of denying, or at least trying to abrogate, the reality of cultural diversity. And so the argument has been going, back and forth, carried by currents of emotion, rather than reason.

And the solution? The difference being one of *emphasis*, rather than of *substance*, there is of course no problem, hence, no cause for discord; just the need for mutual understanding and appreciation of the fact that those who look at the same piece of world through microscopes and telescopes gain different views. *Diversity* among cultures, mainspring and spur of progress, is as essential as is cultural *unification* as the stabilizer against excessive divergence threatening disruption. But diversity does not imply antagonism; nor does unity spell uniformity.

Now, in reading these comments, most everybody will surely have had in mind such cases as hegemonial claims by nations, religious schisms, political doctrinal strife, or "one-world" rule. Yet, what I had foremost in mind are the schisms in the *ideological* foundation of human culture, to which national, religious, and political systems must ultimately be related. I have in mind the hegemonial aspirations of a *scientistic* versus a *humanistic* culture; a *materialistic* versus a *spiritualistic* culture; cultural ideals of *progress* versus *conservatism*; and the like.

Perhaps, if these could be harmonized, harmonization of the more mundane sources of conflict would follow. To harmonize them will take more than just a pious wish. It will take more than just learned treatises and academic exercises. Almost all that could be said on the subject has probably been said and written. But if there has been any effect at all, it has been slight and progress toward the goal too slow, at any rate. And slowness of adaptation is something the world of today can no longer afford if it is to remain viable.

What Can Be Done?

So, what is there to be done to promote the case of true unity in spirit, and to promote it with the necessary speed and effectiveness appropriate to the needs of an ailing world? Some more learned treatises? Some contests, with prizes for the cleverest paper prescription of a cure? Some further paper schemes for remedial action by dreamers unfamiliar with the patient—the *real* world of human nature?

I firmly believe in the need and urgency of some far more systematic, vigorous, and imaginative approach, and though it would be rash to predict success, we simply cannot afford not to try it. I therefore am cheered by every new constructive effort. A few germs of such efforts have been springing up lately in several lands. The setting up of "centers" as rallying points is certainly a useful move. They can serve as the nodal points of the envisaged "co-cognitive" network to be woven from the still disconnected threads of critical and creative thought about the nature of man and his culture.

How can they best serve? First, what should they avoid in order not to jeopardize their effectiveness?

1. None of them should explicitly or tacitly aspire to a monopolistic position. Priority establishes no claim to primacy; unity is based on universality.

2. They should not try to standardize and equalize their various programs and techniques of approach, as long as they keep their diverse courses converging upon a common goal.

3. They should not prejudge the outcome of their search by selecting only searchers known to have consonant ideas.

4. They should not engage in single-shot, incoherent actions, however valuable and conclusive in themselves. Separate unconnected

events, whether conferences, seminars, books, opinion surveys, etc., have rarely proved to leave a major and lasting impress on the course of human affairs.

Now speaking *positively*:

1. They should make the study of the *unity of knowledge* a continuous *process*—"process," not just a series of punctuated spot events.

2. The process must start from an *identification of the problem.* To be acceptable and effective, this must be done not by one-sided precept, but must be left to emerge from *penetrating free and critical discourse* among scholars and men of affairs holding divergent views and philosophies, while groping for common ground in the firm belief that it must and will be found.

3. This diagnostic identification process will proceed in steps as follows:

a) First, the traditional doctrinal areas—the scientific, the religious, the philosophic, the artistic, the humanistic, the legal, etc.—must examine their own basic concepts within their own ranks and test them for reconcilability. In doing so, they will discover that there is a central area of congruity common to all of them as well as a fringe of incongruous peculiarities. The latter belong to the *private* domain of those various areas and need not concern the *public* domain of any group striving for *universality*. This purging process ought to result in the delineation of a core of relevant principles for each area of thought on which knowledgeable thinkers and thoughtful workers in that area could essentially agree; the marginal unresolvable distinctions should not be allowed to interfere with the next step.

b) In this next step, the identified cores of the various ideologies will then, by critical discourse, be subject to the same kind of distillation process in order to delimit the area of congruity or correspondence among them from their particular discrepancies and mutual inconsistencies (which hopefully might yield to persistent further efforts at reconciliation).

The purpose of these preliminary steps is to circumscribe the problem precisely, concretely, and realistically before entering or even contemplating practical ways to meet it. It seems to me futile to try to "unify" the diverse and disparate forms of knowledge by either force of argument or persuasion. The best one can expect is (*a*) to obtain consensus on that common nucleus which is already unified but has not yet been universally recognized as such, and (b) to strengthen and steadily enlarge that nucleus.

A Diagnostic and Pragmatic Program

This is admittedly a pragmatic program. It differs from past and present idealistic, but ineffectual, ventures with similar motives. It also is intended to be, at first, mainly diagnostic. It should point up misunderstandings, misconceptions, misapplications, and one-sided doctrines of whatever origin, as major barriers to the broadening of the base of a unified human culture. Many of those barriers have not been deliberately erected but have come about automatically by the self-confinement (not of individuals, but of groups) to limited sectors of the fields of learning and practice. Much of this can be relieved by "multidisciplinary" discourse, adequately programmed, staffed, guided, recorded, edited, condensed to essentials with the conclusions published serially.

The first outcome of such exercises, I predict, will be the realization and practical demonstration that there is an immensely larger core area of *mutual agreement* than any one would normally have expected. Many of the disagreements generally assumed to be *fundamental* will then fade away as having been *imagined or trivial*, based on limited information or narrow perspective.

The second lesson will be an increasing awareness that "unity of culture" can be manifested and lived in a great variety of diverse forms without at all vitiating the general idea of "cultural community." There is not only merit in such diversity of form, but any attempt to abolish it would only lead to the replacement of old ideological despotisms by a new dogmatism.

Third, it will turn out that man will at last have to learn to cease pitting supposedly irreconcilable opposites against each other to win or lose, and adopt an attitude of "middle of the road," with a tolerable margin of freedom for excursion with impunity.

Summary

What I have been setting forth here are essentially the following propositions:

a) There is a larger *common core*, not only to humanity, but also to human thinking about it, than is generally appreciated and asserted as a guide for the thinking and behavior of people.

b) That core can be made the guiding beacon for the many-sided advances currently aiming at the ideal of cultural unity.

c) To serve as a beacon, rather than as a treacherous will-o'-the-wisp, that core of ideas and principles must be firmly rooted in knowledge. Its substance, now buried in many overlapping sectors of human knowledge and practice, must be extracted and distilled from the content of the different disciplines of learning, from the accumulated experience and wisdom of the human race, and from rational projections and reasonable forecasts of mankind's future.

d) By definition, that "core" will exclude those propositions and features which cannot command universal affirmation, that is, which rest on cultural, philosophical, and political differences of purpose and point of view. Some of those differences are inertial residues, bound to fade; while others are valid, viable, and vital expressions of true diversity and, as such, are spurs to progress.

e) On the precept of "first things first," the prime task in delineating that common core of culture on which men of knowledge, wisdom, and maturity can realistically *unite* is to identify and remove the sources of existing or impending *disunity*. This will be largely a decontamination process, involving the eradication of misconceptions, misinterpretations, spurious arguments, and contradictions based on purely semantic confusion, unfounded premises, faulty logic, incorrect information, and so forth.

f) The resulting purified and clarified nucleus of that common core can then be explicitly formulated, widely disseminated, and hopefully expected to be accepted as a code or, at least, as a universal "rule of thumb" to guide actions of potential bearing on man's future. Without such a common standard, many of the best intentioned moves of man will continue to work at cross purposes and come to naught.

g) The envisaged process of sober, critical, unprejudiced self-examination through discourse shared by men of learning, spirit, and good will from all the major sectors of human knowledge and affairs might well prepare and inaugurate a truly *ecumenical age for mankind*. Of course, it might also fail; but we cannot afford not to try—or to let it fail by our own default. "Concern" is not enough; nor will sheer academic discourse do, unless its lessons can be translated into a pattern of universal tenets for human behavior that will command allegiance for its convincingness and cogency.

Scientific Thought in the 18th Century*

This essay is an unpretentious excursion of a biologist into interpretation of history; it is intended as a sample demonstration of the intellectual indivisibility of our culture, of which scientific attitudes, motivations, and contributions are as much integral components as are its literary and historic facets. I aim to illustrate the intimate and indissociable relation between the culture of an age and the nature of its scientific outlook and productions. The age I shall focus on is the period after A.D. 1700.

Looking back over this last quarter millennium, I discover that the advances of science have indeed been closely related to what went on culturally in those particular centuries. When I say science, I would like to make clear that to scientists, science does not exist as a disembodied allegorical figure, a type that somehow represents an abstract idea. Science is what the men and women of science are thinking and doing; it is carried on by people, whose thoughts, temperaments, knowledge, ambitions, and aspirations are as diverse as are those of other groups of human beings. Because scientific achievement is the product of people, and because people live in definite socioeconomic settings, it is clear that the particular ways in which scientific activities manifest themselves are bound to be influenced by the fashions, modes, and thinking of the period in which they operate—in short, the *Zeitgeist*. And scientists, in turn, contribute to the form of the *Zeitgeist*. This interrelation between the social climate, as it affects the scientist, and the scientist, who modulates the pattern of his time, is a fascinating story of human adventure, which, I believe, has rarely been written in terms of the psychological, sociological, and economic drives involved.

Not only concepts and generalizations, but even the mere assembling of the factual materials of science has at times been influenced by what happened in the world outside. For instance, the mechanics of the flight of birds was never really well understood before the advent of aviation. But then we learned reciprocally to apply what we had learned from the flight of birds to the improvement of aviation. I myself went

* *Reprinted from* INTRODUCTION TO MODERNITY: A SYMPOSIUM ON EIGHTEENTH CENTURY THOUGHT (Ed.: R. Mollenhauer). University of Texas Press, 1965, pp. 13-40.

through this experience when, in my early years, rash and brash, I set up a novel theory of nervous activity, based on certain observations in which an emission-reception correspondence—between an emission system in the inner centers and selective reception by correspondingly tuned nerve cells—was the key to understanding co-ordinated nervous function. I am quite certain that I could never have gotten that idea had I not known at the time about radio broadcasting and selective reception.

In a wider sense, I am not sure whether the present enthusiasm for the exploration of space will not be viewed by some future historian or psychiatrist as an expression of the urge of our contemporaries to escape from what they consider a miserable world. Likewise, the layman's interest in relativity after Einstein was unquestionably a product of the times. Because people had come to sense the instability of what had erstwhile seemed to be eternal values, and because they felt that they could legitimately live lives without anchorage, the notion of relativity seemed plausible to them, though their vague information from magazine articles and popular books did not, of course, provide them with any real understanding of the principle of relativity.

Having made these brief suggestions about the nexus between ideas and the times in which they emerge, let me engage in a few improvisations. Do not accept them as more than that—improvisations on what one man of science can perhaps contribute to a future history of science portrayed against the background of the psychological, economic, and sociological setting in which it occurred.

The nearly half century I have lived with science amounts to about one fifth of the period from 1700 until the present. The latter period, being about one tenth of the whole of recorded scientific history, itself is a sizeable fraction of all recorded history. Its significance becomes even more impressive when we get away from a mere chronological scale. Let me make this fact clear by a consideration of the population growth since the beginning of the Christian era. The first doubling of population took place around 1650. It then took another 200 years to double again, reaching more than one billion by the middle of the nineteenth century. In another eighty years, about 1930, the population had risen to two billion, and present projections indicate that in another 45 years from then, say by 1975, it will have reached somewhere around four billion. In terms of sheer numbers, the present century, therefore, is an historical novelty.

Of course, increase in population is not necessarily a measure of growth of civilization, and indeed, there will inevitably be different curves for economic development, social welfare, public enlightenment and political maturation. Even so, we should take into consideration that we are living in a period in which things occur precipitately. It has been said that science has burst upon this scene with a "knowledge explosion" which showers humanity with more problems than blessings because of man's sluggishness in adapting to, and learning to control, the spirit of this new age and that, for lack of wisdom, man stands to destroy himself by the very success of his ingenuity.

But is this a realistic outlook? Does scientific yield really increase that fast? I am afraid that if we look over scientific history we find that true achievement has not followed a smooth incremental curve of this kind, but rather has had its ups and downs. Times of remarkable spurts have alternated with periods of stagnation, much as in a military campaign, where breakthroughs and mobile warfare are followed by phases of consolidation, or as in economic systems with their fluctuations between oversupply and scarcity. We have, of course, never had a truly valid measure of scientific growth. How does one measure any sort of growth? In a human being, one can take either weights or heights at different intervals, or measure achievement in certain tasks as an index of mental growth. But how does one measure the growth of science? By volume? If the amounts of paper that appear in press are the criteria, then we have been doing very nicely in recent history; very well indeed! On the other hand, if we are to base our measurement on what one might call significant discoveries or major inventions or relevant conceptual innovations, then we note that the ratio of such major advances to sheer quantity of output has not increased; if anything, it has declined substantially in recent times.

This being so, I should rather discount measurements that involve simply quantity of scientific production and not let myself be overawed by its conspicuous proliferation. It is always the few in science who carry it through. As soon as we recognize this, we come back to the human factor and to my original point that man acts under the influence of his social and political environment and, in turn, plays back on it. As a result of this, the growth curve of science has been very uneven.

Let me now review the circumstances during periods of depression in the curve of scientific achievement. Such stagnations, as we might call them, can be attributed to at least four factors:

(1) *Variations of interest.* Periods when people are more practical-minded alternate with periods when people are more interested in speculation and theory. The eighteenth century serves as a good example of a shift from the practical to the theoretical.

(2) *Fluctuations in the support of science.* Patronage, whether it comes from a duke or archbishop or guild or government, has surely had its influence on the productivity of science. This is difficult to assess. I suspect even the support by the Medicis may not have exactly have stemmed from real interest in science as an integral activity of society.

(3) *Variations in employment opportunities for scientists.* This factor has, of course, been extremely variable.

(4) *Intangible variations in external constraints and restrictions.* To some extent, science has been hamstrung in all ages by institutions, whether church, government, social mores, military leaders, or political organizations stepping in and dictating what an individual scientist could or could not do. I mention these repressions mainly because one factor is often overlooked in historic description. It is that ideas, like chemical reactions, have intrinsic kinetics; it requires a certain time for them to mature, and this maturation must be given a chance to occur. Human activities cannot be forced and driven beyond the rate at which human beings, either as individuals or collectively, can develop and advance naturally. By the same token, unfavorable counterpressures during the incubation period of ideas can stifle development altogether.

Keeping in mind these variations which affect scientific development in any age, let us now turn to the eighteenth century and the interactions between its cultural milieu and the scientists working in it. To try to characterize an epoch is always precarious, for generalizations of such broad scope are apt to dissolve under more detailed scrutiny. What, one may ask, is the critical number of exceptions at which a rule ceases to be a rule? At the risk of generalizing, I still perceive some broad characteristics of that century that to me seem to be quite symptomatic. Let me quote G. M. Trevelyan, who in his ENGLISH

SOCIAL HISTORY submits that "the Eighteenth Century, in spite of its educational defects, produced a larger proportion of remarkable and original Englishmen from among those who passed through its schools than our highly educated and overregulated age is able to do." And further down:

"It is only in the years that followed (1740–1780) that we find a generation of men wholly characteristic of the Eighteenth Century ethos, a society with a mental outlook of its own, self-poised, self-judged, and self-approved, freed from the disturbing passions of the past, and not yet troubled with anxieties about a very different future which was soon to be brought upon the scene by the Industrial and the French Revolutions. The gods mercifully gave mankind this little moment of peace between the religious fanaticisms of the past and the fanaticisms of class and race that were speedily to arise and dominate time to come. In England it was an age of aristocracy and liberty; of the rule of law and the absence of reform; of individual initiative and institutional decay. . . .

[There prevailed] the happy belief that the state of society and the modes of thought to which they are accustomed are not mere passing aspects of an evershifting kaleidoscope, but permanent habitations, the final outcome of reason and experience. Such an age does not aspire to progress though it may in fact be progressing; it regards itself not as setting out but as having arrived; it is thankful for what it has, and enjoys life without "deep questioning which probes to endless dole." And therefore the man of this "classical" age looked back with a sense of kinship to the far-off Ancient World. The upper class regarded the Greeks and Romans as honorary Englishmen, their precursors in liberty and culture, and the Roman Senate as the prototype of the British Parliament. The mediaeval period, with its "gothic" aspirations and barbarisms, sank for a while below the horizon of study and sympathy, so that the eye of taste could range back without hindrance across the gulf of time, and contemplate on its further shore the only civilization which could claim to be as classical, as poised, as enlightened and as artistic as the fortunate present.

Compared to the self-complacency of the mid-Eighteenth Century, the proverbial self-complacency of the Victorians is modesty itself, for the Victorians were, within certain limits, ardent and successful reformers."

Obviously, during that time there was a respite from the intellectual upheaval of the Renaissance, with its seventeenth-century "backwash," or what the Italians like to call the *mare morto*: that is, even after the initial force had waned, the tide still carried the big breakers, which, in this case, included many major philosophical and scientific developments. One might cite particularly the creation of the Royal Society, the origin of experimental physics, and the emergence of experimental medicine. On the whole, what followed was a quiet time as if people were tired and had to take a rest from all the turmoil. They settled down to not-too-challenging but tidy work. This obviously led to the sort of scientific activity that concentrates primarily on the collecting, ordering, and analyzing of data. It was not, at least until the close of the 18th century, an age given to synthesis or great and sweeping generalizations.

As Goethe said about that era (I translate): "The eighteenth century is being praised for its preoccupation with analysis, leaving for the nineteenth century the task to disclose the false prevailing syntheses only to start all over again to analyze now the content of the latter."

Much of this, of course, reflects Goethe's personal antipathy towards getting too far away from the observed phenomena. He evidently was unaware of his own flights of imagination and synthesis; otherwise, he would have been a little more charitable about the people who did rise to the higher spheres of theory. But, in general terms, his characterization of the age as being largely preoccupied with tidying up details seems significant.

Before going on to assess scientific achievement in the eighteenth century, let us first look, in general, at the way science proceeds. What is science? What are its objectives? As far as I can see, the ultimate objective of science is to find out the character, composition, and workings of the universe and of all that is in nature, and to create a valid, formal reproduction of it in terms that are rational, logically consistent, universal, and testable (see Chapter 3). The scientific urge undoubtedly stems from man's intimate dependence upon his environment, with the challenges and hazards of which he must learn to cope if he is to survive. For early man to know the products, forces, and perils of nature surrounding him was a biological necessity; he learned to sift the useful from the dangerous by recognizing their respective signs; and their regular recurrence in similar circumstances gave him some power of prediction. Modern man has simply expanded this to the point at which he can formulate the predictions into rules and laws, and from them can, to some extent, derive control over his environment. This is a simple operational definition of science, but little more than that. To express its true spirit, one would have to add a certain set of attitudes and rules of procedure which have to be observed rather rigorously. These procedures may be called the *scientific process*, and they can be described essentially as progressing in six different steps, all of them necessary for the pursuit and the advancement of knowledge (see Chapter 9):

The first step is *observation* of nature, sometimes called fact-finding. It consists of collecting items that one wants to know about. It stems from biological necessity. Curiosity comes in, as well as possessive and esthetic instincts, but utility is perhaps its primordial drive.

The second step is *description*. To be significant, identification must be more than private observation; it must be communicable to others. This does not yet aim at comprehension of the observed phenomena, but simply at the description of their content in unequivocal objective terms. Observations must be put down in words which will ensure that the phenomena appear the same to all.

Third is *comparison*. One looks for what the observed and identified phenomena have in common. The scientist is looking for some order and some sense. He approaches it by assembling the similar and attempting to separate it from the dissimilar.

The fourth step is *classification*—packaging whatever one has found to be similar into common categories. This might be described as a filing and retrieving process. Basically it is a device of the human mind to grasp the immense diversity of nature by parcelling it into simpler and manageable compartments. Classification has taken many forms, and I will reflect later on how it operated in the eighteenth century.

Fifth comes *interpretation*. Here theory is developed. One wants to explain; that is, to reduce to more familiar terms that which has been ordered into categories, and one wants to see inner relations, and eventually relationships, which one can manipulate or with which one can experiment. Here two lines of scientific endeavor become confluent: deduction, in which conclusions are derived logically from past experience already formulated, and induction, in which one learns directly from nature and gradually distills some sense from its lessons.

Sixth is *integration*—an attempt to encompass more and more under a single formula. This stems from the conviction that science is uniform and universal; therefore intelligible cross-communication can be established between the different specialties: the medical man, the physicist, the chemist, the sociologist, the engineer, the mathematician, the philosopher, and, hopefully, eventually all mankind.

How does science approach these tasks? As I remarked earlier, there is no such thing as "science" in an abstract allegorical sense. Science is what people in science think and do. Therefore, the question must be rephrased: how do the men of science approach these different tasks?

In the course of the history of civilization, time and again the human mind, impatient for satisfying explanations, has been tempted to skip some of those consecutive steps and provide answers by short-cuts. Conversely, there have been times when there was little interest and zest in carrying the process to its culminating stage of interpretation and theory. In other words, different links of the total chain were given different attention and emphasis at different times. To keep this composite nature of scientific progress in mind will make an assessment of science in the eighteenth century more instructive and pertinent than if we were to deal with it in terms of a single generality. To draw the average of a picture composed of blacks and whites by calling it gray, deprives the description of all meaning.

Let us now look at the component steps one by one.

(1) *Observation* means disciplined research as contrasted with mere impressions and impressionistic opinion. The eighteenth century has some epoch-making observations to its credit. For example, Luigi Galvani first noted muscle contraction through accidental observation of a frog's legs twitching on an iron grille. His observations then led Alessandro Volta to the study of electricity. Thus, both the sciences of neurophysiology and of electricity stemmed from those observations. Not the least important effect of such findings was that they drew wider interest to the observed phenomena and led to the development

of more refined techniques and instruments for their study. Without amplifying these examples, let me conclude that there were in this era indeed many men with acuity for making significant observations and discoveries.

(2) The *description* of observations, which requires, in the first place, being honest and then, of course, being unequivocally clear in dealing with the language, took an advanced step in those days because instead of relying on personal observation and somewhat flamboyant literary description, people began for the first time to see the need for repositories of type specimens, so that everybody could inspect what had been described and all could view the same thing objectively. It was in those days that John Hunter set up the first museum as a deliberate device for the study of objects of nature. Museums, as well as zoological and botanical gardens, as exhibits of curios or freaks, had existed for a long time, but it must be credited to Hunter, and a little while before him to the Royal Society Museum, to have made the first systematic efforts to dispel by public exhibits the uncertainty attached to verbal description. In the same spirit, Albrecht von Haller had laid plans for one of the first systematical botanical gardens in Göttingen by the middle of the century.

Communication of scientific findings also became well founded in the last part of the century. THE BOTANICAL MAGAZINE, the first biological journal, was started in 1777; the TRANSACTIONS OF THE LINNEAN SOCIETY were begun in 1791, and the ARCHIV FÜR DIE PHYSIOLOGIE appeared in 1795. Therefore, the need not only to observe but also to record and to communicate these records arose during these years in which there was the peace necessary for unhurried systematic fact finding

(3) *Comparison* is, as I indicated before, the source of the determination of similarities and dissimilarities. It is interesting to note Goethe's position on this point. He declares (I translate): "As for the things whose nature we wish to learn, it seems to me we ought to concentrate evermore on what distinguishes them rather than on what they have in common." If this statement was intended to counter-balance a certain prevailing sloppiness in attention to detail, we can pass it as a tactical move. But, in its generality, it is decidedly unscientific. No scientist would state that either focus is more or less important than

the other. Both must be pursued for insight into what things have in common, as well as what distinguishes them from one another. At any rate, comparative studies flourished in that century.

(4) Collecting, ordering, and, perhaps most important, *classification* were, however, the real hallmarks of eighteenth-century science. It is the century that gave us Linnaeus. In his SYSTEMA NATURAE, he grouped living forms into species, genera, orders and classes, in a beautiful hierarchical system which he based on the premise that there were as many species extant as there had been on earth at the time of creation. I point this out because it is one of the clearest expressions of the philosophy of the stable, complacent, smug *status quo* age which Trevelyan descibed. It is not surprising, therefore, that many people of that age, particularly Bonnet and his followers, considered nature as a rigid, once-and-for-all ordered system. As Singer quotes one of Bonnet's followers, for instance: "All beings have been conceived and formed on one single plan, of which they are the endlessly graded variants. This prototype is man, whose stages of development are so many steps toward the highest form of being." In "an age when 'free thinkers' and 'deists,' on the one hand, and Christians, on the other, inhabited sharply-divided camps," one sees that views such as expressed by Bonnet were strictly dictated by religious bias. Thus a social-cultural phenomenon was reflected in scientific attitudes. Then the scientific attitudes, being human attitudes, played back and engendered the rebellious reaction which marked the end of that century.

(5) As for the *interpretation* of phenomena, we are dealing with an age which was fully satisfied with the world and nature. The *status quo* philosophy was further accentuated by the embryological theories of that time. There was emphasis, particularly by Albrecht von Haller, on preformation. Embryology, the development of an individual from an egg, has always been considered a very mysterious affair. Experimentation had not gotten far and there were two opposing theories. The one prevailing then, that of preformation or *emboîtement*, affirmed that every human individual was actually wrapped up in the egg in minute detail as a fully formed little organism. Moreover, that little germ, that little homunculus, also substantially contained his total future progeny. Some people began to figure out how many egg primordia the ovary of Eve would have had to contain. They came out with a figure of 200 billion, which, I suppose, is still conservative. The interesting thing is that they had no misgivings about the fact that this led to the postulate

of infinitesimally small size. The infinity of the universe in the upper dimensions had seemed acceptable. But, infinity downward was something else again, implying that there is no lower limit for the smallest particles of matter. This view, of course, claimed biological support when Leeuwenhoek looked through the microscope and found a mite on a flea; whereupon Jonathan Swift wrote the familiar verse:

> *So, naturalists observe, a flea*
> *Hath smaller fleas that on him prey;*
> *And these have smaller still to bite 'em;*
> *And so proceed ad infinitum.*

In general, the scientists of that time did not really worry very much about where their speculations led them so long as everything turned out to have been nicely and neatly prepared right from the start. All nature had to do was to unfold what had been wrapped up; make explicit the formerly implicit; and relegate all apparent novelty to the rank of a mere display of preordained old and immutable order. Goethe himself said (I translate): "Development by gradual emergence is something that is inconceivable to us; hence, whenever we see something developing, we think it must have pre-existed, and consequently the system of *emboîtement* appears to us quite plausible."

This type of *status quo* thinking, as I have said before, gradually led to an unavoidable reaction. In embryology, for instance, Caspar Friedrich Wolff's theory of epigenesis came to replace the ideas of the preformationists. Wolff postulated that the germ is simply a mass of goo out of which, by consecutive actions and interactions, a body of increasing complexity is shaped, as if an internal spirit or an external sculptor ("entelechy") carved features into it. Blumenbach let it be done by an all-wise *nisus formativus* ("formative drive"). These vitalistic excesses, in turn, found vigorous opposition in equally extreme mechanistic doctrines, which in elaboration of Descartes' ideas, tried to present man as a precision robot (*e.g.*, de la Mettrie in his HOMME MACHINE, 1748).

To return briefly to the earlier preformation ideas, I might point out that it is a quirk of language that "preformation" was also called "evolution," because "evolving" in the sense of the preformationists meant the unfolding of an erstwhile "involved" bud—the way a flower opens. In contrast to this concept of pre-established absolute stability of organization and "prestabilized harmony," our contemporary doctrines of phylogeny tend to vest "evolution" with the exactly opposite power—the limitless creation of novelty. Since the struggle between these two extremes clearly affects public attitudes, it is well to remember the limitations of both. Although rigid preformation has been discarded as a scientific theory, it has retained a valid core of truth. All living organisms, from the simplest to the most complex, including man, have a far greater basic stock in common in their composition, structure, and mechanisms, than is commonly pointed up in our teaching of evolution. We should not eclipse that massive conservative stock of vital properties which all organisms have carried through organic history ever since the beginning of life. Organic evolution has only been reshuffling that stock in novel combinations, improving it, to be sure, but not really creating it. And for that reason the French term *transformisme*, instead of "evolution," has perhaps much to recommend it. One almost recognizes the kernel of truth in the French saying: "Plus ça change, plus c'est la même chose." An eighteenth-century conservative might have added: "Then, why try to change at all?"

It is perhaps no accident, therefore, that in our own age, concomitantly with rapid economic progress to the point of affluence, the concept of rather rigid predetermination in development is coming into prominence again as a result of modern progress in genetics. It rests on a naïve misconception about the manner in which genes operate. One speaks of genes "controlling" or "dictating" this or that feature of either body or mind, as if the course from gene to final property were actually a micro-precisely predetermined clockwork, like the preformation of old. The facts are not this simple and clear-cut. To be sure, the genic endowment sets a highly organized pattern of processes into operation and is, in turn, continuously called upon again to react in specific ways to the products of the diverse processes it has inaugurated, but the precise course of events is epigenetic, far too much subject to the vagaries of external circumstances, hence far too unique and unpredictable, to fit any concept of absolute predetermination of end results. There is plenty of latitude for influencing, for better or for worse, the outcome of development of an organism with a given genic constitution.

The recognition of this fact has deep philosophical, and indeed moral, implications, for it denies that man can do nothing about his fate; quite to the contrary, it places upon him a solemn responsibility to make the most of his innate potential by favoring the development of the better over the worse features of his endowment. The same arguments that invalidate the thesis of blind genetic fatalism thus validate the freedom of responsible self-direction. But personal responsibility is something an age bent on security and risk-free existence does not particularly care to face, let alone advocate. Might there not be an inner link between the prominence given in our day to the illusion of an immutable hereditary fate on the one hand, and the fear of insecurity—social, political, mental, and economic—on the other? The student of the development of organisms cannot fail to note a more-than-superficial resemblance between the earlier parts of the eighteenth century and our own, both tending to affirm the supremacy of a *status quo* of illusory tidiness and perfection, oblivious of the unavoidable reactions such rigid attitudes are bound to arouse, of revolutions then, and stirrings now. Of course, it must be added that, speaking as a student of development, I am still, when it comes to history, an amateur. As such, I sense that preference for one-sided doctrines of either preformation or epigenesis has never rested on the weight of facts alone, but has always had some emotional undertones issuing from the temper of the times.

The antithesis of preformation and epigenesis in embryology also reflects the difference in thinking about the whole problem of the relation between the parts versus the whole. The preformationist view represented the parts as primary; they were there from the start as such, in fitting constellation, and the final organism was but the product of their assembly. The epigeneticist's version was the opposite: in it the organism as a whole was taken to be a primary integrated entity, and parts emerged only as secondary products of differentiating and localizing instructions from the "whole."*

This contrast in assigning primacy to either the parts or the whole has been one of the most intriguing aspects and, I believe indeed, one of the most moving political motives throughout history. Much of our

---

*For a critical discussion of the problem of "the Whole and the Parts", reconciling "Holism" with "Reductionism", see chapter 18.

recent social and political history, which spawned Fascism, National Socialism, Communism and various extremes of nationalism and racism, has been based on the nebulous idea that the "whole," state, nation, race, or collective, has primacy as an entity existing, as it were, independent of the constituents that make it up. Statism, as proclaimed, for instance, by Othmar Spann, thus gained that mythical hold on the minds of the people, without which the horrible excesses of political action that followed would be totally incomprehensible. This contrasts sharply with the liberal and realistic notion that the sole source and agent of social and political thought and action is the individual person, albeit in intelligent group interaction with other individuals. Evidently, if political power is exercised by only a limited number of individuals in a population, whether by arrogation or delegation, and if they are wise enough to heed the lessons of evolutionary progress, they will evince a streak of conservatism, so that when faced with a choice between a reasonably satisfactory *status quo* and an unreasonably violent departure from it, they will decide to hang on to the former. There seems to be thus a direct connection indicated between emphasis on individuality, *i.e.*, on the primacy of the part or members of a group, on the one hand, and a political climate of moderate conservatism, on the other.

Therefore, it may again have been not wholly accident that the eighteenth-century discovery by Hooke that organisms contained subunits, "cells," was soon to be expanded to the claim that those were the true and only living elements and that all functions of the organism had to be referred to them. The "cell theory" thus dethroned the organism as a whole from its position as model of an all-knowing organizer and preceptor. Whether, by implication, this gave specific comfort to those political trends which distrusted centralized power monopolies in general, it seems plausible to assume that the success of the cell theory, with its connotations of decentralized autonomy of member units, at any rate, has had its influence on the political thinking of the subsequent period. One could ask whether, reciprocally, the general acceptance of the cell theory in the nineteenth century, particularly after its articulation and generalization by Lorenz Oken, Theodor Schwann, M. J. Schleiden, Rudolf Virchow, and others, might not have been expedited, if not prepared, by the emergence of political doctrines of liberal socialism. I merely pose the question.

In view of the widespread use, as well as abuse, that has been made of biological models for the purpose of rationalizing preconceived theories of human society, it is significant to keep in mind that the cell theory set up the organism as merely the result of the orderly free interactions among relatively autonomous unit cells, rather than as a super-personality handing down and enforcing assignments to a teeming mass of blind slave subjects. Even though modern science has removed some of the sharpness of this original antithesis, the organism as a state of free members, interacting freely, is still a more valid, and certainly far more desirable, model for civilized human society than is the state of termites, bees, or ants, so often suggested for that role by some of my colleagues in biology for its unquestionably superior efficiency. Our admiration for the high perfection of co-operative group performances among the different castes in insect states cannot obscure the fact that each member is born and reared to an immutable station in life, preordained by the needs of the "superorganism," fixed in advance. Does human progress not aspire to free man from the doom of enforced confinement to a station, let us say, of sterile worker? Since I believe, as I have intimated, that biological and scientific developments in general have a far greater influence on public thinking than we usually credit them with, I am convinced that comparative extrapolations to the modern age of lessons learned from the study of science in the societies of bygone eras can be far more than an academic exercise.

(6) This brings me to my last category—*integration* and *universality*. As the rebellion against the monotony of sheer fact-collecting and the mere dealing with phenomena gained momentum, the concepts of *Naturphilosophie* mushroomed. To become one with nature, to embrace nature, be embraced by nature and take nature as a whole, was set forth as a universal hope. This urge to identify oneself with nature, most markedly reflected in the subsequent romantic period, is too well known for me to dwell on at this point, except that I would like to say that even by the end of the eighteenth century the tendency toward integration and universality had already become noticeable among a few people of sensitivity and perspective. I have already cited John Hunter as one instance. Except for Stephen Hales, no one had ever tried to subordinate plants and animals to the same formula of life: they had been totally separate categories. Hunter made a deliberate effort to put the two together by bringing plants and animals into the same museum;

it amounted, as Herder said, to describing life as an "immense complex organism that comprises heterogeneous realms including that of man." But the man who really achieved a sense of integration was Buffon. He was the main advocate of the unity of nature, the searching for ideal types, or "*Urtypen*." However, Buffon succumbed to fantastic speculations where scientific acuity evaporated into something more appropriately described as the artistic touch. His thinking lacked the discipline of the scientific approach, but it had perspective. Himself no *Naturphilosoph*, he shared with his time the belief in a system; and his all-embracing HISTOIRE DE LA NATURE made the later speculations of *Naturphilosophie* possible.

In all of this, I have tried to indicate that the activities of individuals in science (and particularly in the biological sciences, with which I am familiar) have been strongly influenced by the temper of the times and that, in turn, they may to some extent have exerted a reciprocal influence on the general climate of thought—as vigorous personalities, such as Goethe, have certainly left an impress on their period. Such mutual interactions usually proceed in waves, with ups and downs in the rate of progress. Yet, I believe that despite all these fluctuations, science as a whole has been on a steady upgrade. It will remain so as long as we leave people in their full diversity to exercise their interests, imagination, and aptitudes, instead of trying to cast them into common molds of standard patterns, for science can only thrive in an atmosphere of freedom. And, as we have seen, there were individuals in the eighteenth century who were able to exercise their minds in such an atmosphere. Yet, if they were relatively few, we can perhaps blame it on the fact that it was an age essentially of stagnation, of smugness, of self-satisfaction without aspiration to progress.

I stress this for its bearing on our times. We ourselves are entering a new phase of civilization, not without risks. It is not only the tremendous volume and rapidity with which events overtake us. In the days which we have been talking about men were mostly free agents. In the eighteenth century science and scientists were not institutionalized. Even though some of them may have been in the service of absolute monarchs, they were not working as members of big industrial companies or of governmental organizations. They were just individuals. The modern danger of institutionalization of science comes with the need for large quantities of scientific helpers, technologists, specialists, hands at all stations. The need for them is recognized, but it must not obscure the fact that the relatively small number who will actually carry on science for its own sake, sparked by their own philosophical, scientific, or technical aspirations, need to be protected against excessive pressures of the *Zeitgeist*, of the tempo of life, and particularly the social mores, which try to stamp them into a particular common mold. The most dangerous, stunting, and destructive thing to science is overemphasis of security, for science is adventure. Scientific discovery and theory thrive on intellectual insecurity. Anything that plays up more and more promises of absolute security, not just economic but intellectual security, and illusions of certain and final answers in our time, takes the spark out of the drive of scientific progress. It is precisely this specter of atrophy of the urge to strive which is raised by the signs of complacency and self-satisfaction in our contemporary scene. Heeding the lesson of the eighteenth century may yet put us on guard lest history repeat itself. It could indeed, if consciously counteracted, even lead to a renewed spurt of growth of modern science, not just in quantity and proliferation of minutiae, but in wider mastery and deeper conceptual clarification of the rules of order of the universe, including man.

Science and the Humanities*

Science and the Humanities are commonly placed in distinct categories according to subject matter. To me, this categorical distinction, which implies a dichotomy of knowledge, seems to be spurious. I fail to recognize a sharp disjunction or boundary between them, the separate pigeonholes assigned to them by academic custom notwithstanding. Basically, their differences are not truly *substantive,* but *attributive.* They are differences of aspect, of interest, of attitude, and of point of view, but neither of subject matter nor of methodology. Let me clarify by an example just what I mean.

There was a tree in front of me as I began to write this. In looking at it, I asked myself: "Now, here is a tangible piece of my experience as a human being. Would it not be absurd, unless I were schizophrenic, to try to rate it as *either* a scientific *or* a humanistic object?" Admiring its harmonious shape, I was imbued with *esthetic* pleasure; then thinking of the laws of growth, to which it owed that shape, reminded me of the discipline of *scientific* study, through which that law has been revealed; the record of annual fluctuations of climate, indelibly laid down in the tree rings, turned the tree into a document of *history;* in yielding fruit for nourishment and wood for shelter, a tree becomes an object of mundane *agriculture* and *technology* in the service of human beings,—in short, a subject of concern to *sociology* and *economics;* and then again, as I raise my inner eye to contemplate how the creative *art* of a sculptor ennobles a block of wood by carving from it an even more beautiful shape than was inherent in its original beauty, I found myself come around full circle to appreciating that the world of our perceptions, cognition, and value attributions is a *continuum*—unitary, cohesive and indivisible. Nowhere do I note in it a sign of those substantive boundaries by which our academic world partitions that natural and cultural continuum into a mosaic of ever more specialized fragments ("disciplines"), fenced off against each other by airtight walls, which offer the agoraphobic mind safe shelter from the discomfort of

*Address delivered at the International Humanistic Symposium held at Delphi, September 25—October 4, 1969. Reprinted from Proceedings of the First International Symposium of the Hellenic Humanistic Society, Athens 1970.

intellectual insecurity—the price exacted by the sense of unbounded vision and broad perspective.

The body of human knowledge is all of one piece. To place "science" and "humanities" into opposition, or at best, juxtaposition, as two disjointed disciplines, is but a sign of a growing trend toward dismembering that unitary body artificially for academic purposes. Is there in truth any *logical* or *substantive* justification for such a sharp dichotomy? Or are we simply faced with an instance of a time-honored practice for the sake of administrative expediency?

Let us look at the issue. One notes that "science" is commonly cited in the singular; "humanities" as plural. The underlying logic seems to be that science refers to a single manner of approach to nature, encompassing man and society, embodied in a common code of attitudes and methodology. Conversely, the "humanities" appear as a variegated assemblage of diverse aspects of the specifically human sector, although the record of this conference leaves some doubt as to whether the common root of "human" in the terms "humanism", "humanity", and "humanities" has retained any more than phonetic meaning. This being so, the heterogeneity of things conventionally sheltered in academic schemeta under the umbrella of "humanities" need not surprise us. Of course, the common stem of science has had its offshoots, too, in a plurality of topical branch "sciences", but have the "humanities" reciprocally reintegrated their disparate branches to a common and unified concern with "humanity"—singular? Perhaps this logical asymmetry lies at the base of the issue—to my mind, spurious—of antipolarity of science *versus* humanities. The depolarization of this issue must be our task. Yet, to succeed in it requires first of all that one give up the blind parochial allegiance to the vague generalities on which the standard symbolic designations of academic organizations rest and instead examine the presumed substance of the issue soberly and realistically.

First, what is "science"? As I once put it, "science is man's way of formulating for himself a mental replica of the Universe and all that is in it, in as complete, consistent and *universally communicable* form as is attainable to him through his senses, their extension by tools and logic, and rational ordering." You will observe that this definition confines the domain of science strictly to that aspect of the world, however vast, yet definitely bounded, for which *universal* comprehension by evidence can be attained. It implicitly affirms, as well as explicitly excludes from the jurisdiction of science the infinite realm of "private" relations to the Universe that is the privileged personal domain of the single individual—that stock of subjective beliefs, opinions, intuitions, predilections, fancies and creative urges, which not only cannot be validated by universal consensus, but lie domonstrably beyond the range of objective *validation*.

Note that etymologically the roots of the terms "validity" and "value" are the same. There is an ambiguity in this verbal kinship. It is illustrated by a remark made to me by a prominent humanistic scholar in answer to my question about his test for the distinction between science and the humanities. He said the test criterion is the concept of "value"; in his words, science deals with *facts*; humanities, with *values*. If we accepted this, consistency would force us to go one step further and claim that while values may be the domain of the humanities, validation is the preserve of science. Clearly, this "value judgement" is readily invalidated by pointing out that mathematics, for instance, commonly a member of the science faculties of universities, does not concern itself really with "facts", but is rather a branch of logics, hence of philosophy, which is traditionally ranged among the humanistic disciplines; while history, most of which unquestionably does deal with facts, is surely a respectable branch of the "humanities".

Indeed, no one with open eyes and mind could make a valid case for a sharp delineation between the sciences (for symmetry, set in the plural here) and the humanities on any logical or even methodological grounds. The objects, motivations and procedures of a naturalist in Systematic Botany, who collects, identifies and catalogues new plants as documents for the history of Evolution, or of a chemist who determines the content and configuration of atoms in a large organic molecule, are in no way different in kind from the motives and labors of the archaeologist, who excavates and gathers artifacts, or of the linguist who reconstructs an ancient language from its letter symbols. The deciphering of the genetic code and that of the inscriptions on the Rosetta stone bear close resemblance. And the conception of any scientific theory contains no less of the ingredients of imagination, abstraction and creative artistry than is taken for granted in the arts, which the humanities engulf in their precinct. The practical deliveries of science, exemplified by medicine, technology, or mental testing, are

categorically no different from the utilitarian products of the humanities, exemplified by dictionaries, or calendars of historic data. The
dating of historical events and epochs by means of radioactive carbon,
discussed at this symposium by Allibone, can serve as a further example
of this utilitarian parallelism.

So, let us concede the artificiality of the distinction and antithetical
posture once assigned, mainly for emphasis, by C. P. Snow to the "Two
Cultures", a scientific and a humanistic one. Let us proceed in full
cognizance of the basic unity of human culture, but also in full
appreciation of the wide spectrum of diverse aspects which that
continuum offers and which calls for an equally great diversity of
approaches to its study; approaches, however, which must be pursued
in concert, harmony and convergence, and not in a prejudicial spirit of
fundamental disparity, incompatibility, let alone competition.

I assume that we can agree on this precept in its generality. To
translate it into practical designs and actions is another matter. Not
only have academic traditions, hardened by administrative practices,
grooved a rigid set of linear program ruts from which it is difficult to
escape for resuming free cross travel overland between them, but the
individual travelers themselves mostly prefer to stay in those well-worn
tracks. For the practitioners and the expert specialists, this is a matter
of course. Yet, a growing proportion of scholars begin to show the same
attitude of narrow professional confinement as a matter of choice. For
many, the horizon has also been shrunk, instead of widened, by a
system of education that has become perverted more and more into
indoctrination. True, as I once put it, not every lawyer is, or need be, a
jurist, not every priest a theologian, nor every teacher a scholar. And
similarly, most workers in science are not necessarily "scientists" in the
broad sense of the word. But then, by the same token, how many
people engaged in the humanities are truly "humanists"?

Granting that those chosen to discuss the issue of "science and the
humanities" at this symposium have been selected because, on the
evidence of their past record, they appeared qualified to examine a
broad cultural issue as both "scientists" and "humanists" in the fullest
meaning of those terms; does not this very fact mark us as
unrepresentative of the masses who at the present populate science and
the humanities, with attitudes more self-centered than universally-
minded? Where we would speak out for reunion, integration, and

reconciliation of arbitrarily accentuated antagonisms, the clamor and trend in the academic scene is for evermore splintering and particularization. Scholarly pleading for more attention to the general history of ideas, encompassing philosophy, science, religion, and politics, of universal concern to all mankind, is countered by pressures for more intensive preoccupation with the monomaniac parochialisms of separate and disparate ideologies, sects, and cults. In view of the momentum of this trend, one must concede that academic universalism—Humboldt's "Universitas Literarum"—is no longer universal; neither as a dream, nor as aim, nor as program.

In taking this resigned position, I obviously also give up hope that sheer administrative, curricular, financial, or propaganda measures could significantly advance the harmonization between science and the humanities and redress some of the glaring imbalances between them in the universities sweepingly and on a massive scale. The countervailing force of contending groups with special vested interests seems, for the moment, far too strong to be overcome by reforms based on sheer logical reasoning and idealism. I therefore propose to view our task and chart our course within a much more modest frame, which offers at least some prospect of practical success, as follows:

(1) Let us cease talking in abstract generalities, because insistent repetition of references to a "scientific-humanistic schism" would only go to deepen the illusion of the validity of such an arbitrary cleavage.

(2) Let us give up the fictitious notion that universities can still aspire to being "all things to all men". We must recognize that universities will have to deliver to a society with increasing appetite and claims for the "good life" the practical offshoots of advancing knowledge and the mounting numbers of needed expert practitioners that can render those services competently; and let us not overlook that a majority of students enter the university with the primary aim of acquiring such training in the *application*, rather than the *advancement*, of knowledge, whether in the health services, the building of cities, the teaching of languages, the administration of justice, the care of libraries and art collections, or what not.

(3) Let the Universities learn to identify that decided minority of students which by motivation, aptitude and attitude are preeminently qualified to partake in the general *advancement* of knowledge and guide them toward the optimum combination of the two dimensions of

knowledge—breadth and depth: breadth of vision and perspective, and depth of critical study and interpretation. It is on this level that the demand for breadth must blur, or preferably even wipe out, the artificial science-humanities custom barrier. Yet, in a realistic view, even this requirement does not apply equally to the whole minority group considered under this point; for the rapid growth in volume and differentiation of research and scholarship, as mainsprings of the search for knowledge and understanding, has given rise to corps of technical specialists who operate behind the frontlines of advancing knowledge as essential auxilliary forces, as it were. As such they should be included more appropriately in the category of practitioners, for they are engaged in the *application* of knowledge in the service of the advancement of knowledge, rather than in the frontier steps of the latter process directly. The true pioneering group, however small in proportion, should become the prime target of efforts in higher education at removing the barriers that hamper confluence between science and the humanities, so that there may grow up a generation of almost indistinguishable humanistic scientists and scientific humanists. Here are some pointers to this goal.

(4) As knowledge of a fruit rests on the understanding of the dynamics of the tree that grows it, so scientific knowledge presupposes the understanding of the roots of human cognition—*epistemology and philosophy of science*, branches of the *humanities*. And as the forms—the "styles"—of trees on earth are products of historic evolution, as studied in science, so the fashions of *science* are, conversely, a chapter of *human history*. Presenting both biological and cultural evolution conjointly would distill for the student the common lesson of both, which is the realization of the existence in both of certain fundamental, universal, stable and nearly invariant elements and dynamic rules, combined with an almost unlimited freedom of re-combining those elements in new constellations for the creative emergence of novel styles. It is unpardonable that exposure to the philosophy and history of science as an integral part of the human adventure is not made a cornerstone of the education of a scientist; it is equally deplorable that in the presentation in the humanities of the cultural history of mankind a major share is not given to the history of scientific ideas in its inseparable interrelations with the social, political, religious, artistic and economic aspects of each epoch. Furthermore, as

the budding *scientist* should be introduced to *semantics*—the meaning of words and symbols—, so the student of *history* should be exposed to scientific discipline of rigorously defining *terms* of meaning, with examples of the catastrophic consequences of their misuse in history.

I could go on to add examples to this scant selection, yet I hope to have made my point. It is this. If "scientists" in science education were to re-emphasize the deep "humanistic" roots and outlooks in their fields, and if the "humanists" were to respect more widely not only the limitations, but also the virtues, of critical evaluation of evidence inherent in the spirit of science, the purported divergence between "science" and the "humanities" would surely be not only reversed into convergence, but could lead to a new resurgence of *unified* thought and spirit. Both "science" and "humanities" deal with both facts and values, but above all, both are humane, serving humanity, hence are "humanistic" in the purest meaning of the term. As the seal of my institution, the Rockefeller University, states it: "Pro bono humani generis".

EPILOGUE

Having listened attentively to the speakers and discussants at this symposium, particularly at the session dealing with the interrelations between science and the humanities—or should we say, between their respective images reflected in the public and academic scene—, I recognize that there has been rather general consonance among the witnesses from the scientific sector in their views about the humanistic mission and prospects of science in the furtherance of cultural unity. The utterances from the humanistic sector were far less ecumenically minded, perhaps because of the much wider dispersion of the connotations which "humanists" attach to the term "humanism". The resulting lack of common focus, aggravated by signs of an internal schism between a hard line of status-quo ideologists and a softer line of evolutionary progressists, and further accentuated by the indisputable disparity between scientific and humanistic endeavors in their respective rates of advance and sources of support, makes it not only timely, but urgent, to devise means of counteracting that divisive trend.

To be effective, such countermeasures will have to aim both at the prevention of further disintegration and, progressively, at a firmer consolidation of the *unity of knowledge* on which the sense of cohesion of human culture—singular—, coupled with full preservation of the creative diversity of human cultures—plural—, ultimately depends. Undoubtedly, the industrial age, with its technological profusion and with its growing-pains of reconciling the aspiration to freedom for self-development of the human individual with the demands and restraints imposed on him by an evolving human society, is of itself not conducive to inaugurate, much less, to nurture, such reintegrative moves. And yet, if mankind is to be kept from squandering man's unique dowry of reason by trading an incipient rational and humane trend of civilization for the stultifying prospect of a robotized and dehumanized world, science and the humanities, as now defined, will have to counteract their progressive self-isolation in self-grooving ruts by profuse anastomosing in networks of what nowadays is called "human concern". Such confluence calls for equilibration: more humanism in the humanities and less scientism in the sciences, till their value systems merge. I doubt whether we are faced as yet with "Two Cultures". But I can readily discern two growing *cults*.

The time has come when universities should reassert their time-honored role of leadership in adapting the lessons of the past to the exigencies of the future, Janus-faced. Universities are the major breeding and training grounds for teachers and future leaders of society. While having to spawn the mounting numbers of competent practitioners in the professions, arts and sciences, for whom modern society is clamoring, they must yet, at the same time, defend and fortify their station as trustees of knowledge, caretakers of the past and conquerors of the future. Accordingly, besides their obligation of training specialists for the professions and scholarly experts for the advancement of the diverse specialized branches of knowledge, they must, above all, be prime agents and exhibitors of the *unity, cohesiveness and inner consistency of all knowledge* to set a model for harmony instead of discord. In this sense, the blurring of such sharp academic distinctions as that between "science" and "humanities" becomes a mandatory task for education.

More than a decade ago, I made a similar plea. Not much has changed in the interim. And so, I feel prompted to repeat that plea.

"Alarmed by signs that an abuse of science may lead to humans being treated as merely "cases" for a gigantic statistical processing mill in which they are to be levelled to standards of the average, the common, and the mediocre, I make a plea to science to reacclaim diversity as source of progress (for uniformity means death), including the diversity of human minds in their responsible expressions. And then I make another plea to the non-scientific humanists not to regard themselves as prime custodians of civilization, shunning science as if it were inhuman. Let none of us lodge in the Master's Mansion, but let us all move down into the servants' quarters, so that we all may work together united for human progress in harmonious cooperation. The tasks are large, our forces limited. No group can do the job alone. So, let us all close ranks, the men of science with those in other walks of life, for humanism and against the dehumanization of our culture."

Organic Form: Scientific and Æsthetic Aspects *

Science is usually understood to depict a universe of strict order and lawfulness, of rigorous economy—one whose currency is energy, convertible against a service charge into a growing common pool called entropy. Indeed, in its totality and in the long-range view, reality does ask a price for everything it offers. But on a smaller scale, in the short-range view, the outlook is less dismal and forbidding. Payment can be deferred, and notwithstanding the minus in the final balance sheet, there are in the account factors whose emphasis is on upsurge, growth, and gain, ignoring the downdrafts of drudgery, death, and decay. There is the lavish splendor of animate nature, proliferating luxuriantly at the expense of solar energy. And there is man, its highest creative product, exploiting and thriving bodily on those lower creatures. As his body extracts selectively from nutriment just those substances beneficial for its growth, so does man's spirit gain inspiration from the one-sided concentration on the constructive and uplifting phases of nature's course. In fact, man's spirit cunningly designs forever new devices to accentuate them.

Now, if a scientist may be allowed for once, like people in other walks of life, to overstep his competence, then I dare submit that art is man's supreme device to serve this end: the tool of his creative spirit to break out from the strait jacket of a drab world of realities, in which he figures as but an item in nature's merciless accounting system, into an imaginary world of unbounded ideals and schemes, where nature's laws of cause and effect, of rise and fall, of gain and loss appear suspended. Art seems to be man's striving to temper and to come to terms with nature.

"Coming to terms" implies an adversary. Yet man, whatever else he be, is a part of nature. So his artistic world cannot be one of sharply demarcated opposition to his natural world, but rather must be viewed as a fluid and continuous extension of his domain as ordinary member of animate nature, subject to all the limitations of biological reality,

*Reprinted from THE VISUAL ARTS TODAY, (Ed.: G. Kepes), Wesleyan University Press, Middletown, Conn., 1960: pp. 181-194.

into a realm of irreality of his own making, stripped of those limitations. And since artistic endeavor is thus a direct organic outgrowth of nature, its elements are, of necessity, the same as those of primitive biological experience. The tonal elements of music are no different in kind from those of warning or mating cries; lines and colors of nonobjective paintings are borrowed from the lines and colors that in the context of biological reality delineate, mark, and identify an object as prey or mate or enemy; and gastronomic treats are but recombinations of elements of chemical perception built into our biological organization for the vital, if lowly, task of screening the useful from the harmful in food for nourishment. These are truisms, and I doubt whether anyone would question them. Nature is credited with the supply of elements, but then man's fantasy is purported to take over to recombine them freely in novel patterns of his own creation.

Here is that sharp schism that needs blurring—and blurring from both ends. On the one hand, nature provides much more for our esthetic sense then elements; and, on the other, the free inventive recombination of elements for the creation of emergent novelty is not a privilege of man, although he has carried it to culmination, but is ingrained deeply in all works of nature. Because the schism is due as much to a certain "elementarian" brand of scientific orthodoxy as to the pretentious tenets of "estheticians," I feel impelled to try to rectify the warped perspective, at least from nature's end, in what a scientist—at least this scientist—would rate as a realistic view.

The argument will go about as follows: the universe is built and operates as a hierarchy of dynamic systems and subsystems, each with a defined degree of stability, individuality, autonomy, and durability on the level or in the order of magnitude in which it exists—from stellar bodies through populations, organisms, organs, cells. genes, molecules, atoms, down to subatomic particles. Those less conversant with the facts of science—and even some in science—have been deluded by a sort of shorthand atomistic vernacular, dating back to Democritus, into believing that nature in its scientific version is really nothing but a mechanical conglomeration of elementary colliding particles. As far as substance and energy are concerned, this formulation might be a passable one; yet it does no more than set the frame within which natural events must hold themselves—injunctions, in a sense, as to what *must not* happen. It can yield no specific information on just what *will* happen in given circumstances. The latter can be obtained only from observing and learning directly the behavior of the specific groupings in which the elements are combined into higher entities; the elements are no longer to be conceived as blind and independent agents, but recognized as forcibly restrained in their potential randomness by the higher collectives to which they belong. And it is the orderliness of these restraints which imposes upon the group the over-all regularity of pattern which marks the system as more than a pile of items assembled at random. (For a fuller discussion of this principle of hierarchic order, see chapters 17 and 18.)

The rule of order distinguishes organization from chaos. It must prevail wherever the activities and interactions of component parts are to be integrated and harmonized in the interest of serving the operation and preserving the integrity of the more complex unitary system. The nature, character, and state of the system as a whole remain conservatively stable beyond the flux and variations of its parts, which individually are unpredictable but whose constellation, though varying from moment to moment, is so regulated that the total pattern of activity remains essentially unaltered.

The living organism is such a system; so is each of its constituent cells. A cell remains basically the same despite the continuous reshuffling and exchange of its molecular populations; an organism remains essentially the same despite the incessant shifting, loss, and renewal of its member cells—just as a community can retain its character and structure despite the turnover in population from birth, death, and migration. These being natural systems of supra-elemental order, the establishment of the various rules of order controlling elemental behavior in such systems is as imperative a scientific task as is the description of the elements themselves.

Thus, scientific realism has come to correct its former faith in a naïvely mechanistic atomism by attesting the reality of regulated supra-elemental entities, which can be adequately known and treated only in their own right as integrated wholes. The existence of wholes, in which parts take appointed places in mutual harmony consonant with the total pattern and task, is an established fact of nature, not a privileged property and invention of the human mind.

This, then, concludes my argument. If nature were atomized and inherently chaotic, only creative mind could see and carve into it and from it those patterns of higher order to which we concede consistency and beauty. But nature is not atomized. Its patterning is inherent and primary, and the order underlying beauty is demonstrably there; what is more, human mind can perceive it only because it is itself part and parcel of that order.

But beauty to us connotes something more than sheer orderliness. It specifies a particular kind of orderliness. It postulates order compatible with uniqueness. This may sound like a paradox. The concept of order and regularity is something we can gain only through recurrences—the repetition of events in our experience; yet uniqueness refers to the singular and nonrecurrent. The paradox resolves itself if one considers the true hierarchical structure of nature, as outlined in the foregoing; for this admits of a measure of invariability, stability, and durability in a higher-level system, notwithstanding the variability and changing constellation of its more elementary components. In short, in nature the same over-all effect can recur with lawful regularity, although the detailed events by which it is attained will vary from case to case in ever-novel constellations—hence, be unique. All water runs downhill to the ocean, but the exact course of each rivulet and river is unique.

The lessons of a balanced view of nature can thus be summarized in a formula which bears a close resemblance to—and in my opinion is the root of—an esthetic code: order in the gross, and freedom, diversity, and uniqueness in the small, are not only compatible but are conjugated. This principle is exemplified in all processes of nature whose products have esthetic appeal. A few examples are presented haphazard in the following. They have been culled from a larger list illustrated in an earlier article.* The main points are the following.

(1) The pleasing aspects of organic forms stem from their high degree of general regularity combined with an infinite variety of detail. (2) The order expressed in the developed form, however, is but the result of the orderliness of the underlying formative processes which have led to the formed product and have left their imprint on it: what we read in the finished form is the historic record of its formation. (3) Even if two organic systems were to start out in absolute identity, the fact that in their subsequent developmental histories they would be faced with nonidentical incidents and environmental contingencies would necessarily make for divergence in the details of their final

*Beauty and the Beast: Life and the Rule of Order. Scientific Monthly, vol. 81: 286-299. 1955.

products. (4) Yet, since their over-all results still turn out to be reasonably similar, we realize that capricious and unpredictable deviations from the standard course must have been kept, if not strictly in line, certainly within a safe margin by the governing action of their respective systems, which resist disruption; a system owes its orderly self-realization and self-preservation to its very capacity to moderate or compensate the excesses of its members. (5) The over-all result thus gives us the satisfying impression of a collective task well accomplished by the harmonious cooperation under mutual control of members of a group which, but for these restraints, would yield blind chaos. (6) The viability of an organic form depends on the precarious balance between rigidity of over-all design on the one hand and flexibility of adjustment left to its execution on the other; too much aberrance one side or the other would jeopardize survival. This is the biological foundation of what we call "sense of proportions."

Let us now turn to practical examples. They deal with forms of organisms and their parts—form in the sense of the orderly disposition of parts in space. A lengthwise section through a snail's shell (Fig. 1) shows a pattern of astounding regularity: the pattern and proportions of coiling remain the same from turn to turn, while the dimensions increase in a steady progression. The shell being the incrusted growth record of the animal, its beauty simply reflects the rule of order in the growth process. It is not surprising that for nearly 250 years, since the days of Réaumur, the subject of mollusk shells has attracted the joint

Figure 1

attention of biologists, mathematicians, and students of design. In general, this growth pattern conforms to a curve known as a logarithmic or equiangular spiral. It has many remarkable properties, for instance the one shown in the diagram (Fig. 2), which illustrates that the ratio of any two successive segments meeting at identical angles (in this case $90°$) is constant. As the curve lengthens or "grows," the geometric similitude of successive sectors is preserved. What this implies in actual fact is simply that the width of the turns increases at a fixed ratio to their length. (The actual value of the only ratio satisfying this condition is 1.618:1.)

The beauty of the shell, which lies in its law of growth, has thus been reduced to mathematical formulation. The value of 1.618 has been the subject of serious as well as playful speculation. It is related to what the Greeks termed the divine section, now better known as the golden mean. It gives the proportions of a rectangle in which the smaller side bears the same relationship to the larger one as the larger one bears to the sum of both. Art and architecture of antiquity and Renaissance have made ample use of this highly satisfying proportion. But its biological sense lies in its intrinsic relationship to the logarithmic spiral.

Growth that is steady and equal in all directions ("proportional"), as in this first example, leaves the impression of continuing evolution, which lets our fantasy, once it has grasped the law of growth, extrapolate the momentary product before us into imaginary forms of the same shape gigantically enlarged. Perhaps this "open-endedness" adds vividness to our impression. What we then see is no longer the

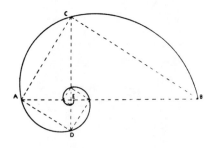

Figure 2

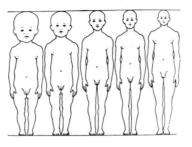

Figure 3

Figure 4

static product, but the dynamic process that has produced it and carries on into a distant future—the specimen being but a sample stage from a time course of unending change, but change within a rather rigid law that stipulates proportionality.

In most forms of organisms the law of growth is much less simple. For instance, if one compares the proportions of the human body at various ages from birth to maturity in reference to the length of the trunk as unit (Fig. 3), one notes that the head grows relatively more slowly, while the extremities grow significantly faster. If carried further than it goes in man, this process of disproportionate growth may lead to rather grotesque forms, as for instance in the fiddler crab (Fig. 4), in which one claw tends to outgrow the rest of the body.

Steadiness of growth is likewise not the ordinary rule. Growth usually proceeds in spurts, with alternating phases of acceleration and retardation or even temporary arrest. If a stylus recording the ups and downs of temperature or barometric pressure writes on a moving tape, it leaves a tracing of the time course of fluctuations. Similarly, the

Figure 5

pattern of tree rings is a tracing of the seasonal variations in the growth
history of the tree. And many patterns of rhythmic banding, striping,
or segmentation in animals are likewise the residual traces of trains of
pulsed production phases during development (Fig. 5). But in contrast
to the tree-ring pattern, which is dictated by the outside climate, the
latter patterns reside in an intrinsic periodicity as inherent in the law of
growth itself as the beat is intrinsic to the heart. And just as the heart
can function only if the actions of all its countless muscle elements are
coordinated and synchronized so that by alternate contractions and
relaxations they can jointly act as a pump, so the pleasing rhythms
displayed in the designs of animals are evidence of the rule of order
exercised by the system over its subordinate elements. A wave could
not arise if each member of the group were to act on its own as
independent agent. A wave front signifies that all points along the front
are beating in unison and pass their rhythm on to the rest of the
system. The system thus submits to coordination, in contrast to
anarchic behavior, in which each element arbitrarily sets its own phase
and its own pace of action unrelated to the others, the whole becoming
a blur of randomness with no design whatever. On the other hand, we
must not forget that even the regular wave, when viewed from close
range, will at any one moment show capricious singularities that will
never recur in quite the same form. In other words, order in the *gross*
does not rule out uniqueness of *detail*, and vice versa.

However, the mechanical wave produced by synchronous rhythmic
excitation, as in the water wave or the acoustic sound, is not the only
model of periodic pattern. At least two other types of different origin
become conspicuous; in both, the inducing agent itself is steady and

continuous, but the excited system translates the steady action into a rhythmically discontinuous response, upgrading, as it were, the degree of order. For brevity, we may refer to these two response mechanisms as "thresholds" and "nucleation."

The prototype of a threshold mechanism is the dripping faucet, where water feeds the drops continuously, but the drops break off only periodically as their weight overcomes cohesion. The same principle builds dunes in sand (Fig. 6): the steady wind piles sand as high as friction will hold it, which leaves a sheltered valley on the lee side, until at a certain distance past the shielded region the wind can become effective again, and so on down the plain. Mechanical determinacy is here replaced by the orderly result of probability, with evidently a wider latitude of expression—or, if one wishes to call it that, a higher content of uniqueness—but still not randomness.

Nucleation occurs whenever at a point in a material continuum there is initiated a change which spreads infectiously from point to point but which is of the kind that depletes the resources in its own neighborhood. An epidemic with immunity in its wake would be a fair analogy. The streaks of clouds on a mackerel sky (Fig. 7) are bands of condensed vapor which have starved the intervening clear zones of that commodity. As one will readily realize, this rhythm is the result of the competition of nucleated zones for limited supplies, the law of order being that no new center can survive too close to an existing one.

In the development of organisms we may expect such patterns to arise wherever local processes are in competition for something from their surroundings, so that another process of the same kind would have

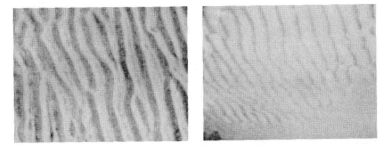

Figure 6　　　　　　　　　　Figure 7

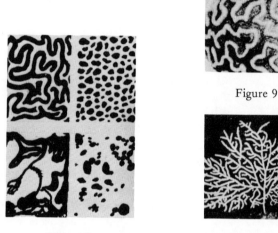

Figure 9

Figure 8   Figure 10

no chance to get started concurrently, except at a safe distance where it can assert its own competitive strength. As a result, there will remain blank no man's lands between the active centers, dividing the space continuum into harmonious patterns of rhythmically alternating properties.

In Fig. 8 the types of ordered patterns resulting from such group dynamics are contrasted with those to be expected from sheer randomness. The left quadrants show two patterns of continuous lines: the lower one, of random dimensions and distribution; the upper one, of more regular arrangement, the rule of order being that the line retains its average width and remains separated from a neighboring line by a standard margin. The right half of the diagram shows this same principle for discontinuous systems. The esthetic (not necessarily artistic) superiority of the upper over the lower is apparent. Although the lack of symmetry marks them as of a lower degree of order than that of our previous examples, they still contrast agreeably with the capriciously disordered randomness of their right-hand counterparts.

A few examples may illustrate how this principle of harmonious space-filling has been implemented in organisms and their parts. A brain coral (Fig. 9) looks like a direct embodiment of the symbolic line pattern of the last diagram. Note how the seafan coral (Fig. 10)

Figure 11

Figure 12

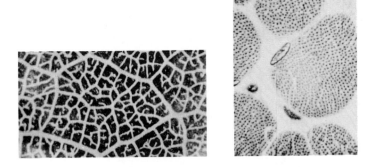

Figure 13

Figure 14

distributes its branches with the same average density throughout the structure, with no big holes nor overcrowding anywhere. The same pattern is found in the dendritic processes of a single nerve cell of the cerebellum (Fig. 11), or in the gastrovascular arborizations of the fluke (Fig. 12), or finally, perhaps the prettiest of them all, in the venation of a leaf (Fig. 13). All these are continuous line systems, branched with or without anastomoses, but always of regulated density.

Next is an example of harmonious but discontinuous filling of a given space. A cross section through a muscle (Fig. 14) shows the individual large muscle fibers set off in space, keeping their distance. If we single out one such fiber, we note that it is dotted with smaller discrete elements, the myofibrils, appearing in cross section as black stippling. We may pick out one such black dot and magnify it enormously under the electron microscope (Fig. 15). A whole island here corresponds to one little dot of the preceding picture (the whole width of the illustration corresponds to approximately one micron). We observe now that each fibril is once more subdivided into a regular array of smaller units hexagonally packed and tentatively identified as the contractile protein chains of myosin and actin. Exemplified here is the identical principle of orderly packing repeated in three magnitudes, from the macroscopic down to the molecular. If we view these same cylindrical units in profile instead of in cross section (Fig. 16), we note a regular lengthwise periodicity with bands and interbands, giving the muscle fiber in the aggregate its familiar cross-striated aspect. Now this rhythmic pattern owes its origin to yet another principle. It is produced by the stacking in tandem of molecular units of standard length, much like the coupling of coaches in making up a railroad train.

Such geometric stacking and spacing patterns along grids of varying degrees of regularity are the crux of organic form. Their elements may be molecules, as in Fig. 16, or single cells, as in the rows of scales covering the wings of butterflies (Fig. 17), or cell groups, as in the rasp on a snail's tongue (Fig. 18). But all of them are subject to a framework of supra-elemental order.

Thus the common element of appeal we have discovered in these manifold patterns is their nonrandomness—the presence of some rule of ordered distribution of units. It starts in the molecular realm and pervades the living structure all the way up to its harmonious total form. Yet, as I have tried to stress, the final harmony we visually admire is but the product of the rules of harmony that have governed its makings. In all these cases we have been dealing with the ordered reactions of orderly elements to an ordered set of conditions, and the result is order. It is this rule of order that we perceive as beauty.

Yet, looking back over the whole series of our examples, we realize that this is order without minute precision, order within which there is scope. Therefore let us not confound rule with fixity, order with rigor, regularity with the concept of stereotypes. Each individual is a unique form of expression of general norms and laws. This uniqueness wants to be acknowledged and appreciated. It reveals the absolute stereotype as fiction, unnatural, unorganic, nonviable if it existed. Observation of nature thus justifies our instinctive rebellion against the stereotype, against a concept of order so mechanized and rigid as to make no

Figure 15

Figure 16

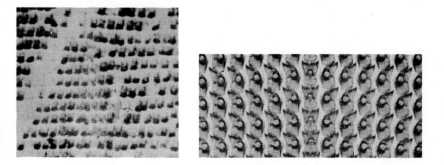

Figure 17

Figure 18

allowance for some degree of latitude for the individual events within it. True organic order, as we know it, sets only the general frame and pattern, leaving the precise ways of execution adjustable and, to this extent, indeterminate. Aesthetically, the principle finds expression in the superiority of handicraft, with no two objects wholly congruous, over the monotony of serial machine production. Biologically, it manifests itself in the superiority of laws of development which prescribe only the mode of procedure but leave the actual execution free to adapt itself to the exigencies of a world whose details are themselves unpredictable.

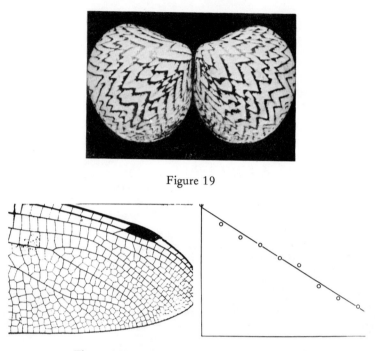

Figure 19

Figure 20   Figure 21

If there is any lesson in the study of organic nature, it is that there is order in the gross with freedom of excursion in the small. Our sense of beauty only confirms it, for it combines pleasure in contemplating the gross, over-all order with appreciation of pleasing variations of detail. Let me show this once more in concrete form. Fig. 19 shows the two halves of the bivalve shell of a single animal. Our first impression is one of exquisite symmetry. Both patterns show, indeed, the very same character. Yet, if we try to compare the details, we promptly notice how greatly they diverge one from the other. Or take another case: the wing of the dragonfly (Fig. 20) shows meshes in its network which in their outlines and positions are individually as unique and arbitrary as the pattern of crackled enamel on a pot; only in general, one notes a gradient of density and numbers from the upper to the lower margin. I subdivided this wing into nine equal horizontal strips and counted the number of meshes within each. Plotted serially, these numbers closely fit a straight line (Fig. 21). This line then symbolizes the general law of

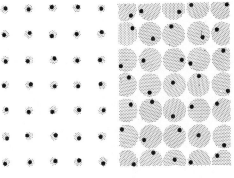

Figure 22

distribution. But just as important as this standard course are the individual deviations of the actual values from the mean, which will be different in each individual case. It is these very differences that make for diversity of individual accomplishment within the rule; they make the individual organism unique, interesting, and, above all, viable.

There is a message, therefore, in the beauty of living things, a message I should like to summarize in a last diagram (Fig. 22). It represents two systems of order as two identical lattices of equidistant points defined by the centers of the stippled circles. The circles symbolize the range within which a black dot inside is free to roam—a range that is much wider in the right than in the left half. The black dots mark the station of individual items or events within the system—for instance, that of atoms in a crystal, cells in a tissue, or organisms in a group. I have let them assume random positions. Now note that in spite of this factor of uncertainty, or, if one wishes, of individual self-expression, the pattern as a whole is well preserved and stands out clearly in the left half; whereas on the right it is completely lost. Does not this spell out for us an organic design for living? Freedom within the law: responsible freedom to move within an orbit as wide as, but no wider than, what is compatible with the preservation of the over-all order that defines the harmony of relationships on which effective living and survival depend. To judge just what the right proportions are calls for a "sense of proportions," to borrow a term from esthetics.

In summary, this has been a very sketchy attempt to show that one can seek and find the roots of art and its philosophy in nature. Man with his powers of perception and aesthetic appreciation is one of nature's products, just as much as are the patterns of organic forms which he perceives in nature around him—the take-off points for his flights of artistic imagination; hence they are both of the same kind of origin and order. If in the limited space of a brief essay it has been impossible to present more than the seed of the idea, perhaps some future effort by one more competent to do so may bring it to germination.

One Plus One Does Not Equal Two*

In school we learned that one apple plus one apple makes two apples. One apple and one pear is just one apple and one pear. If we choose to ignore "appleness" and "pearness," being concerned only with weights and numbers, as, for instance, in counting and weighing parcels for postal shipment, apples and pears would, of course, be reduced to just so many items, to be tallied by sheer summation. In equating such items, we gain as well as lose. We gain an easy way of measurement, but lose what nowadays would be called "information content." Apples and pears do not become alike; we simply discount their differences for a particular purpose.

But can we ever retrieve information about distinctive features once we have tossed it out? If not, can science, as man's striving for as complete and rational a picture of the universe as is obtainable to him by observation, experiment, and logic, stoop to trading loss of information content for the simplicity, convenience and, yes, true elegance, of blotting out distinctiveness based on disparity; for instance, between pears and apples? In fact, in nature, even two apples cannot be equated, if one lies rotting on the ground while the other, still growing, hangs on the tree.

In short, all algebra applied to nature implies abstraction. Sheer adding up always leaves out some relevant information. Whether such omission is passable depends on our purpose, and that, in turn, depends entirely upon our special interest. And since interest, by definition, connotes biased self-limitation, the information thus gained remains incomplete, short of the comprehensiveness to which science in its professed universality aspires. So, how sure can we be that sheer analysis alone—the physical or mental dissolution of a complex into a

*Reprinted from THE NEUROSCIENCES: A Study Program (Ed.: Gardner C. Quarton, Theodore Melnechuk, Francis O. Schmitt) Rockefeller University Press, 1967. pp. 801-821.—Also in P.A. Weiss, LIFE, ORDER, AND UNDERSTANDING. Special Supplement to THE GRADUATE JOURNAL, vol. 8. Austin, Texas, 1970.

shambles of measurable but disconnected units—does not irretrievably destroy highly relevant data about nature? Is Phoenix, rising from its ashes, a true image of nature or just a myth?

In our day, the answers to such questions have become a matter of faith. The success story of learning more and more about less and less, which in the present context means about ever smaller fragments of nature, has grooved our faith in nature as an assembly plant of microevents. No doubt faith in the omnipotence of analytical decomposition has opened the mainsprings for the stream of scientific progress. What we are apt to overlook in our enthusiasm is that there are other sources which could powerfully augment that stream were they not left to dissipate and dry up for doctrinal reasons. Doctrine has barred them from joining the mainstream by artificially erected walls, by conceptual injunctions against admixtures from sources suspected as contaminated because they failed to pass the orthodox test of purity, namely, that *one* plus *one* must be made to equal *two*.

The unorthodox dissenters usually phrased their argument in the age-old adage that "the whole is *more* than the sum of its parts." Look at this phrasing and you will discover the root of the distrust, and indeed, outright rejection, of the valid principle behind it. What did they mean by stating that "an organism is *more* than the sum of its cells and humors"; that "a cell is *more* than its content of molecules"; that "brain function is *more* than the aggregate of activities of its constituent neurons"; and so on? As the term "more" unquestionably connotes some tangible addition, an algebraic plus, one naturally had to ask: "More of what? Dimensions, mass, electric charges?" Surely none of those. Then what? Perhaps something unfathomable, weightless, chargeless, nonmaterial? All sorts of agents have indeed been invoked in that capacity—entelechy, *élan vital*, formative drive, vital principle—all idle words, unpalatable to most scientists for being just fancy names for an unknown X.

Unfortunately, in their aversion to the supernatural, the scientific purists poured out the baby with the intellectually soiled bath water by repudiating the very aspects of wholeness in nature that had conjured up those cover terms for ignorance. And as a prophylactic against their resurgence, they fostered a militantly doctrinaire "reductionism," which axiomatically prescribed that all the relevant macroinformation about nature must, and eventually will, be derived completely from adding up and piecing together the microinformations about the smallest sample units. Never mind that physics had to give up that claim gradually as Boltzmann's thermodynamics, Planck's quantum theory, and Heisenberg's uncertainty principle came on the scene. The life sciences have failed to follow suit and break out of the strait jacket of a doctrine for which their own subject matter furnished the most telling disproof. They might have come around more readily, though, if they had realized that systems with aspects of wholeness are by no means confined to living nature, but are of universal occurrence. In fact, their very universality should clear them of the stigma of vitalism.

Let me take a further step toward destigmatization by pointing to a veiled source of confusion that seems to have confounded past dealings with the problem—the failure to distinguish between a natural phenomenon as such and the symbols of language we have to use in order to describe it. A phenomenon to which we ascribe wholeness is certainly not *more* in algebraic terms than the sum of elementary phenomena composing it. It just is *different*. The difference is that between matter and structure. If there is a "more" involved, it lies in the terms of our description. It is we who, as describers, feel compelled to add extra terms of information for the sake of making the description of the integral phenomenon complete and pertinent.

This neutral and philosophically noncommittal characterization of the problem tries to allay, or if you prefer, circumvent, the present warfare of dogmas. It should soothe the apprehensions of those who have built faith in absolute reductionism as bulwark against onslaughts on their sense of intellectual security, and it should assure those others who felt disenfranchised because of their holist faith, their day in court. There is a current fad to present the subject matter of the life sciences in terms of a dogmatic schism—an antithesis of "molecular" and "organismic" biology, professing a reductionist and a holistic philosophy, respectively. The former is respected for its "rugged naturalism," the latter suspected of flirting romantically with the supernatural. What I shall try to show is that exclusive commitment to either thesis is unnatural. The molecular and the organismic are but two different vantage points from which to look at living systems, neither of them granting a monopoly to insight. They are complementary and co-equal. To document this proposition is the main object of the following discourse; I hope that it will serve as an object lesson.

Specifically, these are the points I aim to prove: (1) that as our brain scans features of the universe we shift range and focus back and forth between telescopic and microscopic vision, as it were; (2) that as we move downward on this scale, we mostly gain precision and lose perspective; (3) that as we move upward, new and relevant features, formerly unrecognizable and unsuspected, come into view; (4) that this emerging novelty pertains to macrosamples of nature—that is, that it reflects properties of *collectives*—of groups, assemblies, systems, and populations, composed of microsamples; and (5) that the required additional terms to characterize such collectives must come from rigorous scientific procedure rather than from anthropomorphic translocutions and allegorical allusions to mythology.

And now I turn from these somewhat pedantic generalities, which to some presumably will seem commonplace, to practical examples by which the validity of those five points can be tested. A brief glossary of our terms of reference may serve as introduction. Let us ask first: Of what do we deprive a system when we dismember it and isolate its component parts, whether bodily or just in our mind? Plainly, of the *interrelations* that had existed among the parts while they were still united. So, in trying to reconstruct the system from the fragments, whether bodily like Humpty-Dumpty, or symbolically in our imagination, we must make up for the deprivation by adding a proper term that specifies the lost relations. This may simply amount to adding vectors to algebraic terms. The requirements for added specifications will vary with the different degrees of order emerging from the union (or reunion) of elements combined in groups. The simplest case involves only a loose and widely variable relation, such as "togetherness"; it displays novelty, but little order. If, besides novelty, the collective shows regularities of pattern which recur with a high degree of invariance, we confer upon it the designation "organized."

But here again we would do well to make a further distinction between true and merely simulated organization. We must distinguish between the genuine order, such as emerges within a group by virtue of its intrinsic dynamics, and a mere semblance of order, such as an aggregate of unrelated units acquires by imposition or imputation from without. Examples of the latter are puppets, or the proverbial camel our fantasy projects into a cloud, or, in fact, any effigy of a natural system, as in the following instance.

Figure 1

Figure 1 shows a meaningless array of dots in inert coexistence, with nothing recognizably in common besides the paper they were printed on. Yet, from a greater distance or, what is the same, at lower magnification (inset), we recognize them as the component bits of information about a continuous, well-structured image. That image, of course, is dead; the dots of printer's ink composing it are physically as unrelated as fly specks. What gives the picture its meaningful integration, are we, the viewers, with our eyes and brain. The dots do not "add up." We add to them. From this we learn that discontinuous and discrete elements can give us the illusion of continuity, but that the mere aspect of continuity alone is no test of inner coherence. Let me pursue this further.

Figure 2 is a picture of the spiral galaxy, Andromeda. Now, if you ask what Andromeda consists of, a census taker would reply, "So-and-so many stars"; a chemist might come forth with spectroscopically discernible distinctions. But would either of these answers add up to a definition of a spiral pattern? Certainly not. Nor would a scientist be happy if the additional feature were taken care of by invoking the magic act of "a spiralizer."

Figure 2

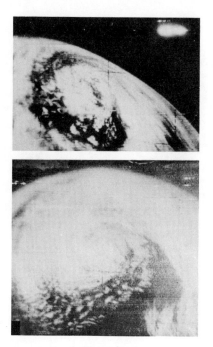

Figure 3

Closer to earth, Figure 3 shows photographs taken by the first weather satellite, Tyros. Note the cyclonic cloud pattern. But what are clouds in analytic view? Droplets of water. Now, could knowing all there is to be known about H_2O ever add up to a picture of this configuration? Of course not: the winds that have shaped it remain invisible. In Christina Rossetti's words,

> "Who has seen the wind? Neither you nor I.
> But when the trees bow down their heads,
> the wind is passing by."

So, here we meet the first caveat against willful isolation of an object from its natural context.

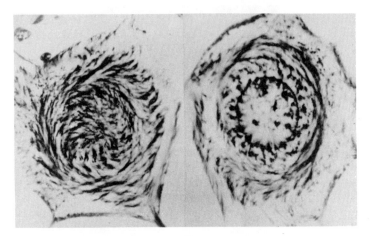

Figure 4

More spirals next, in Figure 4: the neurofibrils in the large motor cells innervating the electric organ of the torpedo fish. To say that these fibrils are made of protein will neither describe nor explain their spiral course. Indeed, from what we now know about their formation, the picture is just a photographic still, a momentary sample of a continuously unwinding record of motion in that cell. These spirals are but the residual traces of a moving stream of substance, the pattern of which must be sought in regularities of the underlying dynamics.

Here lies a general and basic lesson. What we perceive as static form is but the product, transitory or lasting, of formative *processes*. The features of the product—for instance, its geometry—can provide us with clues for the dynamics that underlie those processes. For instance, the counterclockwise spiral spin of water running off a bathtub drain is but an indicator of an asymmetry of forces resulting from the earth's rotation. The order we perceive in structured form thus is not primary, but the expression of the dynamic patterns that have engendered it. Yet this is only a beginning. Through their results, dynamics modify the setting for subsequent dynamics. Dynamically created forms, if somehow consolidated, become molds for the course of further activity. Free-flowing water grooves its bed until the bed begins to channel further flow, as in this instance (Figure 5) of a spiral spout carved by the twisted course of water that drained from a glacier bottom in the glacial age. Once formed, the spiral structure becomes self-perpetuating, gaining in polish and perfection by more erosion.

In passing, let me point out that by this dual action, a whorl can serve as a general model of how dynamic patterns tend not only to preserve, but in further consequence to accentuate, their self-engendered structures. I wish to stress this because of the obvious bearing the general two-step principle has on our understanding of brain mechanisms: of grooving, habit formation, facilitation, and learning theory. If taken seriously and followed up, it might dispose of the necessity of placing rigid fixation and plasticity of neural functions—instincts versus memory—into sharply divided categories, each run on a different principle.

Returning to our main line, we have recognized the spiral wall of the glacial mill as the dead effigy of the unitary dynamic sweep pattern

Figure 5

that has created it. The spiral composition of an artist (Figure 6) is, similarly, the projection on dead canvas of some dynamic process, obeying mathematical terms for spirality, that has been going on in the artist's creative brain. Attempts to resolve this act to mere terms of numerical plurality, whether of neurons or of intraneuronal molecules, would seem to me to be as futile as to derive the spirality of a spiral nebula from our knowledge of single isolated stars.

By now I have exposed three propositions. First, that collectives tend to display novel features not discernible in their component units, hence justly called "emergent"; second, that such features are indicative of the existence of significant *relationships* among the members of the collective, such relationships being severed by physical or mental separation of the members from each other; and, third, that whenever

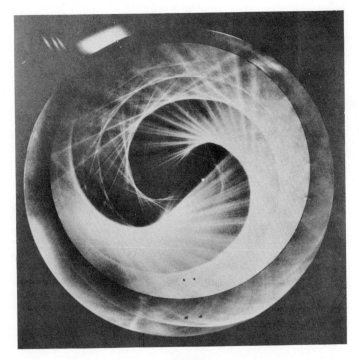

Figure 6

one is faced with static geometric regularities of patterns, he ought to look beyond them—or, rather, behind them—for the rules in the play of forces that have shaped them. In thus raising the sights from statics to dynamics, static *interrelations* become dynamic *interactions*, and in the case of self-sustaining systems with the conservative features of wholeness, simple *interactions* become *interdependencies. States* then appear as but cross-sections through trains of *behavior* along the time-line, *scalar* values must be supplemented by *vectorial* interconnections, and vector systems of specifiable integral properties become realities. Let us then keep in mind that this progression from *elements* to *groups* objectively reflects the ascending scale of supplemental statements we need for adequate description of corresponding objects of our experience. I shall then present samples of such phenomena in that order. By choosing them from various points along that scale, I intend to blur the artificial dichotomy between modes of thought centered either on *elements* or on *continua*, each to the exclusion or invalidation of the other.

I shall use the example of *form* as master indicator of order. Its simplest examples are plain aggregates of identical units stacking up flank-to-flank or end-to-end, according to steric fitting, like key to lock, and chemical conformances. The macromolecular units of the blood pigment of a marine worm (Figure 7), each consisting of six subunits

Figure 7

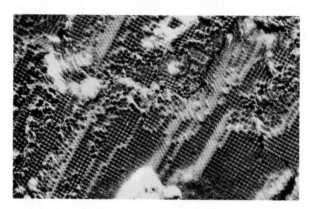

Figure 8

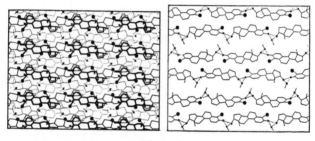

Figure 9

around a hole, stack up in contact: molecules as "modules." The only novelty by which the group differs from a mere sum of units is its predominantly planar array—a significant, yet low, degree of order. The stacking of virus particles (Figure 8), in its near-crystalline configuration, falls in the same class, although the forces interlinking the units so regularly are not equally obvious.

A polymer, as I shall show later, is a linear chain of identical links with couplings, end-to-end, like a railroad train. The linkage represents a first step of order in the assembly. The straightening of the chain from random coils to rectilinearity requires an additional step of ordering. For short lengths, intermolecular forces may serve as an explanation, but ruler-straight arrays over great distances undoubtedly must be referred to straightening effects from the environment; for instance, stretch. Common direction may be imposed by a further polarizing interaction with the environment. And so, in order to describe the formation of, for instance, a connective-tissue fiber, we must construct steps of ever more specifications.

The stacking of lipid molecules into lamellar systems of the so-called smectic state (Figure 9) extends the same principle to *two* dimensions. Here, too, the environment enters as an ordering factor in that it offers to the molecules, as scaffolding for their own planar self-array, a planar interface between two immiscible media. Lacking such guidance, the molecules cluster into so-called micelles (Figure 10), yet by no means as random conglomerations, but in orderly structural patterns determined by their own collective interactions. For each of them the others are part of its environment—a forward reference to our conclusion that the notion of independent "elements" is, in itself, an abstraction, for in reality elements are part and parcel of a single, undivided continuum that embraces units and environment as one integral entity.

Yet, clearly, structural group order in these past examples can still be satisfactorily explained in essence by the microprecise automatic assembly of individual units and subunits, united like an erector set by their steric, chemical, and electrical properties. Such rigid compounding processes can hardly serve as star witnesses in our suit for a divorce from the one-plus-one-equals-two precept of thought. Therefore, let me proceed to a series of further samples, representative of higher-order systems. These are collectives of the following description: their features, "on the whole," show well-defined *regularities* of pattern, recurring consistently from specimen to specimen in each given class; but as one looks at smaller and smaller samples, similitude and regularity decline until, having descended to the elements, one can no longer find any hint of what the structure of the total complex might be like. This is because the *details* of pattern are in each case *unique*, no two microsamples being ever alike, even though the *composite pattern of the whole*, case after case, is of the same standard form. Contrary to the preceding examples, the order of the whole can here no longer be

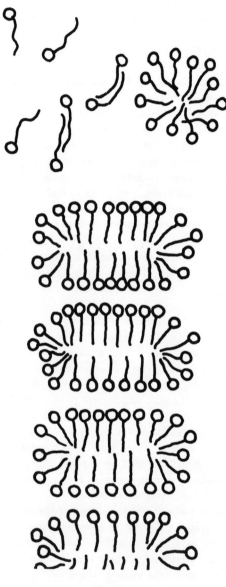

Figure 10

predicted from a simple upward projection of the elemental properties of single units stacked up in module fashion. The following illustrations will make this more specific.

Take, for instance, the bed of blood capillaries in a tissue (Figure 11). They branch and re-anastomose almost at random, yet the resultant network offers an aspect of great over-all regularity. Descriptively, the regularity is reflected in the near-constancy of distances between the branches; dynamically, it reflects a growth pattern elaborated by interactions of the component branches, both among one another and with the cellulated matrix they pervade. In oversimplified terms, the interactions involved are a type of *competition*. This, then, is interaction no longer in contiguity, but at a distance. Each branch may be viewed as surrounded by a shell of influences of graded strengths—*domains*, which keep each other at a respectful standard distance. The term "domain" is used in forward reference to subsequent comments on field and gradient principles.

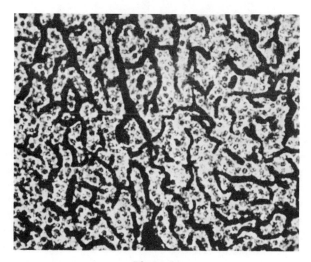

Figure 11

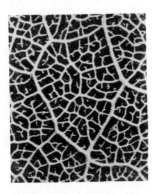

Figure 12

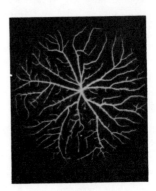

Figure 13

Figure 14

A botanical counterpart to the capillary bed is the venation of a leaf
(Figure 12). But let me at once dispel the notion that growth patterns
of this type are a preserve of organisms. The next picture (Figure 13),
for instance, shows the lightninglike pattern of an electrostatic
discharge from a point source. Ideally, it should, of course, be radial but
in reality, the unpredictable variations of conductance and resistance,
resulting from the random inhomogeneities of the medium through
which it has to travel, establish spearheads for separate and competing
ionization tracks. Despite this capriciousness in detail, the total picture
still emerges as one of systemic order. Growth patterns of snowflakes
(Figure 14) also show infinite variation of detail within a high degree of
constancy of the over-all form of the growing crystal.

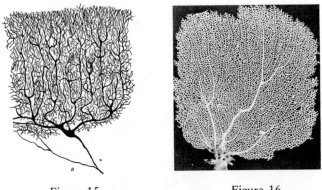

Figure 15   Figure 16

The growth pattern of a nerve cell from the cerebellum (Figure 15) reveals the same rule: the same degree of unpredictability of the details of ramification, yet at the ends great uniformity of distribution among the terminal branchlets. While it is their environment—the matrix of the brain—that offers to the advancing branches a warp and woof of easy pathways, the decision of which of them will be utilized, and in what force and microdistribution, is indeterminate, left to be decided at each branching point by the actual local competition for the limited supply of substance arriving from the common cell body. So, if the common source may have had a "program" for the attainment of the highly regular end result, the precise way of how to get there could certainly not have been spelled out in it in great detail. For those ways are different and unique for each of the millions of cells. The double meaning of the word "design" comes to our mind: design as purposeful planning at the start, ending in stereotyped design as accomplishment, but countless ways of execution leading from one to the other.

Extending our examples upward, Figure 16 pictures a lace coral—a limestone housing development of both great over-all regularity and individual uniqueness, built by thousands of separate little animals in the colony in a concerted pattern of behavior. You may sense already my own design. It is to reorient thinking from static *form* to formative *behavior* across all orders of magnitude. The range extends beyond the

Figure 17

coral colony to human society and to what I take to be its design for living, and indeed, survival: namely, to recognize that individual freedom in the *small* is compatible with the existence of collective order in the *gross*, which reconciles self-determination of the individual with the much stricter frame of rules descriptive of his group.

Were it not for this principle of nature, were the development of every part or branch allowed to pursue its own capricious course without constraints, without a frame of integral interdependencies, we could not have trees (Figure 17) that we could categorize distinctly by their shapes as oaks or pines or poplars even though each specimen is individually unique. Such standardized end form defies any logical attempt to regard the product as just the blind outcome of a bunch, or call it a sum, of microprecisely programmed cause-effect sequences of linear chain reactions in the sense of a naive mechanical machine concept.

The conclusion that countless constellations of convergent micro-events may yield macroproducts of essentially the same standard pattern makes it, by the same token, gratuitous to assume that similar terminal patterns must have had similar mechanisms and histories in common. The treelike pattern of the Colorado River delta (Figure 18)

Figure 18

Figure 19

will prove the point. Let us go on then and reverse the outgrowth pattern of the tree and we obtain the picture of a river forming by junctions of tributaries from many sources; but also, similarly, the inverse "arborization" of cracks in crystals advancing from edge to interior in stepwise confluence (Figure 19, from top to bottom).

Let us now move up to the next step of complexity. Our past examples have been relatively simple. They dealt with interactions among parts of systems which, after all, were still connected and continuous in substance—blood vessels, leaf veins, trees, rivers, etc.

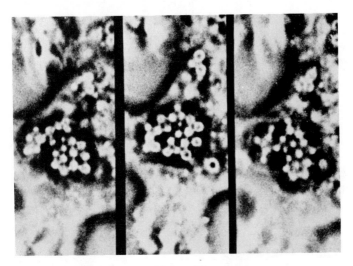

Figure 20

Order emerging in complexes of disconnected, discrete units taxes our explanatory faculties far more severely. As introduction to the subject, I chose Figure 20—three frames from a motion picture film of one and the same cell in tissue culture at brief intervals. They show a group of granules, each about one micron in size. These granules are separate bodies, freely mobile, bouncing around in the soft cell plasma. But as they change positions, they assume preferentially characteristic geometric group configurations—mostly hexagonal, but intermittently an occasional square. Now, since they are separated by appreciable distances, we must infer that in their random buffeting by Brownian motion, they are transitionally stabilized—trapped, as it were—at equidistant equilibrium points in a field of forces established by their mutual interactions, like partners in a square dance or quadrille. If this sounds vague, consider that we can at least describe the various fleeting configurations with relative precision, even though we do not know the actual dynamics defining the grid.

There are other cases, however, in which the operation of group dynamics has lent itself to more concrete definition. Since they demonstrate most cogently that going beyond the one-plus-one-equals-two rule does not mean giving up scientific discipline for the outer space of supernaturality, I shall dwell on them somewhat more extensively.

Let us take two bodies (Figure 21), as centers of emanations and force fields extending radially into the environment, and let them move toward each other from a great distance. Beyond a certain range, interactions between the two are as negligible as the effect of gravitational attraction by the moon is on our stance. Yet as we bring them closer (Figure 22) and as the overlap of their domains increases, their joint effects depart increasingly from the result one would expect from a sheer superposition and algebraic summation of their single contributions. They mutually distort each other's sovereign patterns of action.

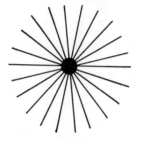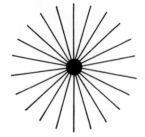

Figure 21

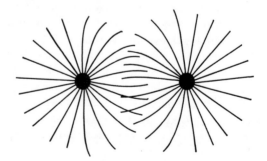

Figure 22

In atomic dimensions, for instance, this yields the redistribution of electrons between atoms (ligand fields), deforming the erstwhile

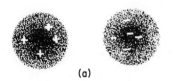

(a)

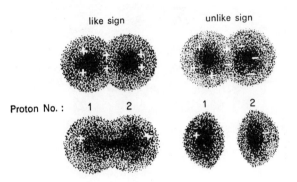

like sign   unlike sign

Proton No. :   1   2   1   2

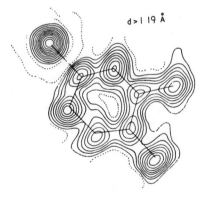

Figure 23

d > 1 19 Å

Figure 24

spherical electron clouds, as shown in Figure 23 (bottom line). The dumbbell-shaped interaction pattern seen in the figure at the left is typical of many cases. The next picture (Figure 24) shows the mapping

Figure 25

of electron distribution in a small organic molecule (specifically a diaminochloropyramidine). Such a continuous field pattern emerges from the group interaction of the constituent atoms and atomic groups, which formerly were envisaged and represented as discrete, neatly bounded entities. More complex molecules—for instance, the protein, myoglobin, shown in Figure 25 in the so-called Patterson projection of its subunit fields—yield maps of still more sophisticated collective fingerprints. One is reminded of the contour maps of mountain ranges. Domains of particles are no more truly isolated than are mountain peaks.

My reason for showing these diagrams is that they express symbolically that patterned processes in space and time form *continua*. To single out and fence in mentally, in such continua, peaks, centers,

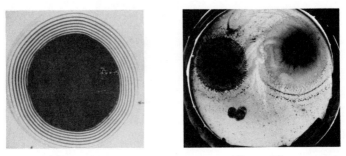

Figure 26   Figure 27

foci, or what not, corporeally isolated from their context, has long been a legitimate abstraction of immense tactical and practical utility in science. Yet, he who forgets that it is basically an abstraction could as well end up trying to extract the center of gravity from a body. One recognizes a kinship between this latter trend and some of the old notions, still not totally extinct, about brain centers as the "seats" of specific functions.

Familiar and accepted as the preceding propositions are for the molecular realm, their equal validity for higher levels, through the cellular to the social, has rarely been pointed up, let along studied and conclusively proven.

Let me again start from an inorganic model, the so-called rings of Liesegang (Figure 26). A drop of silver salt dropped on a gelatin plate that had been soaked in a chromate solution lays down, as it slowly diffuses, periodic concentric rings of insoluble silver chromate. The rhythmic character stems from some sort of threshold phenomenon, formally comparable to the rhythmic response of nerve tissue to a constant stimulus. If we place *two* such diffusion centers sufficiently far apart on a common plate (Figure 27), the total pattern still adds up, in the main, to one-plus-one. Yet, if we narrow the original distance

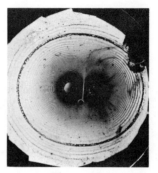

Figure 28

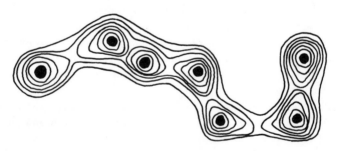

Figure 29

between them, their mutual interference becomes conspicuous (Figure 28): the twin set of circles becomes distorted, the more peripheral ones merge to single dumbbell-shaped contour lines, and the outermost and farthest advanced form a smooth enclosure of both. The two domains have fused. Carrying on the tests, I then placed seven drops on a plate in the configuration of the Great Dipper. Figure 29 shows the outcome of an actual experiment. As one notes, the resulting pattern of silver lines coincides with the pattern of point connections that led man to give the stellar group its name. Does not the unequivocality of this correspondence intimate that a similar dynamic interaction pattern in man's brain had guided his interpretation? Stars do register on retina and brain as single points, but may not the several neural processes thereby actuated engender, on a higher brain level, dynamic interactions that integrate an erstwhile mosaic of local dots into a unitary spatial pattern?

At times, proposals for such physiological underpinnings of Gestalt phenomena have been set forth, couched mostly in symbolic terms of field concepts and related models. Experimental verification, however, has remained scanty. Because cell types other than neurons have furnished far more factual examples of how pattern-determining field effects can arise, I shall turn to those. I shall present two major types of patterning interactions among dispersed cells, first, in a liquid (thermally agitated) environment and second, in a firm cohesive matrix.

The earliest morphogenetic step in the egg of the seaweed *Fucus* is the sprouting of a rootlet on one side. In isolated eggs this sprouting takes place at quite a random spot. When several eggs are combined in groups, however, sprouting is patterned. As Whitaker has shown, pairs of eggs in close proximity sprout at the sides facing each other (Figure 30). However, huddles of more than two sprout toward the geometric center of the group (Figure 30). Thus "mutual attraction," which might still have been conceivable within pairs, is clearly ruled out as explanation for groups of more than two. How then can one account for the phenomenon? Quite simply. When Whitaker placed undivided eggs into a pH gradient (Figure 31), the rootlets sprouted at the more acid side, perhaps because the egg membrane was weakened on that side and sprang a leak through which the rootlet could hatch. Now, eggs may be assumed to secrete their own acid as a metabolic product. This acid cannot diffuse from the confined space within a cluster as rapidly as it can from the outer shore. As a result, an inner-to-outer concentration gradient of acid will develop and polarize the members of the group toward their common center. The additional step that the experimenter had to take to localize root formation the eggs perform among themselves in concert, thus adding what makes two different from one-plus-one, and even three different from the new two-plus-one.

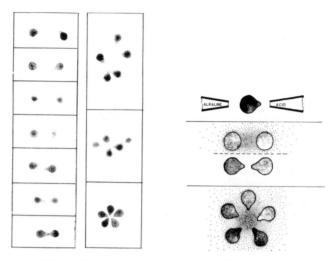

Figure 30   Figure 31

Figure 32

In clusters of explanted embryonic nerve cells (Figure 32), Stefanelli observed a similar convergent growth of dendrites toward the common center, but only if they were not near the outer edge of the drop of culture medium; for near that border, competition between the

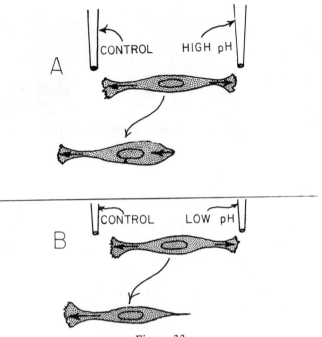

Figure 33

inner medium and its outer environment apparently reversed the gradient, and the dendrites consequently grew outward. The actual agents involved here have not been determined. For other tissue cells, however, we could prove (Figure 33) that bipolar cells in culture, acidified at one end, withdraw that process, thus becoming unipolar. This fairly reproduces what two cells exuding acid will do to each other as soon as they come close enough. Of course, exudates other than acids could have the same polarizing group effect.

Group patterns among cells in semisolid media arise differently. Most tissue cells, as well as nerve fibers, need the support of solid structures—fibrin or collagen fibers, for instance, along which they

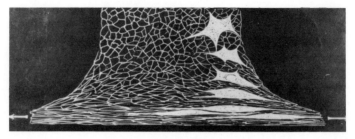

Figure 34

move and grow, like plants along a trellis. The diagram in Figure 34 summarizes the gist of four decades of experiments on this principle of "contact guidance." An untreated protein coagulum, e.g., fibrin in a blood clot, is a random tangle of fibers (top of figure). As illustrated in the lower part, stretch orients the mesh in the direction of the lines of stress. Depending for guidance, like blind men, on the fibrous tracks, the cells then trace the underlying structure. Cell group patterns thus have their precursors in the fibrous matrix in which they are enmeshed. Therefore, if cells could do to the matrix what the experimenter does in applying stretch, they could evidently manage to set up their own physical interconnections and group patterns. And indeed, they can do this. Here is how.

A cohesive fibrous network is under internal tension. Any local disruption of the net makes the surrounding meshes retract to form a ring around the hole, as any lady knows from holes in her stockings. Some spiders (Figure 35) use this as a trick to build a strong-walled nest. Now, cells can achieve the same result, where needed, by local liquefaction through proteolysis of their matrix, or just by local expansion (Figure 36 top). Fibrous and muscular coats around hollow organs owe their circumferential orientation to this effect. More pertinent for us here is the bottom diagram, which illustrates local shrinkage. The meshes are gathered purse string fashion, assuming a radial orientation with focus on the shrinking center. Now, some cells,

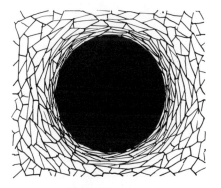

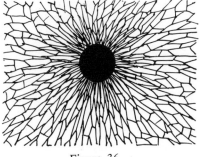

Figure 36

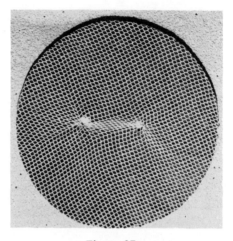

Figure 37

especially proliferating ones, make their surrounding matrix shrink in just this fashion by the release of chemicals that make the meshes squeeze out water, like setting jelly. If cells subsequently emigrate from such a center, they naturally follow their self-created radial routes.

Now, if there are two such cell clusters in a common matrix, will the resulting growth pattern turn out two overlapping stars? Of course not. Let me recall the diagram with which I introduced the two-center theorem earlier in the article (Figures 21 and 22). Two local centers of contraction in the net decidedly do not add up in their effects, as can be demonstrated readily by gathering a taut piece of mesh fabric at two points (Figure 37): the meshes between the two centers are distorted lengthwise into a straight course along the connecting line. In the same way, two clumps of growing cells force fibers in their common colloidal medium to assume a straightline orientation along the shortest distance between them. Three centers generate a structural triangle in their matrix (Figure 38), which then serves as roadway for emigrating cells. Thus, three scalar and erstwhile unrelated local chemical activities become upgraded through vectorial interaction into a well-defined space pattern emerging *de novo*. Figure 39 shows an actual case of such an automatically established triangular interconnection among three embryonic spinal ganglia in vitro.

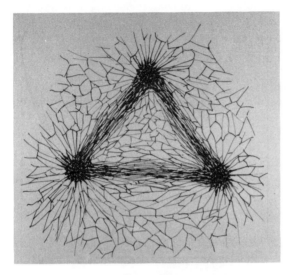

Figure 38

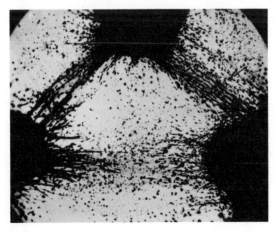

Figure 39

The "beeline" taken by outgrowing cells toward the distant colonies is simply a result of contact guidance. It is definitely not to be credited to any hypothetical "alluring" substances that might have emanated from the distant sources acting as beacons; but there is recent evidence that straight fiber bundles can expedite chemical traffic along their surfaces. So, secondarily, the cell population along the fibrous bridges does gain ulterior benefits from its earlier highway construction. Quite generally in development, structural order, once it has been

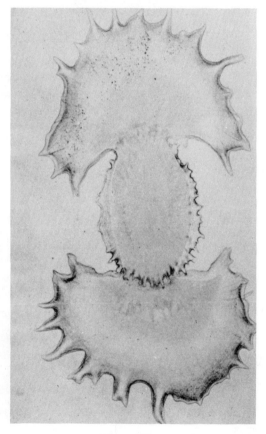

Figure 40

established, creates conditions for its self-promotion and further elaboration.

The architectural effects of a two-center interaction are noticeable in populations at all levels from the molecular to the human. The earliest chromatograms, made by the chemist Runge more than a century ago by letting mixtures of substances diffuse on filter paper, are an example (Figure 40). The confluence of the edges of diffusion from two separate centers immediately sets up a communicating channel, which then drains further substance seepage into its bed. The resulting pattern, reproduced here from one of Runge's original experiments, closely resembles the pattern of mitotic spindles in cell division. Coincidence? Perhaps, but worthy of attention anyhow. And curiously, a recent architectural proposal by Catalano (Figure 41) for

Figure 41

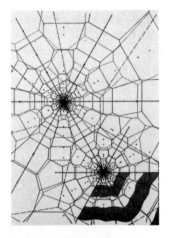

Figure 42

the most efficient structure of a modern growing bicentric city embodies a remarkably similar symmetric pattern of settlement along pressure and flow lines of communication. Population and market distribution between two actual towns, mapped to scale by Isard (Figure 42) bears further witness to the operation of the two-center effect in the dynamics of human ecology.

This mention of ecology brings me to my last set of examples. Ecology is group behavior in free interaction with other groups and with environment. It epitomizes the lifting of subject matter from sheer catalogues of items to paramount concern with their typical differential distribution and, digging deeper, with the patterns of the underlying dynamics. Behavior patterns are ecology's instruments. To explain life, static cell anatomy must become molecular ecology, organisms be comprehended through cell ecology, and societies through the dynamics of human ecology. They all provide us with examples of rigorous scientific propositions that hold for groups but dissolve when efforts are made to reduce them to elemental properties. Here resolution becomes sheer dissolution.

Let us then be emphatic: True, scientific history has grooved our habit of explaining group behavior in terms of the interactive behavior of quasi-independent unit actors, whether molecules or men. Yet this pragmatic, conceptual artifact has serious limitations, and once we reach the limits of its applicability we must relax our historical commitment to exclusive legal recognition of conclusions arrived at analytically and must concede equal explanatory status to collective statements of fact in their own right. Modern physics has done it implicitly in adopting thermo-dynamics, quantum theory, relativity, and statistical mechanics, and the time has come when the life sciences had better follow suit for their own good. They must learn to accept recognized orderliness of the behavior of systems on its own terms. If they can reduce it to analytical terms, well and good. If not, the reality of nature still must be allowed to prevail and override pet micro-mechanistic preconceptions based on predilections. Therefore, regard-less of whether ordered behavior patterns of systems will yield to obstinate analytical efforts at piecing them together through sheer assembly of component pieces—whether of molecules joining to form specific macromolecular systems, of cells to compose organs, or of neuronal circuits to yield adaptive functions—the integral formulations will retain their claim to reality and primacy. Both conceptually and historically, reductionist description is a secondary and limited tactical convenience. Its limits are to be determined empirically and not by prejudice.

Let me briefly pursue this matter on the example of linear arrays, already mentioned briefly earlier. Collagen fibers (Figure 43) are bundles of polymeric chains of protein molecules, linked head to tail and flank to flank. Under certain conditions, homologous subgroups of neighboring chains line up in register, resulting in conspicuous cross-banding. Each molecule is characterized by a specific sequence of amino acids along its backbone. The sequential order being commonly referred to as a code, it justly can be compared to the sequence of letters in a word. Register, then, signifies the sliding of identical letters into alignment (Figure 44), and there is good reason to expect that the molecular mechanism of zipping collagen fibril to fibril by site-matching will be revealed before long. This instance of higher group order then resolves itself simply into a case of assemblage by the orderly stacking of contiguous elements, not unlike our initial examples. But what if similar ordered arrays arise in collectives of linear units without the benefit of mutual contact? How to explain, for instance, the corresponding group pattern of freely mobile, well-separated, linear units in Figure 45, which shows an assembly of trout

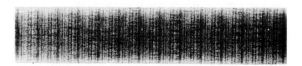

Figure 43

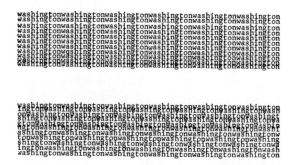

Figure 44

Figure 45

evenly spaced in parallel and register on the bottom of a stream? Clearly, current flow lines and interindividual signals combine in yielding this behavior pattern in grid form, but just how is wholly obscure. How far, then, can we carry the notion of synthesis of such group patterns through the free interaction of their unit elements?

Figure 46 presents an aerial photograph of logging in the Columbia River. The logs are all aligned by current flow and shore lines. Their deposit in register is man-made. In other words, the collective order is strictly imposed by outside forces, which makes it irrelevant to our present context. Not so the next example. Figure 47 is an electron micrograph of rod-shaped tobacco mosaic virus. The units are clustered, and within each cluster the component rodlets are again both in alignment and in register. They look like match sticks; and indeed a group of matches can by analogy serve as a model of the physical mechanism through which such a simple step of order in self-assembling groups can come about. If one scatters matches at random on the surface of water in a dish and then agitates the surface by continuous tapping on the container, the floating matches get into motion and as they collide, they turn into positions of mutual alignment and register—positions evidently satisfying an equilibrium (minimum surface energy) requirement for that particular three-phase (water-wood-air) system. Three stills from a motion picture film of such a model experiment are reproduced in Figure 48, to show the progress in the increase of order by "self-ordering."

Being an instance of ordered group behavior emerging visibly from elementary interactions, the case surely is heartening to reductionist faith. Unfortunately, the argument is open-ended, as can be readily observed in motion pictures of a remarkable rod-shaped microbe, *Bacillus circulans*. Loosely scattered bacilli start out by assembling in physical arrays just like those matches (Figure 49), but once the group has enlarged to a certain critical size, the whole mass adopts a totally different course of behavior: it begins to circle around its own geometric center as fulcrum and keeps on rotating for indefinite periods of time (Figure 50), like a revolving disk, regardless of whether the number of individuals are counted by the hundreds or hundred thousands. There is no sign in the behavior of individuals before their assembly that would have intimated the future rotatory performance of the collective. In fact, although each spinning mass tends to keep its

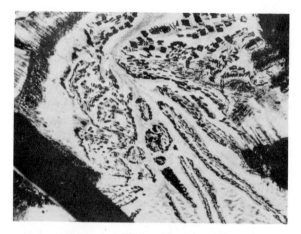

Figure 46

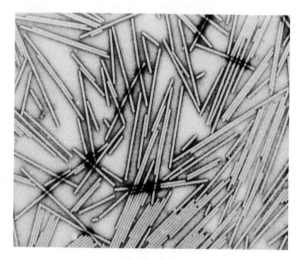

Figure 47

Figure 48

Figure 49

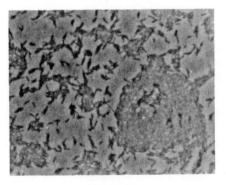

Figure 50

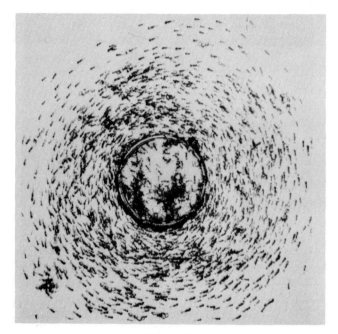

Figure 51

sense of rotation once it has been started, whether clockwise or counterclockwise, fragments that split off may change to spinning in the reverse direction. So evidently the individual units are totally uninstructed as to the direction in which they will be made to spin by their assembled community. Here we are faced with true emergent novelty.

The circling motion of masses of army ants is equally instructive (Figure 51). They keep running round and round a central column, drawing in stragglers, leaving others behind, in an interminable mass circus movement. The infectious pattern of these insect dervish exercises is spectacular. Unfortunately, this running in circles finds a counterpart in human affairs. In fact, in general, there is not too much difference between the laws of human ecology and the ecology of cells and molecules. Dependence on environment, self-sorting by segregation, compounding in groups, recombining for symbiotic reciprocity—in short, self-patterning of groups—occur among molecules and men alike.

Take, for instance, this aerial view of Coney Island on a Sunday (Figure 52). Consider the people as molecules. The heavier border on top is the condensed belt of hydrophobic bodies adsorbed to the water-beach interface. The dark clusters inside the mass clearly mark domains of attractive forces, presumably emanating from sources of nutrient and stimulant attractants. Their equidistant spacing indicates mutual repulsion through forces of competion; and so forth. The analogy is not at all facetious. It cuts deep into the heart of our topic, for it exemplifies basic features of self-organizing systems. I could have gone on, for instance, to relate how a random mixture of isolated single

Figure 52

cells (Figure 53), obtained by dissociating an already functioning embryonic kidney, then scrambled, lumped and properly nourished, can reconstitute itself into a remarkably well-organized miniature kidney (Figure 54); or how similarly scrambled cells of embryonic chick skin in tissue culture can grow into normal feathers (Figure 55); all of this entirely by "do-it-yourself" methods.

Examples of "self-organization" of this kind are numerous. To label them is easy, although gratuitous. To understand them is a long way off. Exclusively reductionist tactics will never get us there, if they persist in "going it alone"; nor, on the other hand, will sheer verbal soporifics. What the task calls for is, first of all, a job of thorough conceptual overhauling and renovation. It requires that we drop self-imposed blinders and admit to view the higher perspective of the whole—not just its bogus literary versions, but its hard scientific core, expressed in such phenomena of emergent collective order as I have illustrated. The venal preoccupation with bits of the materials of nature as such—with "what there is"—must give way to a broader concern with the manner of their operation and use—with "how it all works." And, in this shift of emphasis, one discovers that all the bits hang together; that they are all intermeshed in webs of subtle interactions forming domains or subsystems within the over-all continuum of the universe.

To emphasize the "systems" character of the dynamics of living entities I have, ever since 1923, couched their description in terms of the concept of "fields." Lest this symbolic term again arouse alarm, let me decontaminate it instantly by the following simple example (Figure 56). Let us take a circumscribed body, depending for its maintenance on active exchange with its environment; for instance, an egg in the ocean, a cell in a tissue, a human individual in society. Then let the unit multiply into a few more units; they all continue to have a share in the common interface of exchange and communication with the medium. But let the number of units keep on increasing, whether by subdivision or accretion, and all of a sudden a critical stage arises at which some of the units find themselves abruptly crowded inward, cut off completely from direct contact with their former vital environment by an outer layer of their fellows. The latter thereby acquire positions not only geometrically intermediary, but functionally mediatory, between the ambient medium and the now inner units. From then on, "inner" and "outer" units are no longer alike. A monotonic group of equals has become dichotomized into unequal sets. With the emergence of the

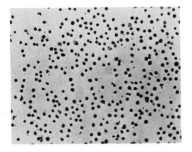

Figure 53

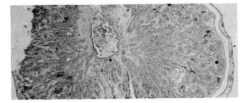

Figure 54

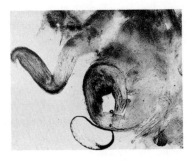

Figure 55

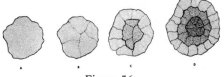

Figure 56

distinction between innerness and outerness, the 1 + 1 = 2 rule becomes inapplicable.

The train of events to follow such a "differentiation" of a radially symmetrical core-crust dichotomy is easy to envisage. Interactions between the "outer" members and their newly established "inner" neighbors would expose to another set of new conditions any fresh units arising subsequently in the intermediate zone between them, and hence call forth in them a third type of reaction. Moreover, polarized influences from the environment (e.g., gradients such as illustrated above for cell orientation) would impose an axiate pattern upon the group. Thus would ensue a train of sequelae of ever-mounting, self-ordering complexity. In all these steps, the fate of a given unit would be determined by its response to the specific conditions prevailing at the site in which it has come to lie, those conditions varying locally as functions of the total configuration of the system—its "field pattern," for short. This principle—long recognized empirically as a basic criterion of systems but not always fully appreciated in its implications—is commonly referred to as "position effect."

The main point to bear in mind is that none of the component members of the group, all erstwhile alike, can know their future courses and eventual fates in advance; can know whether they would become "inner" or "outer" or "intermediate." Nor does it matter for the resulting pattern of the complex as a whole, as is best illustrated by the process of twinning. By cutting in two the cluster of cells that constitutes an early embryo or an organ rudiment, one can obtain two fully formed embryos or two fully formed organs, the way the sorcerer's apprentice, in trying to kill the water-carrying broom by splitting it down the middle, got two busy whole brooms instead. What had been destined to form a single typical organism or organ has yielded two instead, each half assuming the organization of a well-proportioned whole. In principle, we can now understand why: because bisection through the middle has resulted in "innermost" cells coming to lie "outermost" again, whereupon the whole pattern of subsequent dynamic interactions has proceeded, reduced to half-scale, in harmonious proportions. (Of course, the individual parts can respond to their new local cues appropriately only if their original positions in the undivided framework have not already single-tracked them into courses unresponsive to the new demands.)

An inorganic model of this process is, for instance, a sitting drop of mercury. Its convex, lens-shaped form results from equilibrium between opposing sets of forces—gravitation and adhesion, tending to spread the mass, and cohesion and surface tension, tending to hold it together. Disturb the equilibrium by cutting the liquid drop in two, and each half immediately restores its own equilibrium by assuming a convex lens-shape. But freeze the original lens-shaped drop solid before cutting, and then bisect, and each half will retain its former shape of half an oblate; the dynamics that do the remolding in the liquid drop are still at work, but deprived of their free mobility, the elements can no longer yield.

The example of twinning is just one illustration among many for the thesis that strict determinacy (or invariance) of a collective end state is fully reconcilable with indeterminacy (or variance) in detail of the component courses of events leading up to it—a thesis I have tried to contrast with the basic reductionist doctrine that a determinate end can only be reached as the blind outcome of a microprecisely determined tandem chain of component microevents. This latter doctrine, "microscopic" and micromechanistic in the old sense, just is not tenable in the light of facts unobscured by artificial blinders; and yet its popularity has grown steadily because of the indisputable proof that in the progress of science, as I said before, the artifact of reductionist abstraction has had a most signal pragmatic merit. But the time has come when we must check back with *real* nature to find what we have missed by adopting the short-sighted view of close-range analysis as the sole legitimate approach to insight into nature. My early introduction of the "field" concept into biology has aimed at no more than at offering a semantic therapeutic against the spread of this epidemic of myopia and constriction of the visual field, which leaves so many burning problems in the life sciences unattended. The "field" is a symbolic term for the unitary dynamics underlying ordered behavior of a collective, denoting properties lost in the process of its physical or purely intellectual dismemberment. Being descriptive of a property of natural systems, it must not be perverted into a supernatural principle; the study of those properties is, of course, an empirical task and not a literary pastime.

If the young generation were only to realize the origin of the microdissectionists' claim for a monopoly of insight into nature, more of them might turn to problems now kept out of their purview. So let me close with a brief anamnesis of the prevailing conceptual deficiency disease. To me, the crux seems to lie not so much in *a priori* reasoning as in our practice of phrasing experimental results in some sort of shorthand language. I shall explain this on the schematic model of an experiment (Figure 57).

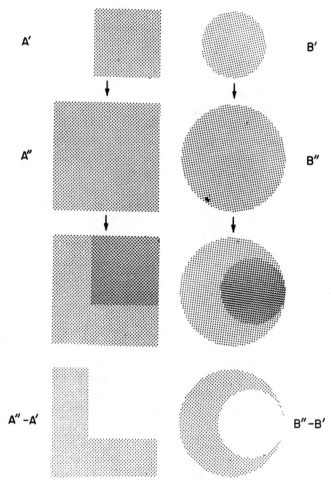

Figure 57

An experiment is motivated by our curiosity about the relationship between two phenomena of nature, A and B. We study them by changing A from A' to A'' and observe a correlated change of B' to B''. We then proceed to correlate the difference (A''−A') with the difference (B''−B'). And basically this is all we can extract from the experiment. But this is not the point at which we commonly stop. We usually go on to endow the *differentials* with an existence of their own, dissected from the context from which they were abstracted in the first place (bottom line in the diagram), and before we realize it, we have personified them as "actors." Genes for the difference between a white and a pink pea became simply genes for white and pink, respectively, throwing the peaness into discard; the differences between integrated brain functions before and after local lesions became transliterated to domiciles for specialist subfunctionaries, as if the rest of the brain were uninvolved; and so on.

In trying to restore the loss of information suffered by thus lifting isolated fragments out of context, we have assigned the job of reintegration to a corps of anthropomorphic gremlins. As a result, we are now plagued—or blessed, depending on one's party view—with countless demigods, like those in antiquity, doing the jobs we do not understand: the organizers, operators, inductors, repressors, promoters, regulators, etc.,—all prosthetic devices to make up for the amputations which we have allowed to be perpetrated on the organic wholeness, or to put it more innocuously, the "systems" character, of nature and of our thinking about nature.

May my presentation have succeeded in documenting that party lines drawn between emphasis either on the whole or on the parts are based on the artifice of predilection, rather than on the realities of nature. And may this realization find its way into human ecology, particularly its political branch, to prove that society is not called upon to choose between two extremes: either a license for anarchic random excursions of its component individuals, or the enforced subordination of individual members to a rigid group order dictated from above, but that, as in all organic systems, order in the gross emerges, not only in spite of, but as a result of, the interaction of free elements with freedom in the small, restrained only by common purpose—or call it program—and respect for nature, which after all, to speak in pre-Galilean terms, abhors not only a vacuum, but disharmony.

The Living System:
Determinism Stratified*

1. *Introduction: Need for the Systems Concept*

Just like the painter, who steps periodically back from his canvas to gain perspective, so the laboratory scientist emerges above ground occasionally from the deep shaft of his specialized preoccupation to survey the cohesive, meaningful fabric developing from innumerable component tributary threads, spun underground much like his own. Only by such shuttling back and forth between the worm's eye view of detail and the bird's eye view of the total scenery of science can the scientist gain and retain a sense of perspective and proportions. My comments presented in the following constitute one such excursion to higher ground, bringing with me those lessons learned in the workshop of observation, comparison, analysis and interpretation, which call for critical collation with those conclusions that have emerged from other specialist channels in a search for overall integration. On a smaller scale, my multivalent experience with engineering, cell biology, developmental biology and neurobiology, have pointed me to the need of, and have given me some practice in, rising from synopsis to synthesis and conceptual unification of biological knowledge.

Although this has brought me close to the portals of philosophy, I have never consciously trespassed into the disciplinary precincts of that branch of learning, for which I would have felt neither equipped nor qualified. I want to stress that at the outset, lest any of my subsequent remarks be misconstrued as pretentious aspirations at philosophical profundity. They are no more then conclusions and postulates cogently derived from pragmatic insights acquired from the realistic study of

Reprinted from BEYOND REDUCTIONISM: NEW PERSPECTIVES IN THE LIFE SCIENCES. ED.: A. Koestler & J.R. Smythies. The Macmillan Co., New York, 1970. pp. 3-42. Also in Studium Generale, vol. 22, pp. 361-400. 1969.
**In references to the author's publications in the text, abbreviated to "P.W."

living organisms. They represent a distillation of experience, rather than the kind of theoretical constructs often erected on a base of imaginative speculation, intuition and logical consistency, but devoid of taproots in the actualities of nature. Considering that in contemporary biology the nexus between inductive experimental fact-finding, on the one hand, and theoretical speculations, on the other, is very tenuous indeed, examples of convergence from both ends unquestionably could speed the rapprochement, and this essay of mine aims to contribute to that goal.

My prime object here is simple. It is to document that certain basic controversies about the nature of organisms and living processes, which have for long failed to melt away in the heat of argument (e.g., reductionism versus holism), readily vanish in the light of realistic studies of the actual phenomena, examined critically and described judiciously in language uncontaminated by preconceptions and predilections. In this light (1) the *principle of hierarchic order* in living nature reveals itself as a demonstrable descriptive fact, completely unrelated to any philosophical connotations that it may carry. And further (2) the necessity becomes compelling to accept organic entities as *systems* subject to network dynamics in the sense of modern systems theory, rather than as bundles of micro-precisely programmed linear chain reactions. A strictly mechanistic notion of a machine-like nature of living organisms presupposes a high degree of precision in the spatial and chronological program according to which the innumerable concurrent component chains are composed and arrayed—a conception later amplified, but in no way altered, by letting the program include equally preprogrammed checking and spare mechanisms to keep the bunch of separate processes from falling apart in the face of the fortuitous fluctuations of the outer world.

2. Animal Behavior: Systems Dynamics

The explanation by Jacques Loeb (1918) of animal behavior in terms of rigidly concatenated reflex sequences, and particularly his proposition of tropisms as paradigms of a precise cause-effect machine principle in organisms, epitomizes that kind of mechanistic preconception. His thesis had, however, two serious flaws. Not only had that particular brand of naïvely mechanistic thinking already become outdated in

physics, but studies of the actual behavior of animals in goal-directed or
other forms of directional performances showed none of the presumed
stereotypism in the manner in which the animals attained their
objectives. True, the beginning and end of a behavioral act could often
be unequivocally correlated with a vectorial cue from the environment;
but the execution of the given act was found to be so variable and
indeed unique in detail, from case to case and from instance to
instance, that it was gratuitous to maintain that the attainment of
essentially the same result regardless of the variety of approaches is
simply the blind outcome of a chain of seriated steps appropriately
predesigned by evolution to lead to that end. In other words, organisms
are not puppets operated by environmental strings; moreover, the
analogy is meaningless, anyhow, if one remembers that the "environment" that pulls the strings of puppets in proper order is another
organism—the puppeteer with his brain or at least some machine
contrived by a brain.

In fact, it was exactly the detailed study of the movements and
tracks by which some species of butterflies assume resting postures
rigidly oriented with regard to gravity and light, that I was prompted to
disavow the reflex chain theory of animal orientation as unrealistic and
to propose in its stead a *general systems theory of animal behavior* (P.
W. 1925). That was forty-five years ago. I concur with the Editor who
prefaced a republication of my article some thirty-five years later (P. W.
1959) by stating that "this paper is one of the earliest examples of
system-theoretical thinking in behavioral science from the biologist's
point of view. . . . Naturally, Professor Weiss would not today subscribe
to every contention and conclusion of the paper. . . . It is remarkable,
however, that the basic tenets of the paper seem to have been so largely
borne out by later developments." Although, unquestionably, my basic
concepts of that time would nowadays be amenable to much
refinement, particularly in the context of cybernetics, I am still amazed
that the main framework has stood the test of time under the scrutiny
of all my broader biological experiences since. As all of my following
discussion rests on that concept, I shall set forth the gist of it here.

3. Analytic Thinking—an Abstraction

To me, as an observer of nature, the Universe presents itself naïvely as
an immense cohesive continuum. However, we usually do not look at it

as such. We are used to looking at it as a patchwork of discrete fragments. This habit stems partly from a biological heritage, which makes focussing on "things", such as prey, enemies, or obstacles, a vital necessity; partly from cultural tradition; and partly from sheer curiosity, which draws our attention and interest to limited "objects". These may consist of well-delineated patterns in our visual field; of repetitive arrays of sounds in bird song, melody or human language; of processes of patterned regularity, such as waves. What makes them the focus of our attention, is their reiterative appearance in relatively constant and durable form; at least, they hold together long enough or recur in our experience often enough to deserve a name, in contra-distinction to the more fleeting, far less regular, constellations, of their surroundings, which we for contrast then call "background". I shall not dwell here on the fact that the distinction between relatively constant and more inconstant patches in the Universe, as we perceive it, is sharpened by peculiarities of our sensory functions (e.g., visual contrast phenomena) and by psychological principles (e.g., those underlying Gestalt psychology). Quite to the contrary, I want to lay stress on the fact that, from a comprehensive perspective, the outer world never confronts us with fractions other than as artificially circumscribed bits abstracted through mental operations from a whole cohesive fabric that is physically indivisible, undisruptable and of intrinsic integrality. No "part" that we might mentally dissect out because we happen to be especially interested in it or because it has forced itself upon our attention, is ever truly isolated or "isolable" from the rest.[1]

The process through which we have come to treat any such conspicuous cluster of properties, called "parts", as ideally isolated, is mostly empirical. We watch the complex move relative to its more variable background, and if we find that it is not perceptibly altered by the translocation, we venture to treat it as independent of its environment. But note the reservations in my phrasing. In the first place, I said "perceptible", which refers to the limited powers of discrimination and perception of an observer and his instruments, rather than to the full repertory of properties of the observed unit; and secondly, in speaking of "independence from the environment", one must allow that since "environment" is ubiquitous, we cannot test, hence never discount, "dependencies" upon any of the features of the

---

[1] See the pertinent and elaborate remarks on this point by Whyte (1949).

cosmic environment which are universal. Temperature or radiation, for instance, are cases in point.

Actually even in that limited definition, independence is not absolute; for all those putatively independent entities are interconnected by the common environmental matrix, in which they lie embedded, so that for every single one of the discrete items, every other item is part and parcel of the former's environment. Our habit of atomizing the Universe mentally into isolated (etymologically the same as "insulated") fragments reminds one of the familiar adage according to which "no man is an island", which simply rectifies the optical impression of the naïve observer from shore by pointing to the submerged connectedness among the visible peaks. Well, similarly, having recognized connections between isolated items, man then goes on to sort those he deems "relevant" from "negligible" ones; which obviously lets the judgement of the describer (or of statistics) intrude into purportedly "objective" descriptions of properties of "objects".

4. *From Analysis to Synthesis*

By raising his sights from single objects to their "interrelations" with others, man reverses his direction from analysis to synthesis. In doing this, he discovers simple rules which describe the interrelations between such entities to his satisfaction without at all shaking his conviction that, to all practical purposes and intents, those entities could be regarded as having primarily an isolated existence of their own, becoming just secondarily coupled depending on "circumstances"; sometimes forgetting that "circumstances"—merely a broader substitute term for "environment"—are never absent. This is, of course, as I have said before, a deliberate abstration, but one to which we must credit the tremendous success of science over the last two millennia.

We have learned that if a finite series of modifications of an entity A is regularly associated with a correlated series of modification in another entity B, a rule can be established from which all future correlations between the two can be extrapolated without further experience. We then proceed to study A in its relation to C, and C again in its relation to B, and so seriatim, to learn how different parts of the Universe, erstwhile mentally dissected and separated, hang actually together. The artifical, but eminently fruitful, method of analysis, adhering to the atomistic concept of Democrit, can thus be partly reversed by putting two and two together, either physically or mentally in our imagination, linking by way of consecutive synthesis such coupled pairs into complex chains and cross braces, constructing compound real or ideal structures, the way a child builds bridges with an erector set.

This brings me to the salient point. The basic streak that runs through practically all of our biological thinking is still that science, given time, will succeed in describing and comprehending, by the consistent application of this synthetic method and without any further conceptual amendments, all that is within the Universe in entities and properties and processes that is knowable to us, including the phenomena of life. It is not for me to expound to what extent modern physics has had already to depart from such a micromechanistic, naïve picture of the outer world (for instance, by arriving at the dualistic concept of fields and particles, or the complementarity principle of Bohr, etc.) for we are not concerned with physics here. We are concerned with *living organisms*, and for those, we can assert definitely and incontrovertibly, on the basis of strictly empirical investigation, that the sheer reversal of our prior analytic dissection of the Universe by *putting the pieces together* again, whether in reality or just in our minds, *can yield no complete explanation of the behavior of even the most elementary living system.*

5. *The Living Organism—a System*

This sentence contains the major key words: "behavior" and "system". A living system that does not behave is dead; *life is process, not substance.* A living system is no more adequately characterized by an inventory of its material consituents, such as molecules, than the life of a city is described by the list of names and numbers in a telephone book. Only by virtue of their ordered interactions do molecules become partners in the living process; in other words, through their behavior. And since this involves vast numbers of disparate compounds, all living phenomena consist of *group behavior*, which offers aspects not evident in the members of the group when observed singly. Now, this fact is generally disposed of by referring to living systems as "complex"; a term uncomfortably reminiscent of the erector set; for "complex" is defined in the dictionary as "comprehending various parts connected together; composite; compound". That is to say, in plain language, the term "complex" need imply no more than a haphazard conglomeration. However, the living system evidently needs one major qualification to be added, and that is the distinctive *orderliness* of the complexes. Therefore, since, as I just said, life is process, the basic characteristic of a living system is that despite of, and in contrast to, the infinite number of possible interactions and combinations among its constituent units that could take place in a simple complex, in the living system only an extremely restricted selection from that grab-bag of opportunities for chemical processes is being realized at any one moment—a selection which can be understood solely in its bearing on the concerted harmonious performance of a task by the complex as a whole. This is the feature that distinguishes a living system from a dead body, or a functional process from a mere list of parts involved, or a sentence from an alphabet, or in biological terms, ecology from systematics. If one omits this fundamental specification, the mere designation of an organism as "complex" is trite.

Although the brilliant progress of biochemistry keeps on increasing the list of opportunities for componental interactions, the rules of order which rigorously restrain them in such coordinated fashion as to yield a harmonious group performance of the collective can only be recognized, appreciated and properly described once we have raised our sights from the element to the collective system; and this, as you will see, means passing to a higher level of conceptualization.

6. *Hierarchy of Wholes and Parts*

The mere mention of "levels" brings me to the fundamental distinction between atomistic, micro-mechanistic terms of explanations on the one hand, and hierarchical concepts of organization on the other. The difference is that the latter imply some sort of discontinuity, encountered as one crosses interfaces between lower and higher orders of magnitude, while the former, trying to reduce all phenomena to the properties of ultimate elements in their various combinations, are based on the premise of a continuity of gradations all the way up from the single elements to infinite numbers of them. To decide which one of these two contrasting presentations of nature represents the reality of biological phenomena is, of course, not to be left to *a priori* conviction, but is a matter of empirical study. If coordinated group performances of a high order of regularity can be proven to be the blind resultant of a multitude of concurrent linear bundles of chain reactions minutely preset in spatial distribution and pre-scheduled in duration and sequence, then the former theory could hold sway. If not, then systems theory would have to be granted primacy for the treatment of organized systems; for the systems concept is the embodiment of the experience that there are patterned processes which owe their typical configuration not to a prearranged, absoluted stereotyped, mosaic of singletracked component performances, but on the contrary, to the fact that the component activities have many degrees of freedom, but submit to the ordering restraints exerted upon them by the integral activity of the "whole" in its patterned systems dynamics.

So, here I have at last put my finger on the sore spot, the touching of which has for ages hurt the protagonists of analytical-reductionist orthodoxy—the concept of *wholeness*. Refusing to look beyond their ultimate and most extreme abstraction, namely, the presumption of truly "isolated" elements of nature, and spurred by the dramatic success of explanations of many complex effects in terms of inter-actions among such elements, they could not help but ask what there could be then in the universe other than elements and interactions. Well, if this is put as an open question, not just a rhetorical one, then I would answer it as follows: The interaction between a positive and a negative electric charge, or between the earth and a falling stone, can certainly be described, at least in first approximation, without paying attention to what happens in the rest of the Universe. And if one watches a multitude of stones falling to earth, the total result can still be represented as the sum of all the individual events. But there is also another class of interactions, which of necessity escape the elemen-tarian observer in his preoccupation with the smallest samples, because they pertain to properties peculiar to larger samples only of the Universe, passed up in the comminution process which led to the concept of elements in the first place. It is in that latter class that the empirical dichotomy arises between *simple complexes* and the type of *ordered complexes* which we designate as *systems*. In other words, systems are products of our experience with nature, and not mental constructs, and whoever without being privy to that primary practical experience would try to abrogate them, would do so only by arrogation.

7. Reductionism and Holism

I shall presently give a concise definition of the criteria that mark a complex of parts for designation as a system, but before doing so, let me put in an aside. As you may have noted, I am skirting here an age-old controversy in biology between the two opposite extremes of "reductionism" and "holism". The former finds currently its most outspoken advocates in the field of so-called "molecular biology". If this term implied no more than a deliberate self-limitation of viewpoint and research to molecular interactions in living systems, it is not only pertinent and legitimate, but has to its credit some of the most spectacular advances in modern biology. If on the other hand, flushed by success, it were to assume the attitude of a benevolent absolutism, claiming a monopoly for the explanation of all phenomena in living systems, and indeed were issuing injunctions against the injection of any but molecular principles into the description of biological systems, this would obviously reflect a patent lack of practical experience with the evidence for supra-molecular order in living systems. Historically, the term "molecular biology" was coined almost simultaneously, though independently, by Astbury (1951) and myself[2]; it was to indicate, on the scale of orders of magnitude, the lowest level of investigation relevant to the advancement of biological knowledge. But nothing in the nomenclature insinuated that it should assume the role of *pars pro toto*. As I once put it, there is no phenomenon in a living system that is *not* molecular, but there is none that is *only* molecular, either. It is one thing not to see the forest for the trees, but then to go on to deny the reality of the forest, is a more serious matter; for it is not just a case of myopia, but one of self-inflicted blindness. Since it bears directly on the crux of our discussion, let me add some diagnostic comments.

[2]On assuming the chairmanship of the Division of Biology and Agriculture of the National Research Council in 1951, I restructured the administrative subcategorization of "biology", previously based on forms of life (botany, zoology, bacteriology, etc.) or on methods of study (anatomy, biochemistry, biometrics, etc.), by a hierarchical system of order according to functional principles in common to living organisms; to wit, in ascending order: Molecular, Cellular, Genetic, Developmental, Regulatory and Group and Environmental Biology (see, for instance, P. W. 1952). This scheme of classification, subsequently adopted, with some supplementations, by the National Science Foundation, has since become rather widely applied in the organization of educational and publication programs.

The colloquial simile of the forest and the trees is actually incorrect because it overstates what the observer of nature means to express by the phrase *"The whole is more than the sum of its parts."* As I have pointed out in a recent, more detailed, analysis of this biological tenet, the term "more" is an algebraïc term referring to numbers. In that sense, a forest is indeed numerically "more" than the number of trees in it, since it contains, besides trees, grass and underbrush and animals and so forth. A living cell, by contrast, certainly does not have more content, mass or volume than is constituted by the aggregate mass of molecules which it comprises. As I have tried to illustrate in the cited article, the "more" (than the sum of parts) in the above tenet does not at all refer to any measureable quantity in the observed systems themselves (P. W. 1967); it refers solely to the necessity for the observer to supplement the sum of statements that can be made about the separate parts by any such additional statements as will be needed to describe the *collective behavior* of the parts, when in an organized group. In carrying out this upgrading process, he is in effect doing no more than *restoring information content* that has been lost on the way down in the progressive analysis of the unitary universe into abstracted elements.

You will recognize that in this neutral version lies the reconciliation between reductionism and holism in that neither extreme pretends to portray the cosmos as such, but only subscribes to different preferences of its students in the ways they look at it. The one likes to move from the top down, gaining precision of information about fragments as he descends, but losing information content about the larger orders he leaves behind; the other proceeds in the opposite direction, from below, trying to retrieve the lost information content by reconstruction, but recognizes early in the ascent that that information is not forthcoming unless he has already had it on record in the first place. The difference between the two procedures, determined partly by personal predilections, but largely also by historical traditions, is not unlike that between two individuals looking at the same object through a telescope from opposite ends, one through the eye piece from in front, and the other in the reverse direction.

8. *System, Operationally Defined*

Whether or not you accept this point of view, I regard here as of no consequence, as I do not want to weaken the conclusiveness of the epistemologically non-committal definition I am about to present. Pragmatically defined, a *system* is a rather circumscribed complex of relatively bounded phenomena, which, within those bounds, retains a relatively stationary pattern of structure in space or of sequential configuration in time in spite of a high degree of variability in the details of distribution and interrelations among its constituent units of lower order. Not only does the system maintain its configuration and integral operation in an essentially constant environment, but it responds to alterations of the environment by an adaptive redirection of its componental processes in such a manner as to counter the external change in the direction of optimum preservation of its systemic integrity.

A simple formula which I have used to symbolize the systems character of a cell (P. W. 1963) could be applied equally well to systems in general. It sets a system in relation to the sum of its components by an inequality as follows: Let us focus on any particular fractional part (A) of a complex suspected of having systemic properties, and measure all possible excursions and other fluctuations about the mean in the physical and chemical parameters of that fraction over a given period of time. Let us designate the cumulative record of those deviations as the variance (v_a) of part A. Let us furthermore carry out the same procedure for as many parts of the system as we can identify, and establish their variances v_b, v_c, v_d, ... v_n. Let us similarly measure as many features of the total complex (S) as we can identify, and determine their variance (V_s). Then the complex is a system if the variance of the features of the whole collective is significantly less than the sum of variances of its constituents; or written in a formula:

$$V_s \ll \Sigma \left(V_a + V_b + \ldots . V_n \right).$$

In short, the basic characteristic of a system is its essential *invariance* beyond the much more variant flux and fluctuations of its elements or constituents. By implication this signifies that the elements, although by no means singletracked as in a mechanical device, are subject to restraints of their degrees of freedom so as to yield a resultant in the direction of maintaining the optimum stability of the collective. The terms of "coordination", "control", and the like, are merely tautological labels for this principle.

To sum up, a major aspect of a system is that while the state and pattern of the whole can be unequivocally defined as known, the detailed states and pathways of the components not only are so erratic as to defy definition, but even if a Laplacean spirit could trace them, would prove to be so unique and non-recurrent that they would be devoid of scientific interest. This is exactly the opposite of a machine, in which the structure of the product depends crucially on strictly predefined operations of the parts. In the system, the structure of the whole determines the operation of the parts; in the machine, the operation of the parts determines the outcome. Of course, even the machine owes the coordinated functional arrangement of its parts, in last analysis, to a systems operation—the brain of its designer.

9. *Hierarchy: a Biological Necessity*

To dramatize the need for viewing living organisms as hierarchically ordered systems, I shall give you the following facts to ponder. The average cell in your body consists to about 80% of water and for the rest contains about 10^5 macromolecules. Your brain alone contains about 10^{10} cells, hence about 10^{15} (1,000,000,000,000,000) macromolecules (these figures may be off by one order of magnitude in either direction). Could you actually believe that such an astronomic number of elements, shuffled around as we have demonstrated in our cell studies (see below), could ever guarantee to you your sense of identity and constancy in life without this constancy being insured by a superordinated principle of integration? Well, if you could, for instance by invoking a micro-precisely predetermined Universe according to Leibniz' "prestabilized harmony", the following consideration should dispel that notion. Each nerve cell in the brain receives an average of 10^4 connections from other brain cells, and in addition, recent studies on the turnover of the molecular population within a given nerve cell have indicated that, although the cells themselves retain their individuality, their macromolecular contingent is renewed about 10^4 times in a lifetime (P. W. 1969a). In short, every cell of your brain actually harbors and has to deal with at least 10^9 macromolecules during its life. But even that is not all. It is reported that the brain loses, on the average, about 10^3 cells per day irretrievably rather at random, so that the brain cell population is decimated during the life span by about 10^7

cells, expunging 10^{11} conducting cross linkages. And yet, despite that ceaseless change of detail in that vast population of elements, our basic patterns of behavior, our memories, our sense of integral existence as an individual, have retained throughout their unitary continuity of pattern.

Those looking at biology exclusively from the molecular end might feel satisfied by calculating that a contingent at any one time of 10^{15} brain molecules in intercommunication could numerically account for any conceivable number of resultant functional manifestations by their mass. However, this misses the real problem. It is redundant for science to confirm as conceivable that which from experience we already know to happen; what it has to explain, is not that it happens, but why it happens just the way it does. And this is exactly where the above molecular computation fails abysmally, for it ignores the crucial fact that contrary to that "conceivable" infinite number and variety of possible caleïdoscopic constellations and combinations, the real brain processes, taken as a whole, retain their overall patterns.

This particular example has taken us right up to one of the highest levels of organismic organization—the brain. One of the great physicists of our age, Erwin Schrödinger, in his lecture series on "What Is Life?" (1945), grappled with the very problem I have tried to dramatize here, namely, the contrast between the degrees of potential freedom among trillions of molecules making up the brain on the one hand (or for that matter, on an even larger scale, the whole body), and on the other hand, the perseverance in an essentially invariant pattern of the functions of our nervous system, our thoughts, our ideas, our memories (and as for the whole body, of our structure and the harmonious physiological cooperation of all our parts). He was forced to the conclusion that, as he put it, "I . . . that is to say, every conscious mind that has ever said or felt 'I' . . . am the person, if any, who controls the 'motion of the atoms' according to the laws of nature."

In order to stay on strictly empirical grounds, let us disregard the implied allusion in this statement to a brain-mind dualism, for the main emphasis lies on the word "control"—the subordination of the blind play of atoms and molecules to an overall regulatory control system with features of continuity and relative invariability of pattern; in short, the postulation of a systems principle. What the theoretical physicist, however, did not seem to have appreciated—and given the lack of detailed empirical familiarity with living objects, could not possibly have apprehended–, is that the integral systems operation, whether of the body as a whole, or of the brain within it, deals with the molecules not directly, but only through the agency of intermediate subordinate sub-systems, ranged in a hierarchical scale of orders of magnitude (see the description of hierarchical order in cells further below). Each sub-system dominates its own subordinate smaller parts within its own orbit or domain, as it were, restraining their degrees of freedom according to its own integral portion of the overall pattern, much as its own degrees of freedom have been restrained by the pattern of activities of the higher system of which it is a part and participant.[3]

This is the gist of all the lessons learned from biology, as one descends stepwise from the organism, through its constituent cells, on through their organelles, themselves composed of macromolecular complexes, down to the macromolecules and smaller molecules, which are the link to inorganic nature. The principle is valid for the single cell as much as for the multicellular community of the higher animal, and for the latter's development as much as for its homeostatic maintenance of physiological equilibrium in later life. On each one of the mentioned planes or levels of this systemic hierarchy, we encounter the same type of descriptive rule summarized in the inequality formula outlined earlier; namely, that any one of the particular complexes that show that high degree of constancy and unity that marks them as system loses that aspect of invariance the more we concentrate our attention on smaller samples of its content. So, at each level of descent, we recognize entities comparable to relay stations sufficiently well defined to be described in their own terms (e.g., organs, cells, organelles, macromolecules; or brain functions, as expressed in concepts, thoughts, sentences, words, symbols), but whose methodical behavior on that level cannot be ascribed to any fixity of regularities in the behavior of the units of next lower order; just as knowing purely the properties of those intermediary "relay" entities would not permit us to describe by

---

[3]Some authors have endowed systems and subsystems of this description with symbolic names, such as "orgs" (Gerard, 1958) or "holons" (Koestler, 1967). If I do not follow suit, it is from fear that such terms might again be naively misconstrued for labels of disembodied superagencies conceived as something that might after all somehow some day *materialize*, distilled off and separable from the conservative *dynamics*, whose special rules those terms aim at categorizing. The history of science has amply documented the conceptual hazards inherent in raising adjectives to the rank of nouns; particularly, in the description of living phenomena, where the temptation to personify nouns is ever present.

sheer additive reconstruction the behavioral features of their next superordinate level in precise and specific terms.

You are aware of what I have been doing here. I have tried to translate the formula, "the whole is more than the sum of its parts" into a mandate for action: a call for spelling out the irreducible minimum of supplementary information that is required beyond the information derivable from the knowledge of the ideally separated parts in order to yield a complete and meaningful description of the ordered behavior of the collective. Our adoption of the traditional reference to hierarchically ordered systems in terms of "levels" is simply a concession to our biological heritage of spatial eidetics. In our imagination, we visualize the system as a whole on one plane; we then dissect it mentally or physically into its components, which we display on another, a lower, plane, the way we teach anatomy to students. Yet, what we must bear in mind is that, in reality, the system and its parts are coextensive and congruous, that nothing need be presumed to have been disrupted or lost in the dissection process except the pattern of orderly relations among the parts, and that what the "level" we are speaking of signifies, is really the level of attention of an observer whose interest has been attracted by certain regularities of pattern prevailing at that level, as he scans across the range of orders of magnitude. He scans as he would turn a microscope from levels of lower to higher magnification, gaining detail at the expense of restricting the visual field, and he finds noteworthy constancies on every level. As long as we remain conscious of the fact that any geometric image (or verbiage) that we might chose as visual (or verbal) model of hierarchic structure is a simplified artifact, reflecting the inadequacy of our faculty for visualizing abstract concepts, it becomes rather immaterial which one we use. In this sense, they all become equivalent, whether one prefers the laminated structure intimated by the term "level" or Arthur Koestler's linear scheme of reanastomosing arborizations or my own preference for "inscribed domains" (see Fig. 6).

10. *Open Systems*

One further qualification of the preceding characterization of systems as phenomena of our experience should be mentioned. In a purist view, if we deny the primacy of the atomistic notion of truly isolated entities in the Universe, then evidently we cannot admit the existence of wholly autonomous, tightly bounded systems of any order of magnitude and complexity, either. It was in forward reference to this point that I have used in my presentation repeatedly such notorious escape clauses as "to all intents and purposes", "relatively bounded", "relatively constant", "essential", etc., and this applies similarly to the distinction between "relevant" and "negligible", both of which must be graded on a scale of "more or less", in answer to such questions as: "Relevant to what? Negligible in what context?"

This reminder is called for because of the justified emphasis placed by Bertalanffy (1952) on "open systems". True to my concept of the primacy of continuity and interrelatedness throughout the Universe, I must, of course, consider *all* systems as "open"—ideally and theoretically. But turning practical, I recognize that I can circumscribe many systems sufficiently broadly to let me deal with them empirically as if they were truly autonomous. In other words, on practical considerations, we accept their putative deviations from absolute autonomy as "negligible" (negligible; not non-existent), treat them as "essentially" autonomous, and call them "closed" systems. If later we discover that we have erred by drawing the boundary too narrowly, that is, by leaving out some "essential" interrelation formerly ignored as "negligible", e.g., interaction with the environment (see p. 266), we just go and correct our error by extending the borders of our definition. Logically, this does not change the system, but merely rectifies our earlier mistake. Basically, all systems must be expected to be open somewhere somehow. But leaving pedantry aside, we might just as well be practical and close them by empirical boundaries, subject to amendment.

11. *Systems—Theoretically Founded*

Having now at length presented the case for the hierarchical organization of living systems in rather assertive form, the time has come to document those assertions. The documentary evidence will have to be cursory, confined to a few illustrative examples. I shall present it in two parts: a brief theoretical one and a more elaborate concrete one dealing with the living cell.

On the theoretical side, there is a strictly logical test for the identification of a system. It rests on the nature of the interrelations between the units conceived of atomistically, through primary abstraction, as isolated, separate and autonomous. As pointed out earlier, as we reverse our steps from analysis to synthesis, we can identify unequivocal correlations between the behaviors of two such units (A,

B) once we have recognized them as mutually dependent. If we then test a third unit (C), whose properties we know, in its dependence on the state of the two others, we might arrive at an even higher synthetic insight, explaining A + B + C, and so forth, by stepwise additions (see the erector set analogy, p. 267). You note, however, that this would apply only for those particular cases in which our original primary abstraction has been empirically validated, that is, on the premise that the abstracted entities have actually been proved to be relatively autonomous. The fundamental distinction of a system is that this premise definitely does not apply as far as the relations among its constituents are concerned. Let us assume, for instance, a triplet of units, A, B, and C, each of which depends for its very existence upon interactions with, or contributions from, the other two. Then, obviously, we could not achieve a step-wise assembly of this triplet, the way we did before by first joining A to B and then adding C; for in the absence of C, neither A nor B could have been formed, existed or survived. In short, the *coexistence and cooperation of all three* is indispensable for the existence and operation of any one of them. This theorem reminds one of the many-body problem in physics.

Regardless of the pertinence of this comparison, however, the fact remains that, in empirical study, processes in living systems reveal themselves as just such networks of mutually interdependent tributaries to the integral operation of the whole group. It is impossible here to elaborate this summary statement any further, but a few simple examples might help to clarify its meaning. Systems of this type of "physical wholeness" can be simulated by inorganic analogies. A self-supporting arch is one example. Except by using mortar to cement stone to stone, one could never close an arch by piling loose stones upon one another because they start to slip off at the curvature. To stabilize an arch as a self-supporting structure, a keystone must be present. In other words, an arch can only exist in its entirety or not at all. Statically, it is a system. Of course, human imagination has found ways of building arches, piece by piece, by attaching every unit to its neighbor by mechanical cements, or by building a scaffolding, which holds the individual pieces in place until the keystone has been inserted to join the two halves and give the total structure its static equilibrium. But those are contrivances of a living system, the resourceful human brain, enabling a system to be synthesized from parts, a feat which could never have been accomplished without such help from another system: System begets system.

This conclusion leads right over to a more proximate example in living systems, namely, the reproduction of the macromolecules in the living cell. Even though this process is commonly referred to as "synthesis", it is radically different from what goes under the same name in inorganic chemistry. If chlorine and hydrogen are brought together, they will combine to hydrochloric acid, even if none of the end product has been present before. By contrast, the assembly of simple constituents into complex macromolecules in organic systems always requires the presence of a *ready-made* model of the product or, at any rate, a *template* of the same high degree of specificity, to guide the proper order of assemblage. The best studied case is, of course, the transcription of genes, segments of a string of deoxyribonucleic acid (DNA), into a corresponding sequence of ribonucleic acid (RNA), the orderly array of which is then translated into a corresponding serial pattern of amino acids in the formation of a protein.

Although this copying process of patterns and its various derivative manifestations, such as the highly specific catalysis of further macro-molecular species through the enzymatic action of proteins, is often referred to by verbs with the anthropomorphic prefix "self"–, these processes are no more "self"-engendered than an arch can be "self"-building; for in order to occur at all, they require the specific cooperation of their own terminal products, i. e., the enzyme systems, which, being indispensable prerequisites for all the links in the metabolic chains, including those for their own formation, thus close the circle of interdependent component processes to a coherent integrated system. Only the integral totality of such a system could with some justification be called "self-contained", "self-perpetuating", and "self-sustaining".

12. *The Living Cell—a System*

These brief theoretical contemplations lead over directly to the practical consideration of a living cell.[4] It is impossible to convey a

---

[4] Much of the specific documentation of examples and conclusions presented in the following sketchy survey of order in the living cell may be found in P. W. (1968).

reasonably accurate conception of a living cell by static illustrations on a printed page or in museum models, even when supplemented by verbal description. As a matter of fact, the frozen immobility and immutability of those text book illustrations has led to such abstruse misconceptions of a living cell that any portrayal would have to dwell more on what the actual cell is not, than on what it is. Unquestionably it has been that lack of realistic first-hand acquaintance with living cells which has been the source of some of the rather fictional current ideas, models and speculations regarding "the" cell, which, while innocent, have not always been innocuous in their effects on theory formation in the life sciences.

Therefore, I took the opportunity on many occasions to show motion pictures of living cells in action under a variety of controlled experimental conditions. The purpose was to free the common mental stereotype of a cell from the strait-jacket to which its static textbook illustrations have committed it. It is true that there are many specialized cell types in which the cell body encases itself in a rather rigid envelope, much as a caterpillar in a cocoon. Bacteria, plant cells, red blood cells, bone cells, are some examples. However, cell life, stripped down to its essentials, is best studied either before the cell has encased itself or after it has been liberated from its captivity in a densely packed tissue. This is done by the method of explantation or tissue culture, in which cells can be observed, manipulated, tested, and experimentally explored in their most basic behavior and reactivity. In studies of this kind, the vitality and viability of the cells under study must be meticulously preserved. Since this puts a natural limit on the scope of such investigations, one complements the limited knowledge attainable from living cells by killing, fixing, sectioning and staining the cell to render it amenable to microscopic inspection, and beyond the limits of the resolving power of the microscope, about two orders of magnitude further down, to examination under the electron microscope.

These morphological methods have opened to our view a microcosm of microscopic and sub-microscopic structures in various arrays of great regularity, specific for each kind and state of cell. But he who is not constantly shuttling back and forth between the observation of the living cell and the pictures of its dead, preserved inventory, is apt to forget that the latter gives us only momentary transient pictures of a system in unceasing change. Thus, what we recognize as static form, must be regarded as but an index of antecedent formative and transformative processes, comparable to a single still frame taken out of a motion picture film. Of course, taken all by itself, a static picture fails to reveal whether it portrays a momentary state of an on-going process or a permanent terminal condition. Unless this ambiguity is fully appreciated and constantly borne in mind, one runs the risk of mistaking the static picture of the cell for evidence of a mosaic of well-consolidated structures. I trust the following examples will clarify these facts.

13. Organelles—Subsystems

Figure 1 depicts a small fraction of a section through a cell as seen under the electron microscope. The two conspicuous sausage-like organelles are mitochondria, which are the "power plants" of the cell. Parallel to them you see a series of collapsed sacs ("cisternae") spaced out at regular intervals. These and the tubules and vesicles, seen in cross-sections, are dotted on the outside with particles, so-called ribosomes, also seen scattered throughout the field. Each mitochondrion shows in its interior transverse folds of surface membrane, spaced out again with some semblance of rhythmicity. What cannot be seen directly, but has been revealed by painstaking further research, is that the walls of these structures are populated by complexes of enzyme systems, not scattered at random, but arrayed in sequential order in accordance with the consecutive metabolic steps which they are to subserve.

Now, to break down in your minds the illusion of fixity evoked by this fixed specimen, let me point out that practically all you see in this picture is fleeting; and that goes even more so for what you do not see. A cell works like a big industry, which manufactures different products at different sites, ships them around to assembly plants, where they are combined into half-finished or finished products, to be eventually, with or without storage in intermediate facilities, either used up in the household of that particular cell or else extruded for export to other cells or as waste disposal. Modern research in molecular and cellular biology has succeeded in assigning to the various structures seen in the picture specific functional tasks in this intricate, but integrated,

Fig. 1. Electronmicroscopic view of an ultrathin section (thickness: 0.00005 mm) through part of a mammalian cell, magnified about 60,000 times. Explanation in text. (From D. W. Fawcett, "An Atlas of Fine Structure: The Cell—Its Organelles and Inclusions".—W. B. Saunders Co., Philadelphia and London, 1966)

industrial operation. There is a major flaw, however, in the analogy between a cell and a man-made factory. While in the latter, both building and machinery are permanent fixtures, established once and for all, many of the corresponding subunits in the system of the cell are of ephemeral existence in the sense that they are continuously or periodically disassembled and rebuilt, yet always each according to its kind and standard pattern. In contrast to a machine, the cell interior is heaving and churning all the time; the positions of granules or other details in the picture, therefore, denote just momentary way stations, and the different shapes of sacs or tubules signify only the degree of their filling at the moment. The only thing that remains predictable amidst the erratic stirring of the molecular population of the cytoplasm and its substructures is the overall pattern of dynamics which keeps the component activities in definable bounds of orderly restraints. These bounds again are not to be viewed as mechanically fixed structures, but as "boundary conditions"[5] set by the dynamics of the system as a whole. I am deliberately phrasing the conclusion in this symbolic and rather vague form in order to leave it noncommittal for future more precise specifications, as the symbolic language of systems thinking matures.

At the present, any more specific phrasing would be gratuitous if account is taken of the fact that a system not only maintains its unitary and integral dynamics beyond internal disturbances, but that the systemic unity and typical pattern can be restored even after thorough disruptions of continuity. The case is best illustrated by the readily observable transformations of that remarkable structure in our picture, the mitochondrion. Not only is it highly mobile, squirming worm-like back and forth across the cell space to places where energy is needed for special work, but it frequently breaks into pieces, which then can fuse again with other pieces. In fact, by placing a cell into a slightly acid medium, all its mitochondria can be made to break up into small spherical beads which, upon return of the cell to normal medium, merge again into strings eventually resuming the appearance and internal structure of a normal mitochondrion, as represented in our

---

[5]The concept of "boundary conditions" in living systems presumably owes its origin, and certainly its articulation, to Polanyi (1968). It is crucial to the position taken in this paper.

picture. On the next lower level, even mitochondrial enzyme systems, when dispersed, can reaggregate into their typical space order, and it has been demonstrated that such clusters can carry out their specific enzymatic function only in those particular ordered constellations.

What we are learning from such lessons is that the features of order, manifested in the particular form of a structure and the regular array and distribution of its substructures, is no more than the visible index of regularities of the underlying dynamics operating in its domain. The near-constant interval, for instance, between the collapsed cisternae or between the internal cross folds of a mitochondrion, reveals simply a rhythmicity in the interactions within such a group, which results in characteristically spaced crests and valleys of conditions favoring the aggregation and assembly of higher order arrays. We encounter here the phenomenon of the emergence of singularities in a dynamic system— unique points, or lines or planes—, comparable, for instance, to nodal points in a vibrating string. This may serve as an example for the "emergence" of sub-patterns within a system with defined boundaries by free interactive dynamics. It is the converse of attaining a given form by the consecutive stacking of modules on top of one another, or of the turning out of a machine product in precisely programmed steps.

Significantly, living systems contain models of *both* types, that is, of free integral systems operations, as well as of serial machine procedures. Much argument in biological theorizing could have been avoided if this fact had been more generally recognized. Even so, the more general and primary type is the systemic one, for when we look at the components through which a very machine-like operation in an organism is carried out—for instance, at the individual nerve cells which compose a stereotyped reflex arc—, we find that these elements themselves operate, within their own active domain, according to the systems principle, so that the "causal chain" reveals itself as a series of systems operations.

Let us remember, then, in summary, that as we move down from the cell as a whole to progressively smaller samples of its entity, we encounter (a) rather well-defined and relatively stable complexes of functional and structural properties which are embedded in, and mutually related through, (b) matrices of much less well-defined, more fleeting configurations, allowing their constituent parts or elements a much higher range of freedom than could be reconciled with a micromechanical concept of a cell.

14. *Ascent to "Suprasystems"*

Let us now proceed in the opposite direction and look at those higher-order cell patterns of which the organelles, dealt with in the foregoing as relatively sovereign units, appear now as subaltern components. I choose as my first example the spermium. It is shown in Fig. 2, in low magnification in the inset, flanked by higher-power

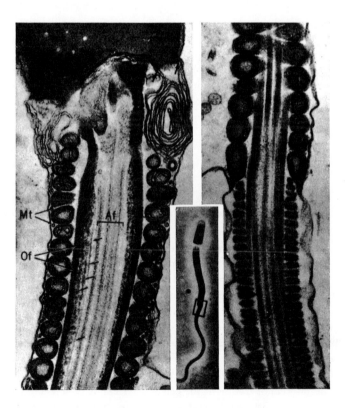

Fig. 2. Spermium, as seen (center) at microscopic magnification and (left and right) in electronmicroscopic views of anterior and posterior regions. (From Bloom and Fawcett, *A Textbook of Histology*. Ninth Edition. W. B. Saunders Co., Philadelphia and London, 1968)

magnifications (under the electron microscope), the left one taken near the head, the right one at the base of the tail. You realize that this whole complicated and beautifully organized structure is the content of a single cell. The two rows of roundish bodies in the sheath are mitochondria (Mt), arrayed in file, while the cylindrical core contains long whip-like cilia (Af) of a remarkable fine structure to be described presently. The detailed architecture of sperm is characteristically different for each species, hence is referred to as "genetically determined" (see later). Unfortunately, we are completely ignorant as to how the germinal sperm cell ("spermatocyte") transforms itself into such a remarkably complex, typically structured architecture. Yet, what we can infer from Fig. 2 is that it is not formed by the stacking up of appropriately pre-hewn pieces, like building a smokestack from bricks, though even such a human construction would not end up straight unless kept in alignment by over-all controls of the assembly process. The individual mitochondria, for instance, are capriciously different from one another, and yet, the composite structure as a whole is of impressive regularity of over-all design. In short, what we have illustrated above for a single mitochondrion, namely, the far greater regularity of the total configuration of the individual organelle, as compared to the capriciousness of detail among its component features, repeats itself now on the higher level, at which those same organelles that we had met as systems in their own right appear as sub-units of the higher system of the cell.

These few examples may suffice to illustrate, first, that in the cell certain definite rules of order apply to the dynamics of the *whole* system, in the present case reflected in the orderliness of the overall architectural design, which cannot be explained in terms of any underlying orderliness of the constituents; and second, that the over-all order of the cell as a whole does not impose itself upon the molecular population directly, but becomes effective through intermediate ordering steps, delegated to sub-systems, each of which operates within its own, more limited authority. What I have tried to summarize here for the internal operation of the cell as a system, is then re-encountered on a still higher level as the basic principle in the functional organization of cells into tissues and organs, up to the body as a whole. To give just a cursory illustration of this ascent on the hierarchical scale, I have selected the following two examples.

Fig. 3 shows a tangential section grazing the surface of a ciliate protozoan. Each one of the round structures is the cross-section through a single cilium. Being slightly oblique, the section takes us through layers of different depths, from naked cores, through the appearance of a sheath around each single cilium, to the presence of a common envelope around each row. Each core shows a circumferential array of nine doublets of fibrils with a little hook, arranged pinwheel fashion, with radial connections to a central pair of fibers. All cilia, from those of protozoans and algae through the whole plant and animal kingdom all the way up to man, are built with only minor modifica-

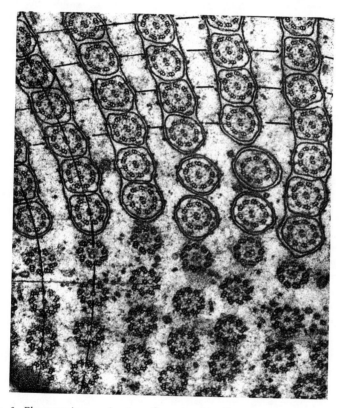

Fig. 3. Electronmicroscopic view of an ultrathin slice grazing the surface of a ciliate infusorium. Magnified about 50,000 times. For details, see text. (Courtesy of I. Gibbons)

tions according to this standard fine-structural pattern. As were the mitochondrial rows in the sperm tail, so here again the individual cilia are aligned in rows into higher-order assemblies, which as you note, combine a remarkable geometric regularity in the gross with capricious deviations in detail. You also note, besides the equidistant parallel tracts of rows, a further lateral alignment among the cilia, which runs crosswise from row to row, as indicated by the lines in the top part of the picture. The fact that the actual positions of individual cilia deviate from the exact nodal points, at which the ideal line systems of this planar grid intersect, gives further evidence of the systemic nature of this architecture with its well defined over-all design, but with departures from it in the details of the component units. It is not too farfetched to see in such grids on the sub-microscopic level an analogy to the lattice structure of crystals—a concept which I have documented under the name of "macrocrystallinity" in several of my earlier publications. To dwell on it here would take us too far afield.

The next hierarchic step takes us now from this highly structured single-celled organism to Fig. 4, which illustrates the occurrence of similar geometric patterns in the tissues of multi-cellular animals. The picture gives a low-power enlarged view of the surface of a leopard's tongue. Two types of sub-structures are visible, representing tastebuds and papillae. As in the previous case, they are again arrayed in a regular grid. In this case, however, each unit is multi-cellular, i. e., consists itself of a large number of cells. Microscopic study shows that even though each unit has the shape, size and orientation typical of its kind, there is not only no corresponding regularity in the detailed configuration of the population of component cells, but there is actually continual change in the composition of the cell population, cell death being compensated by cell proliferation. Each unit behaves as a multicellular system.

Yet, these multicellular units are themselves subordinated to a pattern of still higher order, which defines the positions of the units as the intercepts of a grid of two essentially perpendicular line systems. As before, one notes a sufficiently wide range of departures from mathematical accuracy to rule out any notion that the total pattern could be merely the net resultant of a neat serial stacking of the individual units. It is important to stress that although some irregular-ities of such adult patterns reflect secondary distortions during the

Fig. 4. Low-power photograph of the surface of a leopard's tongue. (Courtesy of the late Professor Zeiger, Hamburg)

growth process, there is plenty of evidence at hand to prove that even the earliest stages in their development fail to display the rigorous microprecision of arrangement among the elements as to position, alignment and interstices which one would have to postulate in order to ascribe the total pattern to a stepwise compilation of micro-patterned building blocks. In fact, if the insurance of an orderly architecture at the end had to rest on nothing but an orderly initial pattern, no such final orderliness could ever be expected unless systemic regulation on the way would hold the pattern together; for otherwise the fortuitous local differences in growth activities would lead not only to the usual minor distortions, but to wellnigh complete obliteration, of the initial pattern.

I do not mean to labor the point further. I have set forth a representative series of examples to document that the study of the behavior of cells and cell groups, whether in development or physiological functioning, makes it imperative to postulate systemic order on *supramolecular* levels; that is, dynamics within collectives which restrains the degrees of freedom of the components in such a manner as to insure concert in attaining, maintaining, and if necessary, restoring, the integral pattern of the whole; and further, that each constituent sub-system in the hierarchy has its own, more limited, degree of systemic sovereignty to deal with its subordinate component units in a similar manner as it has been dealt with as a member of the superior collective.

This statement is, in essence, a purely descriptive one. It is non-committal in regard to preferences for couching systems properties in either "holistic" or "reductionist" terms; for as I indicated at the beginning, and have discussed more fully elsewhere (Chapter 17), both are in a demonstrable complementarity relation in the sense that either one conveys information which the other cannot supply. Consequently, the acknowledgement of *field continua* as ordering principles in systems on the *integral* level is as valid and indispensable as is the practical acceptance, on the *differential* level, of *discrete singularities* within those continua, whether sub-atomic particles, atoms, molecules, molecular assemblies, organelles, cells, or cell assemblies, as in our last picture. I have yet to encounter any phenomena in the living system which could be adequately and completely described without reference to such a dualistic scheme.

Let me also point out once more that my sole aim is the purely pragmatic task of listing, in the spirit of Kirchhoff, the irreducible minimum of descriptive statements necessary for the representation of natural phenomena not only truthfully, but *completely*. This precept must also pervade the terminology we use to express our observations and inferences. Even though such terminology will differ according to whether we move from the undismembered whole down to the parts or back up from the atomized elements, eventually the two versions must become unequivocally related and mutually consistent. This implies that, as I said earlier, nothing need be assumed to exist in a whole separately and separably, than what exists in the totality of its constituent parts. What must be added on the way up is only the restoration of information content of which the system has been deprived in its physical or mental atomization.

15. *The Brain—a System*

It might have been more pertinent to the topic of this discourse to deal specifically with the functions of the *brain* as a hierarchically organized system rather than with the general cellular system. The advantage of the latter, however, is that its morphological aspects provide us with directly perceptible indicators of what remains invariant during a given period and what does not; for as I have indicated before, living form must be regarded as essentially an overt indicator or clue for the less accessible dynamics of the underlying formative processes. Thus, cell structure serves in much the same way as the height of a mercury column in a thermometer or the excursions of a needle in a galvanometer serve to signal changes of thermal and electric states. Yet, for the systems dynamics of the brain we possess no equally reliable recorders. True, our introspective self-knowledge confirms to the private satisfaction of every one of us that all those conclusions about systemic order and its hierarchic structure that I have outlined for the body and its cells are equally valid for our brain activity. But when we look for more "objective" testimony, we find ourselves up against the limits of our methods of detection and assay. Microanatomy gives us only numerical, geometric and geographic data; using electric instruments, we get electric answers; using chemical techniques, we get chemical information; and so forth. However, we still do not have any inkling of how those fragmentary items of information, obtained analytically, could be combined into a faithful image of the unitary and orderly behavior of our central nervous system, of which we are privately conscious and the expressions of which we can observe in the overt behavior of others.

Nonetheless, the outlook is not quite so dim. Critical studies of brain alterations are increasingly providing us with clues, if not on how the systemic behavior of the brain does arise and operate, at least on how it does not. Pertinent evidence comes mostly from neuropathology and the study of experimental brain lesions, but partly also from the poorly exploited field of neuroembryology, which presents us with embryonic brains displaying typically patterned activity prior to any

experience with the outer world, and above all, prior to the emergence
of structures and functional properties, the significance of which would
otherwise have to be tested laboriously and traumatically by artificial
elimination in later life. In a monograph, to which I must refer here for
further information (P. W. 1941, reprinted in P. W. 1968), I have
summarized some of the crucial evidence for the systemic hierarchical
principle of operation of the lower parts of the central nervous system.
That the conclusions reached there can be extended to the brain as a
whole, is not only plausible, but in the light of our foregoing
conclusions about the organism and its cells, axiomatic, since, after all,
the brain is but an organized system of interacting cell complexes.

Of all the features of our subjective knowledge of our brain
activities for which we want science to produce an objective record, one
of the most hotly debated ones has been the aspect of "freedom of
decision" or "free will". The issue has been argued almost entirely on
philosophic grounds. That is a domain which, as I stated in the
introduction, I feel too uninformed and uninitiated to enter. However,
since some of the philosophical discussions have hinged on the
interpretation of certain unfavorable verdicts pronounced by science, it
seems indicated in this place to re-examine briefly the tenability of the
respective positions. The way I see it, looking from the outside in, the
problem of free will has been treated in general as a corollary of the
problem of *determinism*, and the problem of determinism, conversely,
has been laid at the doorstep of science for an opinion. Science deals
with nature; as long as science keeps on presenting nature as a
micromechanical precision machinery run by strict causality, the
concession of any degree of freedom of choice to any natural
phenomenon would be inadmissible by the code of that brand of
science, and hence, would have to be denied to all processes of nature,
including human brain functions. One would then be forced to adopt
the alternative of crediting "free will" to the intervention of extra- or
supernatural powers.

16. *Determinism, Stratified*

To me both of these extreme positions seem to be untenable in the
light of critical scientific inspection. The flaw lies in equating science
with the doctrine of micro-precise causality, or as I shall call it in the

following, "*micro-determinism*". This brings me to the major lesson to which I have been building up in this article and which I have anticipated in the title as "Determinism Stratified", which is precisely what the study of living nature teaches us.

To judge whether or not there are philosophers or theologians who might get comfort from a scientific image of the Universe made up of a mosaic of discrete particles, operating by laws of micro-causality, is beyond my ken. All I submit is that modern science cannot deliver such a picture in good faith, least of all life science; and since all science is the product of human brains and brains are living systems, it is quite likely that this abrogation of scientific rationale for micro-causality applies to science in general.

Scientifically, the term "determined" can only mean "determinable", and similarly, "indeterminacy", whether in the sense of Heisenberg or in the way I shall use the term, can only mean "indeterminability". The scientific concept of "determinability" is of decidedly empirical origin. As we observe a given macrosample of the Universe over a given stretch of time, we note certain unequivocal correlations between configurations of its content at the beginning and at the end of that period of change. If then we find those correlations verified with recurrent consistency, we set them up as "laws", from which to extrapolate future changes with a sense of certainty. As our primary experience in this operation has only correlated macro-samples with macro-samples, predictability based on it can likewise be no finer than *macroscopic*. So, legitimately we could only speak of "macro-determinacy".

The concept of "microdeterminacy" is then derived secondarily by a hypothetical downward extension—"atomization", as it were—of empirical "macrodeterminacy". Microdeterminacy submits that one would observe the same high degree of consistency of correlation from beginning to end that had been ascertained for the macrosample to hold true for every one of those fractional samples. In other words, the structure of the well-defined macro-change would be simply a composite of the mosaic of micro-changes assumed to be equally well-defined, even if not necessarily determinable.

This tenet is demonstrably untenable in its application to living systems. We have recognized the state and changes of such systems as being conservatively invariant over a given period, and hence predictable, without a correspondingly invariant micro-mosaic of the component processes. We had to conclude, therefore, that the patterned structure of the dynamics of the system as a whole "coordinates" the activities of the constituents. In atomistic microdeterministic terms, this "coordination" would have to be expressed as follows: Since any movement or other change of any part of the system deforms the structure of the whole complex, the fact that the system as a whole tends to retain its integral configuration implies that every change of any one part affects the interactions among the rest of the population in such a way as to yield a net countervailing resultant; and this for every single part. Couched in anthropomorphic language, this would signify that at all times every part "knows" the stations and activities of every other part and "responds" to any excursions and disturbances of the collective equilibrium as if it also "knew" just precisely how best to preserve the integrity of the whole system in concert with the other constituents. Although rarely expressed so bluntly, much of this imagery lurks behind such equally anthropomorphic terms as "organizers", "regulators", "control mechanisms" and the like, which particularists have had to invoke in order to fill the information gap between what one can learn from isolated elements and a valid description of group behavior.

The Boltzmann theorem and thermodynamics have realistically bypassed the gap by confining safe statements about macro-relations to macro-samples only. They relate unequivocally the average state of a system at time t_1 to its average state at time t_2, but realize that tracing an individual molecule through that course is not only not feasible but would be scientifically totally uninteresting and inconsequential; for it would in each individual instance and instant be of nonrecurrent uniqueness, hence valueless for any detailed predictability of future micro-events. If physics has had the sense of realism to divorce itself from micro-determinism on the molecular level, there seems to be no reason why the life sciences, faced with the fundamental similitude between the arguments for the renunciation of molecular micro-determinacy in both thermodynamics and systems dynamics, should not follow suit and adopt "macro-determinacy" regardless of whether or not the behavior of a system as a whole is reducible to a stereotyped performance by a fixed array of pre-programmed micro-robots. Since experience has positively shown such unequivocal macro-relations to exist on various supramolecular levels of the hierarchy of living processes in the documented absence of componental micro-determinacy, we evidently must let such positive scientific insights prevail over sheer conjectures and preconceptions, however cherished and ingrained in our traditional thinking they may be.

17. Macrodeterminacy

In order to drive home this lesson, I am adding in Fig. 5 a diagrammatic model of macro-determinacy from a recent book (P. W. 1970), in which I have dealt with the problem more fully. The diagram shows the transition of a living system from a state S′ to a state S″. As is indicated in Fig. 5A, the system S′, comprising sub-systems A′,B′,C′,D′,E′,

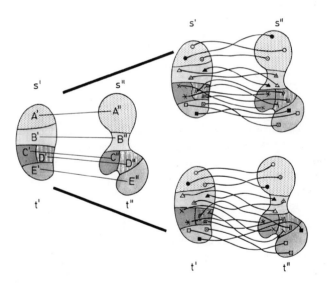

Fig. 5. Diagram symbolizing the changes in the development of two individual germs from the stage at time t′ to that at time t″; the upper and lower courses correspond in "macroview" of overall pattern, but differ in "microview" of detail, as explained in text

develops between times t_1 and t_2 into the modified system, S″, each sub-system of which at t_2 can be traced back to a corresponding sub-system at t_1; this makes the pattern of t_2 explicable, that is, predictable, hence, determinable or "determined", as a direct transform, piece by piece, of the macro-constellation of component sub-systems at t_1, the sub-systems having kept their relative positions and relations.

This kind of mosaic correlation between two stages permits an embryologist, for instance, to identify specific regions of an early embryo as being the predictably earmarked forerunners for the formation of heart, liver, kidney, brain, etc., respectively. Yet, in looking at the diagram 5B, we note that such clearcut correlations no longer hold for smaller samples of each sub-system, represented by the various symbols. In other words, if we were to follow individual cells of these various prospective organ areas from the earlier into the later period, we would find them to take far more fortuitous courses, differing individually from case to case; this is indicated by the lack of correspondence between the upper and lower sets of lines connecting symbols from S′ to S″ for two embryos of the same species. This fact is so well established in embryology that one has even gotten to referring to the process which changes a cell from its originally "indeterminate" and multivalent condition into one definitely committed for a given fate, as the process of "determination".

The same principle as illustrated here for development repeats itself at all orders of magnitude: Let us review, for instance, the establishment of organelle structures within the cell, or of the finer substructures within organelles.

A mitochondrion, in being reconstituted after fragmentation, will order lipid molecules into the characteristic lamellar configuration seen in figure 1, but the new position will not be a precise replica of the former one, nor will the lipid molecules in the pool know which ones will be recruited. Likewise on the next lower level, the enzymes in regularly seriated clusters, which are to dot the new mitochondrial lamellae (see page 284), do not know their final arrangements until they are in place; and so forth.

I could go on to confirm the validity of this principle of *determinacy in the gross despite demonstrable indeterminacy in the small* for practically any level and area of the life sciences. In order to take account of this hierarchical repetitiveness, I have suggested the simile of "grain size" of determinacy as an empirical measurement for the degree of definition and predictability at any given level. The mosaic of organ rudiments mapped out in the early embryo, for instance, is very "coarse-grained", whereas the mosaic of genes in the chromosome is far more "fine-grained" (see below). It is immaterial at this juncture whether or not the principle is rigorous in a philosophical sense. What counts is that, scientifically speaking, it is as realistic and logical a proposition as we can deduce from the facts accessible to scientific observation and experimentation.

As you will note, one could turn this renunciation of the primacy of micro-determinacy into a positive scientific declaration in favor of the existence of "free will". I prefer to give it a more restrained interpretation, for it really implies no positive commitment. What it does, is simply remove the spurious objections and injunctions against the scientific legitimacy of the concept of freedom of decision that have been raised from within the scientific sector, or from other camps leaning on supposedly scientific verdicts. I cannot see that science can prove free will but, on the other hand, I can see nothing in what we know in the life sciences that would contradict it on scientific grounds. To go beyond this neutral statement, would be a matter solely of private belief, conviction, or opinion, without objective evidence, and hence quite irrelevant to a public discussion.

18. *A Canon for Determinacy*

Lest there be misunderstandings about my thesis of macrodeterminacy which is not explainable in terms of aggregates of microdeterminate events, let me review briefly the major way stations to this conclusion.

1. Nature presents itself to us primarily as a continuum.

2. In scanning this continuum, we recognize complexes of phenomena which retain identity and show a high degree of stability and persistence of pattern, in contrast to other samples with less cohesive features.

3. Success of science over the ages has validated the abstraction involved in our dealing with such reasonably constant entities as if they had an autonomous existence of their own.

4. Some phenomena of nature can be reconstructed in practice, or at least in our minds, from the analytical knowledge of properties, interrelations and interactions of such putatively isolated entities.

5. Some of the sciences, particularly the physical sciences, have confined themselves mostly to the consideration of phenomena amenable to the treatment according to Point 4.

6. In the life sciences, there are likewise many questions which can be answered satisfactorily by the recombinatory method according to Point 4.

7. Understanding of the integrality of a living system, however, has proved, on logical grounds, refractory to the same methods, and the empirical study of life processes has discounted, on factual grounds, the probability of future success.

8. The preceding point implies that it is logically and factually gratuitous to postulate that the methods of Point 4, successful in Points 5 and 6, must necessarily also be sufficient to restore completely the loss of information about the dynamics of *systems* suffered in their analytical atomization. By the same token, restrictive injunctions against descriptions of living phenomena in terms other than those compatible with Points 5 and 6 can no longer be upheld.

9. The *systems concept* proves applicable to the description of those phenomena in living systems which defy description purely in terms of micro-mechanical cause-effect chain reactions; it thus lends substance to the principle of systemic organization.

10. Applying the systems concept, an organism as a system reveals itself as encompassing and operating through the agency of sub-systems, each of which, in turn, contains and operates through groups of systems of still lower order, and so on down through molecules into the atomic and sub-atomic range.

11. The fact that the top level operations of the organism thus are neither structurally nor functionally referable to direct liaison with the processes on the molecular level in a steady continuous gradation, but are relayed step-wise from higher levels of determinacy (or "certainty of determinability") through intermediate layers of greater freedom or variance (or "uncertainty of determinability") to next lower levels of again more rigorously ascertainable determinacy, constitutes the *principle of hierarchical organization*.

12. Although I have emphasized for didactic reasons the relatively conservative features of systems, the uni-directional change of systems

must not be overlooked. We find it expressed, for instance, in the mutability of systemic patterns in evolution, ontogeny, maturation, learning, etc., as well as in the capacity for systems to combine into what then appear as super-systems with the emerging properties of *novelty* and *creativity*.

This set of twelve points represents a sort of conceptual canon, based on empirical studies, against which theoretical pronouncements and formulations in the life sciences ought to be checked. As you will recognize, some statements in the current literature would fail the test of validation in terms of these criteria, while some others would even seem totally irreconcilable with the principle of *stratified* determinism. One in this latter class that comes immediately to mind is the prevailing notion of *"genetic determinism"*. A few comments on this issue are therefore called for. A less cursory discussion of the subject may be found in the book referred to above (P. W. 1970).

19. *Genetic Determinism, Scrutinized*

The term "genetically determined" means three different things to three different groups of people: (1) the broad-gauged student of genetics, who is thoroughly familiar with the underlying facts and uses the term simply as a shorthand label to designate unequivocal relations between certain genes and certain "characters" of an organism; (2) scientists in various other branches who are not familiar with the actual content of the term and accept it literally in its verbal symbolism; and (3) the public at large, to whom the term frequently imparts unwittingly the fatalistic outlook in life, frustrating in its hopelessness, of an inexorably pre-set existence and fixed course toward a pre-ordained destiny. In the present context, I shall concern myself only with the first of these three groups, because many of its practitioners seem addicted to a doctrinal orthodoxy that is clearly at variance with the picture of living processes I have tried to present in this article. The source of the discrepancy is easy to spot. It lies not in factual inconsistency, but merely in the phraseology used, which, if one stops to think, turns out to be a queer hybrid between brilliantly established analytic facts and scientifically spurious anthropomorphic lingo. Like the mule, the hybrid has proved to be viable but not fertile. Very briefly, here is an account of its origin.

Basically, genetics proceeds by the same analytical technique that I have described in the early part of this article as the progressive dissection and subsequent mental isolation of features of the world around us that have aroused our interest by their constancy. As we sharpen our view, our attention is drawn to specific *differences* between entities whose generic aspects are indistinguishable. Eyes, as the organs of vision, are in essence the same throughout a species, but the iris of some appears black, in others blue, and in albinos transparent. And similarly, the same object, hair, occurs in distinctive varieties of dark or blond, or red, as well as straight or wavy or krinkled. In our analytic mood, we then abstract those various differential criteria from their generic carrier objects and confer upon them mentally a measure of autonomy, which they may or may not merit. Since "genetically determined" black pigment, for instance, can be bodily extracted from black eyes and black hair as a proteinaceous substance and since the "genetically determined" absence of it in blue eyes and blond hair is traceable to a gene defect, we feel entitled to deal with it without regard of the eyes or hair that carry it, that is, to concede to the gene-color correlation substantive identity. But does this also entitle us to think that an eye can really be resolved simply into a bundle of such "gene-determined" attributes, so that if we just kept on stripping them off one by one, we would end up with no substantive entity left over of which those attributes were merely qualifying variables? In other words, what makes for "eyeness" in the integral formative dynamics of an eye? Evidently, by consistently promoting in this manner *adjectives* to the rank of *substantives*, we have, by definition, vested genes with the exclusive "responsibility" for organization and order in an organism. (It is worth noting, incidentally, that the term "responsibility", so commonly interspersed in reductionist "explanations", is again an anthropomorphic reference to a system—the human brain.)

It has been one of the most spectacular triumphs of analytical science to have demonstrated that many of the observed *differentials* among features within a given species of organisms can be unequivocally correlated with corresponding *differentials* between the chromosomes of the respective varieties and that these chromosomal differences can be further resolved into differences in the array of sequences of nucleic acid residues along the backbone of the helical macromolecule of deoxyribonucleic acid (DNA). Segments of those gigantic macromolecules for which such differences of composition can be demonstrated or compellingly inferred are, therefore, the molecular counterparts of what with a purely symbolic term for units of inheritance of characters used to be called "genes". So far, so good. Overt differences between "characters", that is, specific attributes of a body, have been linked indisputably with specific differences in the structure of a macromolecule. This is all beautiful and straightforward.

One then was faced, however, with the major problem of how it would be possible, true to the spirit of scientific parsimony, to reconstruct from the knowledge of those elemental units the higher entity of an harmoniously built and coordinately functioning organism. Let us recall that genetic methodology can only test *differences* between organisms. As I just pointed out, it can deal with differential properties of eyes or of hair, but cannot elucidate the nature of "eyeness" or "hairness", as such. In other words, we know of no "genes for eye" or "genes for hair" that could explain the basic formative dynamics by which those systems attain and retain their generic configurations, even though we know plenty of genes referring to differences in their specific styles of architecture and properties of building stuffs.

Lest there be further misinterpretations, let me remark that such phrases as "genes for eye*less*ness" (anophthalmia) or "genes for hair*less*ness" do not refer to properties of eyes or hair at all, but signify differentials among other conditions of the body, either permissive or repressive, as the case may be, for the processes of eye formation or hair formation, without being in the least concerned with the organizational pattern of those processes themselves. In conclusion, there is neither logical nor factual support for the supposition that organization can be explained in reference to gene interactions *alone*.

Nevertheless, the claim of the gene for recognition as the sole ordering principle in organisms persists with undiminished tenacity: the rigorously and conservatively ordered array of components in the molecular gene string is proclaimed as the sovereign source of *all* order in an organic "system"; the term "system", in that event, being decidedly a misnomer. As far as I can discover, this claim rests on sheer assertion, based on blind faith and unqualified reductionistic preconceptions. But if one examines the phraseology in which the claim has been presented, one recognizes that its proponents have by no means been unmindful of the problem of the organizational wholeness of the organism. Their error lay in the manner in which they tried to overcome, or rather, gloss over, the difficulty of the problem.

Instead of reversing the rigorous objective methodology, which has marked the successful descent from the organism to the gene, and exploring how far one could effectively synthethize any system of higher order from nothing but genes in free interaction in an environment devoid of order, they took recourse to pretentious anthropomorphic terms, which evaded and obscured the issue. One simply bestowed upon the gene the faculty of spontaneity, the power of "dictating", "informing", "regulating", "controlling", etc., the orderless processes in its unorganized milieu, so as to mold the latter into the coordinated teamwork that is to culminate in an accomplished organism. It is at once evident that all those terms are borrowed from the vocabulary of *human systems behavior*, especially the brain; in short, terms reserved for precisely the kind of complex group dynamics that cannot be pieced together by sheer summation of componental contributions. Therefore, to contend that genes can "determine" the systemic wholeness of the organism, while at the same time being driven to invoking the systems analogy of brain action in order to endow gene action with the required integrating power, is logically such a circular argument that we can readily dismiss it from serious scientific consideration.

Besides this *logical* flaw, the speculation about gene monopoly in organization meets also with *factual* contradictions. They pertain to the very premise that genes operate in a random, disorganized matrix. In the first place, unless we want to vest genes with animistic powers, we cannot grant to them the faculty for spontaneous "action". They can only *interact*; but interact with what? With a disordered molecular population, to which they, as the expression goes, "transmit the needed ordering information"? The transfer of order from DNA through RNA to protein is well-attested, comparable to the translation of *words* from one language into another. But how to get from words to the meaningfull *syntax* of language? One might concede that the change from the coded polypeptide chains to protein and tertiary conformations of the latter into highly specific configurations might be regarded as steps up to a next higher level of organization, like forming words from syllables. But then, where do we go from there: Even considering that proteins with enzymatic functions are instrumental in the synthesis of the other species of macro-molecules, this still would leave us only with a bag of molecular units milling around in thermal agitation. And if one were to point to the further fact that such compounds can link up chemically into still more complex composite units with solid structure, one would get even further away from the realistic picture of a living cell, which, as I have indicated, rules out any portrayal of organization that intimates a piece-meal origin through the consecutive assemblage of building stones.

20. *Development—a Hierarchic Systems Operation*

The conflict vanishes with the realization that genes, highly organized in themselves, do not impart higher order upon an orderless milieu by ordainment, but that they themselves are part and parcel of an ordered system, in which they are enclosed and with the patterned dynamics of which they interact. The organization of this supra-genic system, the organism, does not ever originate in our time by "spontaneous generation"; it has been ever present since the primordial living systems, passed down in uninterrupted continuity from generation to generation through the organic matrix in which the genome is encased. The organization of this continuum is a paradigm of hierarchical order. I have schematized it in Figure 6 by concentric shells which, in this case,

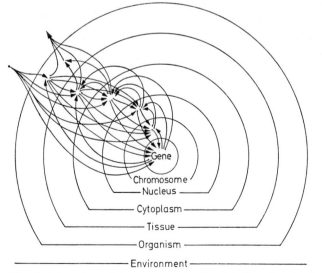

Fig. 6. Interactive relations among the hierachically ordered subsystems of an organism. (From P. W. 1968)

coincide with physical enclosures. The diagram is self-explanatory. The profusion of arrows indicates pathways of all possible interactions that must be taken into account in studying the dynamics of this system, organism.

Now, let us start our consideration of the time continuum of living generations with a particular egg, containing in its nucleus the inner sanctum, the chromosomes with their genes. An egg is not a nutrient solution for the genome to feed on, but it is a full-fledged organism, equivalent in its systemic features with other single-celled organisms (e.g., the protozoans illustrated in Figure 3), having derived these features directly from its prior existence as a germ cell in the maternal body (see below). We know that in its crust, the egg cytoplasm consists of an orderly mosaic pattern of fields (see P. W. 1939), the typically different properties of which map out the dynamics of specific organ districts, as was mentioned earlier (p. 296). As the egg nucleus divides, the derivative daughter-nuclei, therefore, come to lie into specifically disparate domains, which later, in their ensuing interactions with the nuclear genome, become further modified; and as this interplay between plasma and nucleus in the steadily increasing cell population continues, the genic environment becomes progressively diversified. In all this, the genes themselves do not significantly change; their pattern is replicated stereotypically in practically all cells of a given individual throughout development. Yet, each cell's genome is, and always has been, a captive of an *ordered* environment. While the genome contributes to the specific properties of that environment in mutual interactions with it during the whole course of embryogenesis, it is only by virtue of the primordial frame of organization of the *cytoplasm* of the egg that an individual can maintain from the very start the unity of overall design, to which the masses of freely mobile scalar entities of lower order, including the cells and nuclei with their chromosomes and genes, owe the "microdeterminacy" of their eventual fates.

In this incessant interplay, the latitude for epigenetic vagaries of the component elements on all levels, indicated by the arrows in Fig. 6, is immense.[6] And yet, the end products turn out to be far more similar than one could expect if there were no conservative systems dynamics

---

[6] For a penetrating discussion of the epigenetic course of development in relation to genic participation, consult Waddington (1962).

in operation to guard the over-all design. Hierarchic stepwise delegation of tasks to sub-systems is ostensibly nature's efficient device to let an organism keep order without having to deal with all its trillions of molecules directly.

In conclusion, genetics alone can account rather precisely for the differences between attributes of such systems as cells or organs or organisms, but for a complete definition of the integral subjects which carry and display those attributes, genetics must call on *systems dynamics* for supplementation; and reductionism must call on holistic succor, often disguised by anthropomorphic phraseology. The dynamism of organization is *dualistic*. The coarse-grain macrodeterminacy of the systemic plasma domains, in which the genomes reside, is, through the interactions with the fine-grain microdeterminacy of the rigorously structured genes, progressively translated and consolidated into more detailed and specific definition—"from the general to the specific"—, without the organism or its parts ever losing their free systemic dynamics entirely while they are alive. The loss of those integrative dynamics is the mark of death.

In order to make more concrete this necessarily general and formal presentation, let me just give one specific illustration for the systemic network operation through which the macro-pattern of an egg is progressively converted into the detailed structural and functional pattern of the mature individual. Fig. 7 is a flow chart of some of the major tributary processes that lead from the egg with its dual endowment,—genes, embedded in ooplasm (top of figure)—, to the finished functioning brain and spinal cord (bottom of figure). The boxed-in titles are labels for some of the major component processes that have been singled out from the total developmental fabric for analytical study; the arrows represent actually identified dependencies between those processes, that is, pairwise dynamic connections between boxes, each of which in isolated consideration, appears as a linear cause-effect chain. But as soon as we raise our sights back from the artificially detached single threads to the total context, we recognize the true intricacy of the systemic fabric, in which "everything depends on everything else", just as I have outlined it above for the lower level of the molecular ecology of the cell.

If the total network were not so coherent and conservatively unitary in its overall dynamics, no two nervous systems could ever

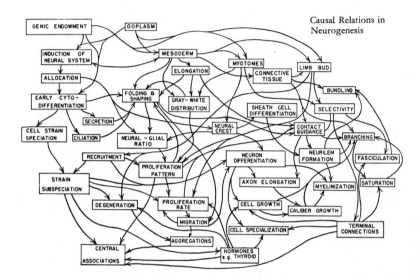

Fig. 7. Some demonstrated interdependencies and interactions in the development of a mature nervous system (bottom level) from a fertilized egg (top level). (From P. W. 1968)

resort ffom the developmental cauldron with even the faintest mutual resemblance; for it has been precisely the analytical study of the single "cause-effect" nexuses which has impressively demonstrated the enormous unpredictable variability of each tributary component from case to case, which mountingly compounded, as ontogeny proceeds, would blur and finally obliterate all initial order. So, what holds them all together in coordination under an overall design? The usual answer is: "control processes." If these are visualized as coequal to arrows, the answer is partly correct, partly misleading. As I pointed out earlier (p. 284), there are examples of programmed linear "feedback" pathways to be found in organismus. But they are decidedly *not* fair samples of the general method of organismic systems operation. Paraphrasing the

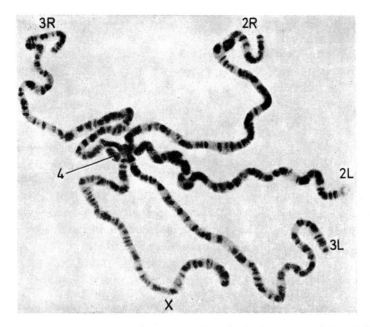

Fig. 8. Giant chromosomes from the salivary gland of an insect. The aperiodic "banding", expressing the linear sequential order of genes, is as strictly identical among the chromosome sets of all cells of an individual as are all the telegraphic tapes on which the same message is printed in Morse code. (From Sinnot , Dunn and Dobzhansky, Principles of Genetics, 4th ed., McGraw Hill 1950)

dictum about "the whole and its parts", the development of the nervous system is "more" than the sum of arrows in the diagram, even if additional "feedback control" arrows were included; incidentally, to satisfy the facts, the number of the latter would have to be infinitely larger.

21. *The Dualism of "Interaction"*

Since much of this last comment was called forth by the unduly broad innuendo of the term "genetic determinism", especially in its articulated version of "genetic information", I might be pardoned for the following, slightly facetious, pictorial analogy to language. Fig. 8 shows a set of fixed and stained giant chromosomes of an insect; their aperiodic band structure corresponds to the underlying stereotyped aperiodic ("coded") seriation of the genes along the chromosomal axis. Fig. 9 is from the frontispiece of a translation of Nietzsche's "Thus spake Zarathustra", which I discovered at the Pratt Institute in New York. It shows sentences exuding from the poet's mouth (though hardly simultaneously). The resemblance between the two pictures is not entirely fortuitous, for the meaningful seriation of letters in a word has been rightfully used as model for the meaningful serial linkage of molecular elements into genetic subunits to serve as code for the transcription of "information" form DNA to RNA and subsequent translation to protein. Quantitatively, the alphabet with its twenty-six letters is richer than the genetic code with only three-letter "words", but otherwise the analogy is of intriguing pertinence. In fact, the visual counterpart to the analogy, shown in our two pictures, goes even one step further; it does so by what it fails to show, for both figures depict senders without receivers, implying "action" without "reaction". Unless heard and understood, the poet's utterance would be that of a "voice crying in the wilderness"; and unless faced with an appropriately "interlocutory" field structure around it, the gene string, likewise, cannot make sense.

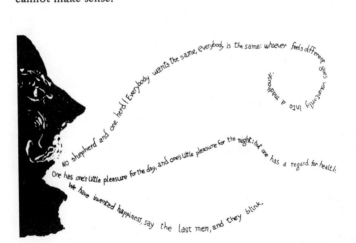

Fig. 9. Signature for an English edition of a book by Nietzsche with quotations (Courtesy of Pratt Institute, New York)

The simile of dialogue here alluded to is just another reminder of the inevitability of a dualistic reference scheme for the exhaustive description (= explanation) of living systems, as exemplified by the whole-part, field-particle, cytoplasm-gene, etc. relationships. Due to the understandable prevalence of the analytical methodology and reductionist phraseology of our scientific past, we are faced with a conspicuous asymmetry of knowledge in favor of the second member of these conjugated pairs. Some signs of redress of that imbalance, however, have appeared, and it would have been profitable to accentuate them further on this occasion; for instance, by presenting examples of *field effects* as concrete demonstrations of the macro-determinacy of systems. If I have steered clear of this, it was because of limitations of space and readers' patience. But as a parting bid for the acceptance and exploration of field concepts of group behavior in biological systems, I want to give at least a glimpse of a simple model, which I have found helpful in the past both for making "field principles" more tangible and for keeping mysticism out-of-bounds.

The model, diagrammed in Fig. 10, starts from a single unit, let us say, a cell (A), assumed for simplicity to be internally homogeneous, but in steady equilibrated interaction (e.g., exchange of substance and energy) with the ambient medium across its free surface. Let us then increase the number of such units, either by cell division or aggregation (B). At first, all the members of the group are equal and share in the free surface, hence continue to exist as before. But as their number increases, all of a sudden, when a critical number is reached, a new situation emerges (C) which splits the mass of erstwhile equivalent units into two radically disparate groups—an *outer* group, still in direct

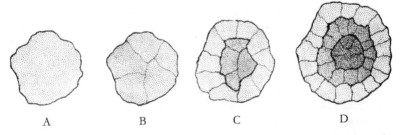

A   B   C   D

Fig. 10. Diagram, illustrating the emergence of differentials in collectives of erstwhile equivalent units as a result of numerical increase. (From P. W. 1968)

contact and exchange with the original medium, and an *inner* one, shut off from access to the old medium and encircled instead completely by its former equals. As the inner units (cells), in response to this drastic change of their conditions, switch into a different (metabolic) course, the formerly uniform group acquires a core-crust (inner-outer) differentiation. If then the outer layer interacts with the newly modified inner group, a third type of unit will arise between them (D), and so forth, in ever mounting complexity, but obviously conforming to an orderly overall architectural pattern. This inner-outer differentiation is one of the most elementary instances of a group pattern being definitely predictable as a whole, while at the same time the fates of its components are still indefinite, thus illustrating macrodeterminacy in the absence of microdeterminacy, as in Fig. 5. Yet, the main point is not just this early indeterminacy of the members of the group, but the fact that their future fate is determined by their place within the dynamic configuration of the whole group and can be predicted and understood only in reference to the "whole." For example, if such a group were cut in two, then future "inner" units would become "outer" ones, and the whole, though of reduced size, would turn out as of harmonious structure and proportions. In essence, this is the story behind the phenomenon of "twinning."

22. *Epilogue*

I herewith rest my case. It states what I have learned from observation and experimental study of living systems: that as biology has made spectacular advances by the adoption of the disciplined methods of the inorganic sciences and mathematics, it has not widened its conceptual framework in equal measure. My comments have tried to illustrate not only the need, but the feasibility of such adaptive move. It may entail attempts in physics to enlarge its conceptual structure so as to be able not only to encompass living nature, but to fulfill the postulates raised by the realities of phenomena germane to living systems. But pending a successful achievement of this task, and even if it were doomed to remain short of accomplishment, biology must retain the courage of its own insights into living nature; for, after all, organisms are not just heaps of molecules. At least, I cannot bring myself to feel like one. Can you? If not, my essay may, at any rate, have given you some food for thought.

Bibliography

Astbury, W. T.: *Adventures in Molecular Biology.* Harvey Lectures, Series 46, 3-44 (1951).

Bertalanffy, L. v.: *Problems of Life. An Evaluation of Modern Biological Thought.* New York: J. Wiley 1952.

Gerard, R. W.: *Concepts of Biology*—National Academy of Sciences-National Research Council. Publication 560, Washington, D. C., 1958.

Koestler, A.: *The Ghost in the Machine.* London: Hutchinson 1967.

Loeb, J.: *Forced Movements, Tropisms, and Animal Conduct.* Monographs on Experimental Biology. Philadelphia—London: Lippincott 1918.

Polanyi, M.:*Life's irreducible structure.* Science *160* (1968) 1308-1312.

Schrödinger, E.: *What is Life? The Physical Aspect of the Living Cell.* Cambridge: University Press 1945.

Waddington, D. C.: *New Patterns in Genetics and Development.* New York—London: Columbia University Press 1962.

Weiss, P.: *Tierisches Verhalten als "Systemreaktion". Die Orientierung der Ruhestellungen von Schmetterlingen (Vanessa) gegen Licht und Schwerkraft.* Biologia Gen. *1* (1925), 168-248.

— *Principles of Development. A Text in Experimental Embryology.* New York: Holt 1939.

— *Self-differentiation of the basic patterns of coordination.* Comp. Psychol. Monogr. *17* (1941) 1-96.

— *Medicine and society: The biological foundations.* J. Mt. Sinai Hospital *19* (1953), 716-733.

— *Animal behavior as system reaction: orientation toward light and gravity in the resting postures of butterflies (Vanessa).* General Systems: Yearbook of the Society for General Systems Research, *IV*, (1959) 1-44.

— *The cell as unit.* J. Theoret. Biol. *5* (1963).

— *1 + 1 ≠ 2. (When One Plus One Does Not Equal Two.)* In: G. C. Quarton, T. Melnechuk, F. O. Schmitt (Eds.), The Neurosciences: A Study Program, 801-821. New York: Rockefeller University Press 1967.

— *Dynamics of Development: Experiments and Inferences*, 624 p. New York: Academic Press 1968.

— *"Panta' Rhei"—and so flow our nerves.* Proc. Am. Philos. Soc. *113* (1969) 140-148.

— *Life, Order and Understanding:* Special Supplement to the Graduate Journal, vol. 8, The University of Texas: Austin, Texas, 1970.

Whyte, L. L.: *The Unitary Principle in Physics and Biology.* New York: Holt 1949.

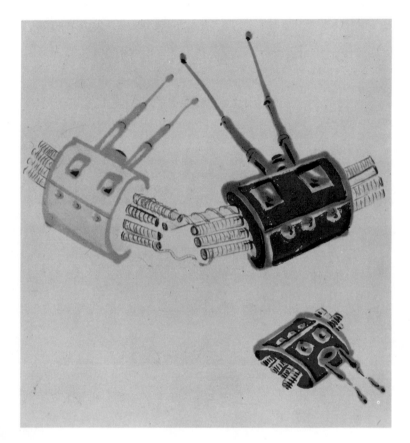

Life On Earth*

The year is 2064. Interspace Airways conducts monthly round-trip flights to Mars. Terrestrial Fulbright scholars in cryptography and comparative linguistics have VIP priorities. They have come to outrank the physical scientists of the hardware variety and the biological scientists of the garden variety, who only had confirmed that, after all, mass is mass, and energy is energy, and those telescope-discovered green patches up there are just ordinary grass. And so most research on Mars has been entrusted to the "Neo-Socio-Humanities," whose scientific status symbols are electronic scanners, counters, computers, and probability calculus. They have been asked to check some vague reports about weird, elusive objects on Mars, said to roll around with a metallic noise, behaving much like living creatures—perhaps the Martian version of man. On orders of The World Security Board, teams of investigators went up to look, and here are the results:

There are indeed lots of bodies tumbling around up there, shaped like drums with sturdy rods protruding from both sides. Hard to the touch, they clang and clatter harshly whenever two of them collide, as they quite often do. They definitely are some sort of animate hardware, or rather metallic organism. An artist's rendering of those curious structures appears on the left. They all carry tapelike wrappings around the rods and, most amazingly, when two such bodies meet, some of the wrappings unwind partly from each of the bearers and coil around the other's rods.

What is supposed to be the meaning of all this? It did not take long for our investigators to find out. By sheer good luck, they came upon some dumping grounds littered with scraps of Martian tape to which they helped themselves in quantity. Back on earth, acting on a hunch, they ran these fragments through the transcriber of a magnetic tape recorder. Miraculously, out came long sequences of squeaky sounds, not unlike Morse code. Computer people and cryptographers got busy and in short order managed to decode the Martian language.

Reproduced with permission from THE ROCKEFELLER UNIVERSITY RE-VIEW, vol 2, No. 6, Nov/Dec 1964, copyright © The Rockefeller University Press

This, then, was the way in which Martians communicate. The rods are evidently magnetic recorders, committing language symbols to metallic tape, to be read off from there by the receiving rods of the accosted partner. (The baby in the picture, as you note, is still short on taped information.) How sobering for man to contemplate that once again nature has scooped his proud technology.

As more and more of these taped records were collected, collated, and connected, they yielded an amazingly coherent chronicle of Martian life, civilization, and history. Its publication on earth was a bombshell. Indeed, for a while, it shook man's faith in his own security. For the Martian story revealed with unassailable certainty that more than a century earlier a Martian expedition had visited the Earth without being detected. Just how they had escaped detection, despite the radar screens around the globe, is still a mystery.

At any rate, the excitement eventually died down and people turned their attention to the substance of the Martians' story of their expedition. This brought the next wave of astonishment. The Martians' report asserted that they had discovered beyond the shadow of a doubt that there was *life* on earth; more lowly than their own, but true life all the same.

Thanks to the efficiency of the terrestrial decoding and interpreting machines, the Martians' account of their epochal discovery could be fully reconstructed. It speaks highly for Martian literacy that the description is so articulate, lucid, and pictorial that it was easy for a terrestrial artist to compose a pictorial record of the whole story. That story is not only exciting; it is also a superb model of cogent logic—the equal of the peak achievements of inductive reasoning by man. And here it is—the Martians' story of "Life on Earth"—transcribed to a first-person rendition for effectiveness. The accompanying pictures, although apocryphal, are certainly no less authentic than those gracing the illustrated editions of Homer's *Iliad* and *Odyssey*.

LIFE ON EARTH

BY A MARTIAN

"We had timed our approach to earth to fall into the dark phase of the diurnal cycle. Yet, as we came nearer, we noticed that not all was darkness. There were streaks of light like knotted ribbons. They seemed

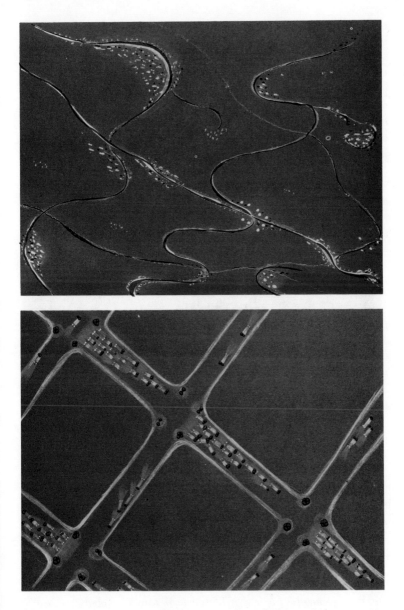

"If life is motion, here was life, attracted by a flickering light source"

to move in waves, mostly in one direction. From a still closer view, the knots proved to be separate bodies; they moved indeed, in spasms of alternating spurts and stalls. If life is motion, here was life. Each luminous knot was obviously an individual organism. Each had the polarized appearance of a wedge and seemed in finer resolution to consist of smaller subunits; something like cells. Why they should move in file and unison did not become clear to us until we came in still closer and saw the cause: they all were positively phototactic, attracted by a flickering light source, toward which we likewise now steered our course. Hovering over it, we recognized our first mistake: the knots, which from a distance had looked to us like single individuals, had dissociated into the putative "subunits." These latter thus revealed themselves, by their separate existence and independent motility, as the true elemental carriers of life on earth.

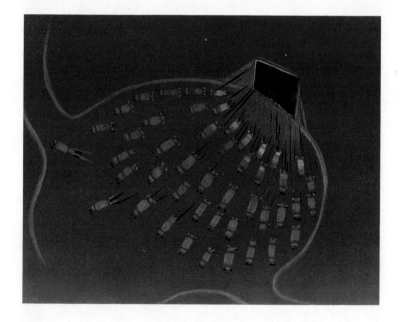

"the true elemental carriers of life on earth formed a handsome sort of crystalline array"

"inside each unit we perceived a pair of structures squirmings,"

So we kept watching them. Rather than rush right on into the attractive light source, they stopped just short of it and formed a handsome sort of crystalline array. For some time after, they remained immobile and soundless. The only sounds we heard came from that light trap. We thought they slept. So, we took courage to land and inspect them. That was when we noticed that motion had stopped only superficially. For inside each unit we perceived a pair of structures that kept on squirming. Whether these were peristaltic internal organs or some sort of wriggly endoparasites, we had to leave unresolved, for our inspection was cut short abruptly when suddenly the light went out and the various creatures resumed locomotion, all in the reverse direction, though not all at once.

In order to study life on earth in more detail, we decided to wait for daylight, fully prepared to be discovered. Unaccountably, this never happened. We therefore were able to go about our explorations undisturbed and at great leisure. And what we learned was truly unexpected, almost incredible. To sum it up: Life on earth has so many features in common with our own that we must concede the possibility that Martians and "Earthians," as we shall call them, might be akin. Unpalatable though this deduction may be to the glorious leaders of our superior Martian people, in our conscience as scientists we cannot evade it, provided we can document its premise. And document it we can. For we can prove that Earthians metabolize, eat, drink, and groom; generate heat and light and sound; proliferate and die; and they, like us, vary in size and mood; in short, have individualities.

In structure, they are, like us, of symmetrical build and slightly polarized, although one cannot always tell the two ends easily apart, a

"of symmetrical build and slightly polarized"

feature perhaps correlated with their ability to move in opposite directions. Just how they move at all, we are unable to explain. What confounded us was that while most of them make contact with the ground at four points, others use only two; should the latter, more unstable, perhaps be rated as degenerative forms?

"most of them contact with the ground at four points,
others use only two"

In volume, the majority fall roughly into three size classes. These evidently represent three different age groups, mass increasing with age, though not continuously, but rather in metamorphic steps. Moreover, our measurements of locomotor speeds revealed a striking inverse relation between velocity and size, which would bear out the familiar rule that vigor and speed decline with age.

"three size classes represent three different age groups"

As we kept on observing, we could not fail to be struck by one peculiar and constant attribute of Earthians: they had invariably associated with them some rather unimpressive bodies of much smaller size. These we have now definitely identified and classified as obligatory parasites of the Earthians, for the following good reasons:

1. They are lodged, for the most part, in the interior of Earthians.
2. Although at times they are disgorged to the outside, they never stray far off, and soon re-enter their hosts.
3. They are more numerous in larger hosts. Therefore, since host size reflects host age, the accessory bodies obviously multiply inside the hosts as the latter grow.
4. Even when detached from their hosts, the little bodies show only extremely limited capacity for independent active motion. Whatever

"invariably associated with them some bodies of much smaller size identified as parasites"

motility we could observe contrasted drastically with that of Earthians by its sluggishness and, above all, its lack of direction.

5. Lastly, the fact that they make only unstable two-point contact with the ground likewise puts them into the degenerative class.

We have given these parasitic bodies the name of "Miruses." Because of their plainly ancillary nature, we shall ignore them in our detailed story, which now returns to our main subject—*The Earthians* themselves. The evidence that these are truly living creatures is overwhelming.

In the first place, they metabolize; that is, they take in substances from the environment, extract energy from them, and give off wastes, mostly as gas and smoke. Intake is mostly liquid, through two holes. One is in back; the other one in front. The front one seems to be much more important because it is quite near the brain, protected by a huge operculum. In fact, the two seem to have totally different functions. We judge this from a test made by a daring member of our party who managed surreptitiously to cross the feeder tubes. The Earthian so

*"Intake is liquid, through two holes. One is in back
the other one in front"*

treated became completely paralyzed; his parasites, by contrast, showed signs of extreme agitation, the source of which remains unexplained.

Although most Earthians thus live on liquid food sucked in through tubes, the largest, hence oldest, of the race seem to have formed the habit of gulping solid matter with special organs sprouted for this purpose.

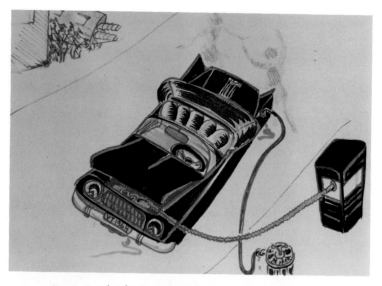

"crossing the feeder tubes, they became paralyzed"

"the oldest of the race gulps solid matter"

Some of the energy derived from intake goes into heat; and more than once we saw it explode in spouts of vapors. The functional utility of these geysers is obscure. Some other part of energy, as noted earlier, is converted into light, and still another part, into sound. The volume of this sound grows as the square of traffic density.

"energy from intake goes into heat in spouts of vapors"

Off and on, we noted signs of grooming by a wiping motion, but only in front. Astonishingly, this was started and stopped in synchrony by all the members of the population, as if they obeyed some secret commands. Does this imply that they have brains?

"grooming by wiping motion in synchrony"

Unquestionably, they do have an organ designed to integrate and shape data of information from the outside world into concerted actions—a sort of brain. For we found under their front operculum a wild profusion of lines and tubes and links, so utterly mixed up and tangled that our "systems analysts" have persuaded us of its basic resemblance to a thinking machine much like our own.

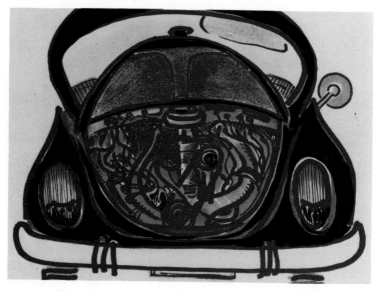

"an organ to integrate information—a sort of brain"

Life for the Earthian, as it must for all living beings, ends in death. Death either comes slowly, heralded by a phase of disarray, unsightly appearance, and frequent breakdowns, or suddenly, in a violent noisy disintegration. As you will see, the fast kind has deep vital significance. Much as in our own world, the corpses are collected in heaps destined, at least in part, for some sort of reincarnation. In fact, it was from this source that we could gather clues as to the amazing method by which the Earthians propagate their kind. It took us an inordinate amount of time, effort, and imagination to reconstruct their mode of reproduction. Our conclusions, based partly on observation, partly on deduction, are these. The Earthians definitely do not reproduce by fission or budding. New Earthians are the products of true synthesis from

"the corpses are collected in heaps"

elementary nonliving parts which are assembled stepwise in an orderly nonrandom sequence—a code. Life comes into them only at the end of this process. The elementary constituents themselves are of uncertain origin. However, a series of lucky incidents has made us favor the following theory.

On several occasions we noted two Earthians, fiercely attracted to each other, embrace in a crushing hug, losing their shape, vitality—indeed, identity—in the encounter. They evidently gave up their individual existences for a higher union. We could not help being mystified by this sacrificial act, till we discovered that it marked not an end, but rather a beginning: a renascence. In following the fate of the devitalized scraps picked up by other Earthians, we saw them vanish in a complex of huge structures which spouted fire and colored smoke and later re-emerge as handsomely molded parts, preformed and ready for assembly into new Earthians. From this experience, we are convinced that the observed crash encounters are truly a mating of two individuals, which in loving abandon expunge their lives so that their merged substance may be reincarnated in living offspring. At times, a considerable lag period separates the act of love and the reprocessing of its products to new life.

"two Earthians, attracted to each other, embrace"

"New Earthians are the products of true synthesis from elementary nonliving parts"

A rather curious correlation ought to be mentioned in this context. It was not at all uncommon for us to find pairs or groups of Earthians resting motionless in rather isolated spots. It could not escape us that, in the vicinity of such locations, the incidence of the described mating collisions was significantly higher. We wonder if this is sheer coincidence, or whether, perhaps, the observed phase of quiet togetherness might not be a sort of prelude to the mating crash.

"Earthians resting motionless in rather isolated spots"

We could go on documenting the living nature of these Earthians still further. However, we rest our case, having proved to everybody's satisfaction that they possess at least three of the basic attributes of life—metabolism, motility, and reproduction. That they are alive cannot be doubted. Being metallic, they might conceivably have come from the same primordial stuff as we ourselves. If so, they must have evolved at a much slower rate to have remained on such a primitive level of behavior as we succeeded in recording. This gives us comfort; for it assures us that they could hardly ever come over to our lands to bother us. Far from disheartening, the discovery of life on earth has, on the contrary, strengthened our faith in our Martian supremacy as the unequaled climax of evolution.

Moreover, by actually witnessing the stepwise assembly of Earthians from nonliving scraps, our expedition has once more confirmed the brilliant deduction of our chemists, reached long ago, that *all* living matter can be synthesized from scratch. Not that we needed confirmation; for have we not *known* that life, wherever in the Universe it may exist, was not created, but has originated?"

The Martians' summary report ends here. No doubt it sounds utterly farcical to us genuine Earthians. What an absurd trick their logic and inductive reasoning has played them: those smug, vainglorious, and self-assured creatures imagining they had the key to life, its essence and its origin. We,who know better, glory in our superiority. Would we ever let ourselves be deluded by such glib contentions? Would we, in comparable circumstances, not exercise our native faculty for sober, balanced, critical, restrained, and undogmatic judgment? Would we?